Science Ponders Religion

Science Ponders Religion

Edited by HARLOW SHAPLEY

APPLETON-CENTURY-CROFTS, INC.
New York

The quotation on page 150 is from a poem "The Second Coming" by W. B. Yeats which is included in *Collected Poems by W. B. Yeats*, copyright 1924 by The Macmillan Company. It is used with the permission of The Macmillan Company.

PREFACE

ON STAR ISLAND, a rocky and treeless member of the Isles of Shoals a few miles out to sea from the shores of Maine and New Hampshire, a group of some two hundred explorers and analysts have in recent years held week-long summer meetings to ponder on the inborn nature of man, his goals, and the types and justification of his various beliefs. We study man's place in space, time, and biological evolution, his meaning to the world, and the world's meaning to him.

"We are citizens of the universe," one of the Star Islanders reminds us. The proper study of mankind should therefore not be only man himself, as Alexander Pope would have it, but should be the Universe—its contents, its mechanics, the atoms in time and space, and the molecules in organisms; it should be the electrochemical operators that we call nerves, brain, and mind, and the socializing impulse that puts simple atoms into molecular complexes, that puts bees and ants into colonies, and men into civilizations. These paths to understanding should all be followed for the proper study of mankind.

The Star Island group, consisting of laymen, clergy from various denominations, and scientists from several disciplines

v

and from a score of universities and colleges, come together to inquire, discuss, answer—and some of them put their thoughts on paper. From their writings I have selected eighteen essays that we would now like to share with a larger audience. All were written by scientists.

The Star Island project, which includes visits of scientists to theological seminaries and which has culminated in the forming of an Institute of Religion in an Age of Science (IRAS), had from the beginning the support of several clergymen of the Boston area. They had become concerned with the possible influence of the scientific method and scientific discoveries on religion as formally exhibited in church, chapel, and synagogue. They invited a number of leading scientists to Star Island to discuss these matters, and somewhat to their surprise the scientists accepted the invitations. Apparently many had been hoping for a *rapprochement* of modern science and religion. The two groups have from the first sincerely worked together.

It became clear very soon that science, in a wide sense, could enrich the holdings of religion, and that religion could perhaps ennoble the concepts of science. Scientific knowledge could possibly encourage a proper use of religious myths; the religious attitude could emphasize the value of knowledge for courage and right doing. Religion, when defined as the belief in spirits and matters spiritual, is found by anthropologists to be an inherent part of all cultures, primitive and advanced. It is natural. The human search for answers to deep questions leads us to reach out boldly and resort to imagination when the rational interpretation of evidence is beyond us. Before meteorology, the gods handled the lightning; before astronomy, mythical deities managed the planetary motions; before psychology and neurology, the devil inflicted our psychoses. Irrational beliefs arise naturally and persist, and sometimes usefully. But with the present explosive rise of science, primitive beliefs are in retreat. Effective religions must now pay closer attention to reasonableness, and salute more diligently our expanding knowledge of a myriad-starred universe with its probably very rich spread of organic life. The anthropomorphic one-planet Deity now has little appeal.

The scientists recognize the finiteness of their knowledge. Much is to be done before we are out of the half dark. These eighteen contributions are asking and partially answering many questions. For example:

Is the administration of the universe purposeful?

Are the "great" religions, the most widely spread cults, on their way to extinction because of the rise of science and naturalistic philosophy? Or rather, do the religions have a validity and a capacity to revise that provide a continuing light unto men's feet?

Will the now widely accepted hypothesis of highly developed sentient life throughout the stellar universe affect religious creeds?

Have other biological societies and civilizations on the earth arisen independently of religion?

Is the "reverence for life" (Schweitzer) a cramped version of humility and reverence—a cramped idea in view of what we now know about the emergence of life out of the lifeless? These facts make logical an equal reverence for the inanimate *and* the animate. Would it not be more reasonable to be humble before the phenomenon of *total* existence rather than only before a biochemical digression or before a display of atoms and stars?

Will it be possible to develop an ethical system more suited to our dramatic times than are the ethical systems of less sophisticated cultures?

Does Pantheism make sense—a world view where the natural is divine, where Nature is God and God is Nature?

These questions are among those to which our contributors turn their thoughts and reports. If this book wherein

"Science Ponders Religion" is found to present a useful account of the way some scientists think about religion, perhaps we should hear from the clergy of the Star Island conferences, and others, by way of a companion volume on "How Religion Reacts to Science."

There is no particular significance in the order of the chapters of this book; no communication depends directly on the preceding. But to assist those readers who would start at the beginning and proceed methodically toward the end, I have put first two essays that are of orienting value—mine, which deals chiefly with the setup of the physical universe and man's position therein, and Hudson Hoagland's "Reflections," chiefly reporting on factors and ideas in the physiological and mental world.

Ralph and Frances Burhoe, who have been leaders in the origination and operation of the Institute of Religion in an Age of Science, have assisted me in assembling the manuscripts for this volume.

HARLOW SHAPLEY

Sharon, New Hampshire,
October 1960

CONTENTS

ix

Science Ponders Religion

CHAPTER 1

Stars, Ethics, and Survival*

by HARLOW SHAPLEY
Harvard University

A HUNDRED YEARS AGO Darwin's *Origin of Species* was published and, as a consequence, our concept of man forthwith underwent a major mutation. This sudden change in attitude was comparable in effect to those slow physical changes that had in preceding millennia differentiated the body of man from the bodies of his anthropoid ancestors. We have appropriately celebrated Darwin and his brave collaborators; and in doing so we have extended that basic Growth Principle (evolution) far beyond the point of emphasis of a century ago, when only the origins of plant species and of animal species were explored. We now go much farther back than Darwin and the paleontologists went. Also we timidly look forward. Along with Robert Burns we may say to the panicked mouse that she is fortunate compared with the human plowman, for

> The present only toucheth thee:
> But, Och! I backward cast my e'e
> On prospects drear!

* This chapter is adapted from the inaugural lecture of the Barnett R. Brickner Memorial Foundation, delivered at Fairmount Temple, Cleveland, Ohio, December 9, 1959.

1

An' forward, tho' I canna see,
I guess an' fear!

Let us cast our e'e backward as far as we can before we look and guess timidly forward. We shall start with the birth and growth of atoms, and steadily progress through a myriad of atomic and cellular stages to ethical man—indeed, toward either a kind of superman or toward the dreaded extinction of this planet's human race.

Hence the title, the ambitious title of this presentation: "Stars, Ethics, and Survival"—*Stars*, in which are born most of the kinds of atoms that compose solid and human matter; *Ethics*, on which human and other civilizations are nurtured; *Survival*, based on the hope of avoiding the extinction with which the distortion of civilization now threatens us.

For the race of men and for the individual we seem to hear ominously of birth, struggle, and the finalizing curtain.

Or might it be birth, social wisdom, and a glorious survival in an atomic world?

Stars burn their abundant hydrogen fuel into helium ash. They thus provide the energy of radiation that generates life and warms and feeds us all, feeds all protoplasmic creatures. Man himself, who is one of the late products of that hydrogen mutation deep in the sun, now also knows how to change hydrogen into helium and thereby provide energy which, misused, can extinguish himself and others. As a hoped-for alternative, man can peacefully use that nuclear energy for the enrichment of human culture. He can at least slightly modify the earth, explore the solar system. Beyond that, however, little progress, little effect.

We need not be concerned about what man, at his most explosive worst, may do to the universe. We need not worry about a cosmos that has human ingenuity running wild. For man's power, cosmically speaking, is negligible. He can do himself in, of course; possibly blow up his planet and put an end to terrestrial biology. But it would be only a local disturbance. Such an episode would leave the stars untouched and unconcerned.

The Stuff of Stars and Man: Atoms and Radiation

In the beginning was the Word, it has been piously recorded, and I might venture that the word was hydrogen gas. In the very beginning were hydrogen atoms, so far as we now see, but actually there must have been something antecedent. Whence came these atoms of hydrogen, these atoms, 20,000,000,000,000 (plus 66 additional zeros) in number—atoms that we now surmise have become the material make-up of the universe? What preceded their appearance, if anything? That is perhaps a question for metaphysics. The origin of origins is beyond astronomy. It is perhaps beyond philosophy, in the realm of the to us unknowable.

Ordinary physics and astronomy suggest that if several billions of our years ago we had all that hydrogen and the natural physical laws, what we now see would have followed without the intervention of miracles and without supernatural intercession. Gravitation, radiation, and eventually photosynthesis and genetics—with operators such as these and the widely dispersed hydrogen atoms, the universe of galaxies, stars, planets, life, and man would have emerged.

A most amazing and simplifying evolution of the chemical elements, of which all matter is made, has recently come to our knowledge, thanks to the present-day erudite studies in nuclear physics and astrophysics. The evolution of the whole series of elements is concerned, from hydrogen and helium (the lightest atoms) through carbon, oxygen, iron, and threescore other middleweight atoms, to lead, radium, and the devil atom uranium. The interiors of the stars provide the locale of the syntheses. High temperatures are required. Here on earth, or in the earth, there are no atomic mutations —except the natural radioactive breakdown of radium and some others into lead, helium, calcium, argon—not even the simplest mutation, $4 H = 1 He + radiation$, occurs here on earth where there is no natural temperature high enough for that operation. The same holds for the other planets. Nor is it hot enough on the surface of the sun for the hydrogen burning, or on the surfaces of other stars, or in the diffuse nebulosities from which stars apparently are born.

To start this transmutation, first involving helium and then the heavier elements, we need temperatures in excess of ten million degrees absolute. In the middle of the sun, such temperatures prevail—hot enough for the hydrogen-into-helium reaction, but not hot enough for the "cooking" of the heavier elements—not hot enough for the further steps in the evolution of complex inanimate matter. How were these heavier elements born? They appear to be built out of hydrogen "blocks"; the common carbon atom is 12 times the weight of the hydrogen atom; iron, 56 times; uranium, 238 times.

Our question to the cosmographer is: How are these complicated heavier atomic structures evolved from simple hydrogen and helium? The sun, we have said, is not hot enough. It can produce helium, and in collapsing after the hydrogen supply approaches exhaustion it may produce some carbon and oxygen, but apparently not iron, nickel, gold, and the other middleweight or heavy atoms.

But suppose the sun should blow up, and become a nova. Every year there are scores of such disasters in our own star-populated galaxy. Something goes wrong with the control of the energy output. A star in such trouble suddenly increases its size and brightness. It blows off its outer atmospheric shells.

If the erupting star were, for example, the sun, the brightness would increase in a single day to five or ten thousand times its normal brightness. The internal temperature would rise toward 100 million degrees, and some of the helium atoms, which had been born more calmly out of hydrogen, would be violently turned into heavier elements. At the same time the explosion would have scattered into space some of this new material as well as the helium and unburned hydrogen.

It is from this scattered gas mixture that eventually new stars are formed as a result of a second gravitational contraction. They would radiate with a higher central temperature, because the heavier elements are now involved. They start again their risky life where thermostatic controls may fail to function and novation may again ensue.

Supernovation

Ordinary novae, however, are not competent to do the syntheses of the heaviest elements. Their central temperatures are not hot enough. And it is here that another violent operation enters—the supernova.

In the year 1054 A.D. a dazzling new light appeared in the sky—a starlike radiator that apparently outshone all others. The oriental astrologers made a record of it. It was visible in the daytime for some weeks and visible at night for a couple of years; but then it faded away from the sky and from the memory of man. Centuries later, however, in the same position among the constellations, a faint nebulosity was found. It was named the Crab Nebula, because of its fancied shape. It was not much unlike other nebulosities, such as the famed one in the sword of Orion. But examination with the photographic and spectroscopic tools of the astronomer showed that it is expanding, and at such a steady rate that,

counting back, the time of its origin can be accurately dated.
The nebula is indeed the product of the explosion recorded
in 1054, which actually occurred some four thousand years
ago. It took about forty centuries for the light from the explosion to get to the earth. This explosion was not a simple
blowing off of the upper atmosphere, but the essentially complete annihilation of a star. The temperatures involved in
this supernova explosion were what astrophysicists had been
looking for, a temperature source high enough to produce
the heavier elements.

Many details of this evolutionary process are yet to be
worked out, but the general sketch is clear—contraction of
the primeval hydrogen gas into stars, explosive return of some
of the gases to space to again assemble in stars, which again
may novate. In the course of these catastrophes the chemical
elements evolve. Our sun, it is surmised, may be a "third
generation" star, for it is composed of all kinds of elements.
Of most of the atomic species, however, there is as yet only
a trace; hydrogen and helium still dominate the sun. The
following percentages for the solar system are based on es-
timates of atomic abundances by Dr. Lawrence Aller:

Element	Percentage
Hydrogen	86.84
Helium	13.00
Oxygen	0.06
Neon	0.04
Carbon	0.03
Nitrogen	0.01
All others	0.02

We have, therefore, in the centennial of the Darwinian
biological evolutionary theory, found that *physical* evolution prevails on a much greater scale. It is exhibited not only
by the birth and growth of stars, galaxies, and planets, but

also by the mutation of the chemical elements. An evolutionary thread seems to run through all nature, inanimate and animate. Again I point out that modern science has removed the need of appeal to miracles or the supernatural for the origin of molecules, or the origin of life, or the origin of trees, or the origin of man and his curiosity. All these evolve naturally.

Much can be said about stars—volumes and volumes about star myths, and star-generated poetry; about telescopic appearances and mathematical analyses; about the youth of stars, their evolution and senility. For the examination of our principal theme—biological survival—we shall refer to but a few stellar problems. For example, are there planets other than those of the solar system? Are there minor bodies like the earth circulating endlessly around hot gaseous giant bodies like our sun-star?

Many stars are double, or triple, perhaps more than half of them. Clusters of stars are common, the open variety, like the Pleiades, and the rich globular clusters that have tens of thousands of members. Still larger aggregates are the galaxies, one of which is our own Milky Way organization; and there are clusters of galaxies, and the sum of all, the Metagalaxy.

In general, the double stars are hostile to planets like the earth. They permit no travel in circular or nearly circular paths around them. In fact, they would probably not permit the forming of planets from pre-planet material. The same holds for other close groups, like the multiple stars, and probably for the centers of globular star clusters; perhaps also for the nuclear regions of spiral galaxies like our own Milky Way organization. From sampling the contents of space with the largest telescopes to distances in excess of a billion light years, we estimate that there are more than a hundred billion galaxies and a total population of stars in excess of 10^{20}, in excess, that is, of a hundred thousand million billion. If only one star in ten were single like our sun, there would still be a tremendous number of single stars, namely, more than 10^{19}.

The Frequency of Life-Bearing Planets

In a speculative frame of mind let's say that only one in a hundred is a single star, and of them only one in a hundred has a system of planets, and of them only one in a hundred has an earthlike planet, and of them only one in a hundred has its earth in that interval of distance from the star that we call the liquid-water-belt (neither too cold nor too hot), and of them only one in a hundred has the chemistry of air, water, and land something like ours—suppose all those chances were approximately true, then we would find a planet suitable for biological experiment for only one star in ten billion. But there are so many stars! We would still have ten billion planets suitable for organic life something like that on the earth.

In the opinion of most scientists who have pondered this situation in recent years, I have here greatly underestimated the frequency of good planetary sites for biology; we should increase the number by a million times at least, increase it to ten million billion.

Planets, Then Life

Our next problem concerns the probability that life really does exist on some of these accommodating planets. We have life here on earth, but are we unique? Are all the millions of other suitable planets barren of the products of natural biochemical evolution?

We on earth have no advantages that are denied others.

In fact, we are very humbly placed in the stellar world. Our planet is small. It circles a very average, yellowish, middle-age star. That star (the sun) is located in the thinly populated outer structure of a large galaxy that contains some hundred billion other stars, of which many billion must be essentially identical with the sun. That this planet is the one and only place where life has emerged would be a ridiculous assumption. Those who know about the number of stars, about the natural ways planets can be born, and the apparently automatic way life emerges when conditions are right—they no longer hesitate to believe that life is a cosmos-wide phenomenon; and that belief is giving many of us a reason for rethinking our philosophies of man and his function. Rethinking our religious position. Contemplating a stellar theology.

We have long suspected that the animate evolves somehow from the lifeless. But how? The scientific literature has in recent years frequently mentioned the Russian biochemist A. I. Oparin and his speculations about the conditions on the earth's surface before the earliest life appeared. Also well known is the Urey-Miller experiment of putting an electric discharge through an atmosphere of methane, ammonia, water vapor, and hydrogen, and producing amino acids, the building blocks of proteins. We believe that the earth's primeval atmosphere was much like that of the experiment; the electric discharge simulated the primitive lightning. In other words, the Miller experiment was what could have happened, and evidently did happen, on the earth's surface two to three thousand million years ago, for here we are!—the offspring of rather nauseating gases and of the turbulent primeval lightning.

The Miller experiment has now been successfully repeated in many other laboratories. Other attacks on the problems of life's terrestrial beginning involve deep studies of photosynthesis, viruses, and the nucleic acids. They now convince us that when the physics, chemistry, and climatology on a planet's surface are not unfavorable, life will emerge and persist. Astronomers through their spectroscopic studies are able to say that the same chemical atoms as those found in our sun are present in other stars; and apparently the physics is the same the universe over. But even if only one in a hundred of the suitable planets has actually got life well under way, there would be more than a hundred million such planets. No, we are not alone!

The evidence is strong, though not yet conclusive, that there is life on Mars. If space researches should develop to the point of *proving* the existence of life on Mars, our argument of life's inevitability anywhere when conditions are right would be greatly strengthened.

The high probability of cosmos-wide life of the kind we know is certainly a thought and dream producer. That any form exists just exactly like the higher primates on the earth is very unlikely, for there are millions of variations on the animal theme. However, protoplasmic developments that are far more complex than ours are probable.

Will we forever be out of physical and mental contact with sentient beings elsewhere? Some scientists think not. They even discuss possible techniques for communicating, by light and radio signals, across the emptiness of space. The suggestions are amusing, instructive, if not yet very practical. It is properly assumed, I think, that organisms, more advanced than we are, probably exist on some planet not too far away. But effective signaling would be difficult. Perhaps we should first attempt a two-way conversation with a horse-radish or a scarab beetle, or with a termite queen-mother, who represents the highest natural societal organization known on this planet.

Probably no suitable planetary station is nearer than ten light years (sixty thousand billion miles). Question and answer would take more than twenty years. So far no one is seriously contemplating velocities of travel or of signal greater than the velocity of light. The physical laws seem to be universal. We are indeed isolated from other life-bearing planets by the physics of the situation.

The Ethical Crisis

Our concern, however, need not be with the rather bizarre project of space communication; we have a more serious problem on our hands. To appreciate its seriousness we must look back to our account of the early history of the chemical elements. The stars, we noted, are kept hot mainly by the natural evolution of hydrogen into helium and by other transmutations. We humans have learned to turn the trick artificially. As a by-product, enormous energies can be got out of the hydrogen-to-helium mutation. We do not need the resulting helium, and the loss of hydrogen is of no immediate consequence to us. But the explosive heat produced by the mutation is so enormous that all mankind is deeply concerned with its discovery and development.

Here is where ethics enters our discussion. The hydrogen atom is capable of doing great things for mankind. It is an inexhaustible source of energy; and that cannot be said of wood or coal or oil. *If* we can learn to control it properly, the hydrogen atom can easily give us essentially free energy anywhere on the planet. The imagination boggles at the grandeur of man's future, *if* hydrogen is his ally. But that happy collaboration is for man to create—not by some single act but by a series of deliberate acts aimed to serve fellow man, to serve all men.

From the scientific progress on many fronts emerges the need for ever new attitudes toward religion and philosophy. We need an ethical system suitable for now—for this atomic age—rather than for the human society of two thousand years ago. Cautiously we must modernize, but certainly.

We need a new set of principles for the guidance of today's deciders and today's actors on the international stage. The scientist's atom has made good will, good fellowship, social justice more than ever necessary, if degradation or even extinction is to be avoided. To our problems, especially to our multiracial, multinational problems, peaceful approaches are demanded. Angry men cannot resolve our social and political dilemmas. Big national angers can no longer be tolerated if man is to survive. For anger leads to action and reaction and counteraction. If atomic war tools are available to angry and vain and stupid men, and are used—then a grim final curtain will close the human play on this planet. It will be truly a judgment day—a day of our own *bad* judgment. The galaxies will continue to rotate, without concern for little Planet No. 3 and its highest life (which is not quite high enough). The sun will bountifully pour its energy into space, but not for *Homo*. He will be through because he has not learned to live with himself.

But let us turn the page and be optimistic; let us consider some elementary short-term alternatives to the extinction of *Homo sapiens*. Short-term protections they will be, but long enough, I hope, to give us the opportunity to establish the long-term working schemes such as enforcible world law that may restrain indefinitely the genocidal, suicidal madness of man's worst enemy—man himself.

Alternatives to Extinction

It may require less than fifty years or it may require more than two hundred, but optimistically I foresee a civilization on this planet sufficiently unified and intelligent to forestall the annihilation of the human race. Before that hoped-for stability arrives, we shall probably suffer some difficult times—even small wars. But the desire to live in an increasingly attractive world is so strong and so widespread that I believe political concessions and life-saving adjustments will be made. Thoughtful planning will be required, however—not thoughtless drifting.

But first some remarks on *coexistence* as national policy. It must be, and probably will be established. It is already widely operating, and agreeably so, except in the USA-USSR socioeconomic fields. For instance, a dozen or more different nationalities coexist in Russia (how pleasantly I do not know). Differing and inherently antagonistic religious sects coexist in the majority of the large nations of the world. Political parties of comparable strength exist peacefully, though sometimes noisily, in the United States, Canada, England, Germany, and elsewhere.

The socioeconomic differences between the USA and the USSR seem deep, but they need not permanently menace our modern civilization; both programs appear to work fairly well in their own states. Probably there is as much sincere and passionate grousing about "Party" men in the USSR as about labor dictators in the USA. Ours is open grousing and apparently ineffective; theirs not so open and possibly more dangerous to the Party. Both political systems of course have faults that are more apparent to others than to themselves. We can continue to boast of our free or nearly free press, keeping quiet about the Negro problems and political corruption; the Russians can boast of Sputnik and their intense educational policy, and maintain silence about war and political prisoners and no free press. It is not entirely unrealistic to suggest that we and they may gradually draw nearer together than now—that we both will soften the sharpest antagonisms and learn to appreciate in each other some virtues as well as real and imaginary vices.

How can we attain mutual and peaceful understanding?

It is a difficult task; man is naturally combative, and most politicians are naturally greedy for power or property. Politics thrives on confusion. Here are, however, a few suggestions bearing specifically on the solving of the USA-USSR problems. Some of the suggested projects could be widely international. When and if needed, similar programs, involving other pairs of nations, could be undertaken. For example, India and Pakistan, Poland and Germany. But the USA and USSR first, for without amelioration, without softening of the strain between them, the future could be dark and sudden.

1. Increase the student interchange until ten thousand visiting students from each nation are continuously involved. This will be expensive; but all-out preparation for or against war is much more so. A war could destroy civilization. A massive interchange might save it. Hopefully, the students from neither country would be deliberately brainwashed, either before the exchange or during the residence. Spread the visiting students over the two countries, I suggest, and let natural friendliness do its work of adjustment and understanding.

2. Continue indefinitely in several scientific fields the beautifully working projects of the International Geophysical Year, which brought not only the USA and USSR, but more than sixty nations into intensive scientific co-operation. The first trip under arctic ice, the first man-made satellite, the first moon-approach rocket, the first complete exploration of Antarctica, the discovery of a mysterious radiation belt —these are but five of the accomplishments of the 1957–1958 international attack on the earth's problems as a planet.

3. Inaugurate international "years" in other than geophysical areas. For example: (*a*) in the elimination of the major human, animal, and plant diseases; (*b*) in the study of prehistoric man; (*c*) in the building and exploitation of deep Plutonic (subterranean) laboratories; (*d*) in the creation and

geographical distribution of new food plants; and (*e*) in the rescue of arid lands. To illustrate this last: More than a billion acres of unwatered land are distributed over all continents. Depending on the future development of cheap atomic energy, we can eventually bring water to all arid areas. To activate such a world-wide project we need heroic international research programs on the inexpensive purifying of salt water, on the developing of edible salt-water vegetation, and on the amelioration of widespread food taboos. We might bring back from the deserts some of the paradises of old, and create new ones.

4. Award decorations (or prizes) to artists of each other's country, the recipients to be selected by juries mainly from other nations. For example, a Tchaikovsky prize given by Russia for the best new American symphony; or a Frank Lloyd Wright award to the best architectural design or construction by a Russian in Russia.

5. Establish in each other's capitals, and possibly in each other's largest cities, theater-concert halls devoted in America wholly to Russian productions (classical and modern), and in Russia to American productions. Again an expensive dream—yes—but hate and suspicion are more so; and this educational program could be started modestly.

6. Encourage with cash and applause the present two-way traffic in farmers, artisans, students, artists, and scientists.

The extensive interchange of goods is, of course, important, but not so effective in saving man from his follies as would be the interchange of nonpolitical and noncommercial ideas.

Americans and Russians should both keep in mind that their political and economic inheritances have greatly differed for a long time. All the Russians of age forty-five or less, and there are probably more than a hundred million of them, have lived under no other system than that of the present day;

why expect them to understand fully our methods and goals? And the 170,000,000 Americans, mostly contented Americans, have lived under no other system than that which now prevails in America. Little wonder that we worry about other governmental policies than ours. Are we able to understand sympathetically other systems?

The Russians have now and then quietly adopted some "capitalistic" methods. The Americans have permanently adopted a number of socialistic practices that would have shocked into hysterics the "capitalists" of half a century ago. Wide differences between the two still exist. "And our system is the right one for the future," says Sam, the American; and says Ivan, the Russian, "Our system is the one for the future."

CHAPTER 2

Some Reflections on Science and Religion*

by HUDSON HOAGLAND

Worcester Foundation for Experimental Biology

IT IS OFTEN SAID that a major reason for the decline of leadership in the Western world is our loss of religious faith, and that since our ethical and moral standards have been built upon divine sanctions, revealed through the Judaic-Christian tradition, this loss in the faith of our fathers leaves us floundering like a rudderless ship in a storm. Arnold Toynbee, in the last volume of his *Study of History*, expresses the view that only a renaissance of religion can save our civilization from further decline, and this view is held by many thoughtful people. The advancement of science is often blamed for our loss of religious faith and this in large measure may be justified. It is my belief, however, that the loss of traditional religious faith does not in itself imply the analogy of a rudder-

---

* Much of the contents of this paper was presented at a meeting of the Institute of Religion in an Age of Science. The paper, somewhat modified, is reprinted with the publisher's permission from a book edited by Stewart G. Cole entitled *This is My Faith* (New York: Harper & Brothers, 1956). Copyright © 1956 by Stewart G. Cole.

less ship or a collapse of ethics, and that the values by which men live are not contingent upon supernatural sanctions.

A study by Anne Roe, called *The Making of a Scientist*,[1] consisted of interviews and psychological tests applied to sixty-four eminent American men of science. The group was selected by a sound sampling procedure in terms of criteria of eminence in the physical, biological, and social sciences. Nothing was known of the religious backgrounds of the men when they were chosen for the study. In the group of sixty-four, five were from Jewish homes, the parents of one were strong "freethinkers," and fifty-eight came from Protestant families. None had Catholic backgrounds. Of the scientists themselves, only three of the sixty-four were at all active in church affairs, and a few others attended church occasionally but were not concerned with institutionalized religion. These findings are in general agreement with the personal experiences of many of us. Scientists for the most part are agnostics, and reasons for this are not hard to find.

I have heard the physicist P. W. Bridgman define science as intelligence in action with no holds barred. Over the past three centuries, accompanying the development of science, there has been repeatedly tested and satisfactorily confirmed an hypothesis that the most fruitful way to knowledge is limited by one's capacity to ask meaningful questions, to observe objectively, and to reach conclusions based on sharable observations relevant to the questions asked. Experimental procedures with adequate controls, logic, and mathematics are tools to assist this process and to enable one to draw tentative conclusions and proceed to more questions and testable hypotheses. But logic of the best can give no better answers than are inherent in the observations to which it is applied, and no amount of skillful reasoning can reach sound conclusions if the questions are meaningless, the assumptions invalid, the operational procedures faulty, or the observations

[1] (New York: Dodd, Mead & Company, 1953.)

inadequate. Most scientists have had the experience of working on highly limited problems in their fields of special competence and arriving at convincing conclusions only to find later that the answers were wrong because of errors in assumptions or technique.

As a result of experiences with the elusiveness of truth in limited fields in which much is known and where technics are highly developed, the scientist is skeptical of conclusions arrived at by methods devoid of control and independent of his criteria of evidence. Thus logical proofs of the existence of a beneficent personal God are to most scientists meaningless because they cannot accept the assumptions upon which the logic operates. The historical bases of divine revelation are devoid of the evidential qualities essential for conclusions. Psychological interpretations of religious experience offer to many a more probable foundation for these phenomena than do the interpretations of the theologian.

In 1942, in that year's volume of the Second Conference on Science, Philosophy and Religion, I wrote:

> All that we know is a product of the functioning of our nervous system. Our neurosensory apparatus is itself a direct product of biological evolution. We, together with other contemporary living organisms, are here today as the resultant of an extremely inefficient process of elimination. For every surviving species, many thousands of species have perished. For every living organism, many billions of potential organisms in the form of their parents' germ cells have perished. Animals eliminated in the course of evolution are, in large measure, ones that as a result of genetic accidents have failed to develop suitable physiological mechanisms to cope with the vicissitudes of their environments. All knowledge of our universe, including a knowledge of God, comes to us strained, if you will, through a series of highly involved physicochemical events, constituting sensory reception and responses mediated by the central nervous system (the brain). We experience not the properties of ob-

jects but the properties of our own nervous systems. We can thus have no direct knowledge of reality beyond the symbols that we learn to agree upon with others who have similar nervous systems. Since all normal men have in general similar nervous systems, it is impossible for some of us to accept indefinable and unsharable ways to a superior knowledge of God. In addition, naturalistic interpretations of religious phenomena in anthropological and psychological terms preclude for many of us the type of faith enjoyed by others.

Mystical experience appears to be no less a product of the nervous system than is the reflex reaction to a pinprick or the appreciation of a Beethoven symphony. Experiences of transcendent mysticism may be produced by the action of drugs on the brain. Thus the ingestion of half a gram of mescaline can produce remarkable aesthetic and mystical experiences, as Aldous Huxley has so well described in relation to his own experience, in his little book *The Doors of Perception*.[2] This substance, a product of the cactus plant, has long been used by the Indians of the Southwest for the purpose of inducing mystical experience in conjunction with religious rites. One of a number of other interesting substances producing psychological changes is lysergic acid diethylamide. A hundred-millionth of a gram of this substance, diluted in the body to one part in a billion, by its action on brain chemistry can produce in normal men weird and psychotic-like experiences lasting for eight to ten hours. Thus subjective mystical experiences can be brought about experimentally by subtle modifications of brain chemistry, and interpretations of religious experience, based upon functional properties of brain mechanisms, seem to some of us more probable than their interpretation as insights revealed by a supernatural external agent.

One property that nervous systems have is an ability to

[2] (New York: Harper & Brothers, 1954.)

co-ordinate response of the organism as a whole in terms of the total environment. This ability to react to total environmental configurations on the part of animals, including man, has had great biological survival value. In the 1942 Conference volume referred to above, I suggested that man's drive to explain and make sense of his world and his relation to it may be a consequence of this fundamental property of his functioning brain, a property necessary for his survival as an individual and as a species. Thus the drive for a monistic viewpoint and a monotheistic god may be an attempt on our part to close a Gestalt and to unify our universe. There are primitive counterparts of this tendency to unify the environment in the behavior of animals. Similar motivation, in the main subconscious, may play a role in much of science and art.

While we know all too little about the nervous system, intensive work of the last century and a half has never necessitated an hypothesis concerning its action that transcends physicochemical concepts of its workings. Modern views of mechanism are quite different from the materialistic clockwork concepts of the nineteenth century, and seem adequate to account for elements of purposive behavior, memory, and learning, since these functions have been incorporated in electronic devices containing appropriate feedback circuits. This matter has been interestingly discussed by, among others, F. C. S. Northrop.[3]

The scientist cannot accept supernatural revelation as a way to knowledge. Revelation based on either secular or theological authority is alien to his way of life and thought. It is clearly alien to Bridgman's definition of science mentioned earlier, since it insists that some "holds be barred" and such authoritarian restriction destroys objective inquiry.

Man appears to be one form of a large number of organisms that inhabit a minor planet which is a satellite of one

---

[3] "The Neurological and Behavioristic Basis of the Ordering of Society by Means of Ideas," *Science*, CVII (1948), p. 411.

of many billions of stars in one of many billions of galaxies. Because of its mass, distance from the sun, and rotation, the earth happens to present a set of remarkably restricted physical conditions that make life upon it possible. Ever since 1828 when Wöhler synthesized in the laboratory the first carbon compound (urea), it became clear that organic compounds do not require any vital principle for their formation, as had been thought, but follow the laws of chemistry. Organic compounds (i.e., the carbon compounds), of which hundreds of thousands are known, can be made in the laboratory as well as in living cells. In 1936 A. I. Oparin discussed from a fresh point of view the possibility of the spontaneous generation of carbon compounds as the beginners of life in the remote geologic past. Such compounds might serve as the building blocks of living organisms. Based upon considered geological evidence, he suggested that in very remote times the earth's atmosphere lacked free oxygen but was rich in methane (CH_4), ammonia (NH_3), and water vapor (H_2O). He postulated that electrical discharges in the form of lightning might produce a synthesis of amino acids, the building blocks of proteins. Recently Harold Urey and S. L. Miller have tested Oparin's hypothesis. They circulated a mixture of these gases continuously for a week in an enclosed glass apparatus past an electric spark. At the end of the week it was found that amino acids had indeed been formed with a surprisingly high yield. Glycine and alanine, most prevalent building blocks of proteins, were found, with lesser amounts of aspartic acid and four other amino acids, together with some thirteen other organic compounds produced by living organisms. In an article on the origin of life, George Wald [4] has discussed these findings together with other important aspects of the problem, including probability considerations and energetics. While the nature of the origin of life has certainly not been proved, the probability of its chance spon-

[4] "Origin of Life," *Scientific American*, CXCI (1954), p. 44.

taneous generation without the intervention of a directing agency is certainly strongly indicated.

It is believed that primitive life could begin from soups of organic molecules in primordial pools, and with the operation of natural selection and vast eons of time a wide variety of organisms, including ourselves, could have developed. Man seems nowhere to display a break in his continuity with nature. Viruses, which display some properties of living organisms, have been shown to be large nucleoprotein molecules. Viruses can be crystallized and, when put in a bottle, the virus looks like so much salt. Inside the congenial environment of a suitable host organism, these molecules reproduce themselves and produce diseases after the manner of bacteria.

In a sense, living organisms, including man, appear to be by-products of natural selection based primarily upon the combining properties of carbon, nitrogen, oxygen, and hydrogen. Man has become most differentiated in the course of natural selection from other animals by the elaboration of his brain, rich in complex electrical feedback and control mechanisms. Both conscious and unconscious drives are properties of his brain's action, and he is aware of himself and of aspects of his relation to his environment. He, along with other contemporary animals and plants, seems to be the end product of entirely chance variations in the arrangements of the special nucleoprotein molecules constituting the genes. Natural selection has eliminated innumerable less well adapted genetic mutations. As a result of this, man appears to have been selected by design, as do all other forms of life that have survived the inefficient process of elimination resulting from chance variations in genetic mutation. Evolution is creative but is so because of natural selection, in which no evidence of design is found. Accounting for the order man sees about him, in terms of Divine purpose, fulfills a basic biological urge to unify himself with his threatening environment and to put himself in an especially favored position. While these views may seem bleak, they cannot be removed by wishful thinking. They may, of course, also be wrong, but the general picture is consistent with the results of scientific inquiry.

This brief consideration of the nature of man is presented, not to convince anyone that it is correct, but merely to indicate some lines of thought that may help account for why many scientists are agnostics. Science deals with probabilities. Absolute and final truth is not within its province. But science can ultimately yield so high a degree of probability as to become certainty for all practical purposes. Thus, for example, it is certain that the earth is round, not flat. Biological evolution by natural selection is no longer a theory but is so highly probable that debating its validity has become futile. Newtonian mechanics as a first approximation for phenomena of intermediate dimensions is true, despite relativity and quantum mechanics with their different views of the physics of the very large and the very small. The social sciences are as yet too young and their phenomena too poorly controlled to have given answers to a degree of assurance characteristic of the physical and biological sciences, but much may ultimately be expected from them. Some events are more probable than others, and to many the phenomena of religious experience and beliefs are more probably explicable along naturalistic lines than in terms of the traditional views of theologians. The existence of God can neither be proved nor disproved, and honest agnosticism becomes the only answer for some of us in spite of the will to believe. It seems probable that, for better or for worse, agnosticism may increase in the future rather than diminish. If this is so, a frank facing of the situation is in order. If we assume as a working hypothesis that good and evil are purely products of man and his relation to his environment, particularly to his social environment, what can he do in support of the good life?

In terms of these views on the nature of man, what becomes of human dignity and ethics? In the Judaic-Christian tradition and in that of other of the great religions such as

Mohammedanism and Buddhism, man has dignity because he is made by God in His own image. His ethics have been a result of his religious sanctions as interpreted for him by theologians. God had revealed a way of life, for example in His commandments given to Moses, and this is the justification of ethical conduct. If we reject this idea of revealed truth, what have we left for a basis of values?

I suggest that in practice the agnostic scientist is an ethical person. His conduct is not different from that of those who profess conventional religious beliefs. The scientist has developed a high regard for truth and spends much time in trying to ascertain it, and the fraternity of scientists transcends national boundaries and class and color restrictions. As Bronowski has pointed out, a scientist can be wrong without being wicked, in contrast to thinking in spheres that are dominated by authoritarianism in religion and politics. Scientists can function effectively only when they have mutual respect for each other's integrity. The scientist has learned to say "I do not know" to questions where others are sure they do know the answers on the basis of meager evidence or no evidence acceptable to him. He knows that some of the most unethical conduct of history has been the result of religious belief. He recalls the cruelty of the Crusades and of the Protestant and Catholic wars of the Middle Ages. Surely witchcraft, superstition, and the tyranny of organized religion, as featured by the Inquisition, have contributed little to human dignity.

Communism in operation may be thought of as a modern secular religion with its doctrines according to Marx and its icon worship of pictures of political leaders and symbols. A monolithic state replaces God, and science and the arts become slaves of the state. The intolerances of great faiths have generally resulted in concentration of power in the hands of a few and the suppression of the many. As Lord Acton said, "Power corrupts and absolute power corrupts absolutely." More blood has been shed in the name of authoritarian religion and politics than over any other issues. In view of all this, it is reasonable to ask if there is any enduring, positive relationship between restrictive authoritarian faith and the good life.

In many ways the practice of science validates the conception of the brotherhood of man and of democracy. It furnishes no comfort for race and caste prejudice. While marked differences exist between achievements of, let us say, Englishmen and those of South Sea Islanders, these differences appear to be due to environmental, cultural, and historic factors rather than to intrinsic biological genetic differences. Within any given group of people, intelligence as measured by tests that are reasonably culture-free indicate no significant racial difference. A similar bell-shaped distribution curve seems to apply to members of all racial groups in terms of measures of abilities. Man is one species displaying marked individual differences in abilities and endowments, but these differences are intracultural. When racial groups are compared, evidence indicates there are as many brilliant people and morons in one racial group as in another. Genetic difference in intelligence and abilities do not follow color lines or natural boundaries.

Just as a locomotive will continue to run for a time along the track after the fire under its boiler has been extinguished, it might be maintained that most agnostics are well behaved because of the momentum given to their ethical values by the Judaic-Christian tradition and that this momentum will be lost in time by a society that loses its belief in a personal, beneficent Deity. There are many who sincerely believe that only a revival of belief in a supreme personal God on the part of secular leaders and people in general can save Western civilization. Many scientists, schooled in rigorous views of validity of evidence, find it is not possible to have faith in the existence of something for which there is to them inadequate evidence. Such persons are humbly aware of the mysteries of the unknown at every hand and of the inadequacies of knowledge and of science to give certainty. But to accept a faith in a personal Deity, who has specific concern for personal problems of good and evil, on the basis of ignorance and mystification, is simply not possible for many persons. Mystification both humbles and challenges, but for many of us it cannot in itself interpret and yield a basis for positive faith.

Since the existence of God can neither be proved nor disproved by methods acceptable to most scientists, it might be held that empirically the assumption of a beneficent personal God makes for a better and more workable society, and on pragmatic grounds therefore confirms the hypothesis of the existence of God. We have considered reasons for questioning the validity of the generalization that religious dogmas make for better societies, and to many the concept of revelation is intrinsically unacceptable. It might also be maintained that belief in divine revelation was historically important in leading men to higher standards of values. These values of ethical conduct have then withstood the operational test of use so that the scaffolding of supernaturalism used in building them is no longer necessary. The completed ethical structure can stand by itself in terms of the important role it plays in daily living. Thus, for example, it matters little how the use of traffic control lights came about. Their continued use as a form of ethical regulation is assured because of their merit in an automotive age.

Altruistic behavior is not limited to man. The sacrifice of life of mother animals in protecting their young, the protection of members of the herd by the organized behavior of animals, even at the cost of their own lives, are forms of conduct which in us would be called ethical. Such behavior has survival value, preserving the group and the species in a hostile world. Symbiosis among plants and animals is of great significance in survival and advancement, both of the individual and of the species. The remarkable ecological aids afforded to each other by plants and animals, even between widely different species, can teach us much about the es-

sential value of mutual co-operation in human societies. Evolutionary progress may in a sense be measured by the development of complex multicellular plants and animals from
primitive single-cell forms. The service of individual cells in
special organs and tissues to the functioning of the total
organism characterizes the metazoan and emphasizes the dependence of each cell upon the activities of the others. In all
of these considerations the concepts of teleology and en-
telechy have added nothing to our understanding of biological phenomena. Such hypotheses have only confused the
issues.

In the course of evolution within a system, various
writers have pointed out that new properties of the system
emerge. These properties are intrinsic to the system but as
emergents they may be entirely novel. Thus, modification in
the course of evolution of the anatomy of the forelimbs of
certain terrestrial animals has resulted in the novel property
of flight. In man, elaboration of the brain has brought about
properties of behavior found only in rudimentary form or
not at all in other animals. Man's use of the spoken and
written symbol is a case in point. The use of language, an
emergent property of his highly developed brain, has been
essential for social evolution and the developments of civilizations. It has been suggested that the vast elaboration of the
human cerebral cortex may result in the ultimate elimination
of man as a species, that phylogenetically the great brain may
be a sort of cancer operating to produce nuclear weapons,
bacterial warfare, and other forms of destruction that could
eliminate him as a species. An oversize brain may be as great
a phylogenetic liability as may have been the great bulk of the
dinosaurs. Just as animals and plants have used their special
physiological and anatomical advantages to survive and
prosper, so must man use his especially advanced brain to control himself in relation to his fellows if he is to survive and
prosper. His great forebrain makes possible the binding of
time—past, present, and future—for his advantage. It also

serves to inhibit and modulate appropriately the basic drives of brain stem and midbrain mechanisms. Thus, control for longtime objectives of aggressions, appetites, and fears is possible as in no other species. In other terminology, man has developed in the course of emergent evolution a conscience. If one wishes to use Freudian terminology, his id and ego are controllable by his superego.

Of all the concepts of ethics, that of the dignity of the individual seems to me to be most essential for advancement of man's welfare. The value of this concept appears to run through all historical human progress. This value seems to be an emergent property in man as a social organism. Nothing quite analogous to it seems to exist in ant and bee colonies or in the wasteful propagation of species in which only two of billions of germ cells form an embryo and become an adult organism, whether man or fish. The value of the individual per se does not seem to be inherent in the principles of natural selection responsible for survival of the species.

In many animal societies and in human societies individuals stand in certain relations of dominance and submission to each other—the pecking order in birds is a case in point. But the concept of the dignity and value of the individual man as it operates in ethics is more than this, and tempers the human pecking order in favor of a better life for all. It seems to me that this is the result of the operation of values based upon intelligent appraisal of their consequences, and that this, after centuries of testing, sanctions the values. Slavery has been abolished because of man's belief in individual human worth. Nazism has been destroyed because of man's belief in the dignity of the individual. Tyranny has repeatedly surrendered to this belief. There are many crucial tests of the workability of value concepts that are part of the historical record of the past three thousand years. Intelligent appraisal and insistence on these values and their modifications when they fail to work seem to be the best hope for man. Civilization depends upon social life controlled by accepted values. In the past, through ignorance and its accompanying prejudices, hatreds, and fears, men often lost for generations their earlier advances. The rapid decline of Athenian civilization is one example in point. Science can be of inestimable value if applied objectively to the testing and evaluation of values as they operate in society. There certainly can be a science of values. The social sciences deserve every encouragement lest our advanced knowledge in the physical fields prove our undoing through devastating world wars with modern weapons.

I believe that basic values from our cultural heritage contain the ingredients needed to solve the problems that plague our world. From the ancient Greeks primarily came our belief in the importance of intellectual honesty and free inquiry. From Judaism and Christianity has come our faith in the brotherhood of man—this means man as such, not just members of the tribe or nation or race. Primarily from England we have derived our humane legal code which holds that a man is innocent until proved guilty, and is not guilty when charged. From Magna Carta on through eighteenth- and nineteenth-century liberalism and our Bill of Rights has come our conception of the rights of man. The state is for man, and man must not be a pawn of the state. All of these things add up to our belief in the dignity of the individual with his freedom to choose and, if he wishes, to be unorthodox in the honest choice of his opinions.

What Chief Justice Holmes has referred to as the right of dissent—the right to disagree with authority—is essential for the survival and advancement both of science and of the democratic society. Without the exercise of this right, knowledge ceases to grow and democracy is turned to tyranny. The norms of ethics, the purposes and values by which we live, are not static but dynamic and subject to education and evolution, and we have a moral obligation to be intelligent, as well as honest, in appraising the consequences of action and so directing our values in terms of these consequences. Much that ails the world today appears to be a result of the fact that many people everywhere have surrendered their freedom of choice in favor of the easy, ready-made ideologies and slogans of dictators with their false solutions and authoritarian panaceas. These surrenders are in part a consequence of the failure of traditional religious beliefs. They are probably more the result of anti-intellectualism, ignorance, and disrespect for the tested values that have given men dignity and integrity over the ages.

Since I have spent over a quarter of a century doing research in the biological and medical sciences, it is inevitable that my beliefs should be colored by this background. While I believe that science is a technique of the greatest importance for the acquisition of knowledge and that truth is intrinsically good, I am fully cognizant of the limitations of science. In our daily activities we must usually act upon the basis of evidence that would not withstand the tests of scientific validity. The frontiers of the unknown hem us in on all sides, and we are aware that according to the rigorous criteria of a laboratory we know little about many things. These limitations are especially conspicuous in the realm of values and human relationships. Aside from the austere, rigorous approach of science, there are other approaches to reality. Thus, literature, history, the arts, and the experiences that come from living with one's fellows offer different aspects of great importance of the world about us. An objective scientific approach to human relations has much promise for mankind. It has never really been tried on a large scale or for a significant period of time.

Reason and the basic sciences have emancipated us from the superstitions of the Dark Ages. I believe that life can be rational and that reason and loyalty to our historically tested values, derived by the struggles of free men over the centuries, can do more than anything else to resolve the tragic problems of our generation. This is not an easy road, but I know of no short cut.

CHAPTER 3

Creation and Evolution

by KIRTLEY F. MATHER
Harvard University

THE CENTURY SINCE the publication of Darwin's *Origin of Species* in 1859 witnessed a remarkable evolution in the intellectual life of man. To an extent unequaled in any other period of equal length, reasoning minds have found response in a rational universe. Countless superstitions have been erased by increasing comprehension of the intrinsic orderliness of the world around us. The unprecedented progress toward valid understanding of the nature of the world and of man has not been confined to the physical, biological, and social sciences; it also appears in the thinking of large numbers of intelligent theologians.

Particularly indicative of this progress is the change of mental attitude toward the two nouns joined together in the title of this essay. Rarely indeed is the perplexed inquirer told today that they are antithetical, that "you must choose between belief in God, or in the Bible, and belief in evolution." Any contemporary writer who entitled his essay "Creation versus Evolution" would be considered illiterate by scientists and theologians alike. The concepts for which these words are symbols have come to have such meanings that they are almost identical. Nevertheless, there are shades of meaning or overtones of emphasis that indicate subtle but significant differences between "creation" and "evolution" as symbols for concepts, especially when they are used in the context of religion as distinct from that of science. These differences are worthy of careful consideration. Their examination will lead to certain obdurate problems which theology inevitably encounters in an age of science.

The Scientific Point of View

From the scientific viewpoint, creation is an orderly, continuous sequence of events, each of which is amenable to analysis with the expectation of discovering how it occurred. At every stage, as far back as the mind can reach, it involves the transformation of previously existing matter or energy into something new and different. There can be no thought of any actual "beginning," no suggestion that something was ever produced from nothing. More important, each transformation of matter or energy is confidently believed to take place in accordance with the regulations that make the universe a cosmos rather than a chaos. In other words, creation is a process. For this creative process, the scientist uses the designation "evolution," including the evolution of stellar and planetary systems as well as that of animals and plants. Although much is still to be learned about many aspects of the complicated procedures in evolution, no scientist imagines any rational explanation of the creative process that cannot be appropriately designated as evolution, with its connotations of orderliness and continuity.

The concept of continuity deserves special emphasis. It brings to mind the hypothesis of "continuous creation" proposed a few years ago by some of the astrophysicists to replace the "big-bang" theory that had been in vogue in preceding years. The "big-bang" theory asserts that five or ten billion years ago all of the matter and energy of the entire universe was concentrated in a single nebulous mass of relatively small dimensions. It then began to expand with explosive violence and has been expanding ever since. Early in this process, the countless galaxies of stars were organized and planetary systems were evolved. Since then the stars have been radiating their substance outward into the vast reaches of interstellar space. The eventual fate of the universe will be like that of a clock set running but not rewound. Entropy will increase as the availability of energy is decreased in accordance with the second law of thermodynamics. The time will come, many billions of years in the future, when no star will be able to shed life-sustaining energy upon any planet.

In contrast, the "continuous creation" theory implies that the universe as a whole is in a "steady state." Although the entropy of existing stars is necessarily increasing, new organizations of matter-energy are emerging in interstellar space. New concentrations of mass-energy arise, new stars are "born," new planetary systems evolve, even while the older ones proceed toward their eventual "heat-death." For such a universe, there is no suggestion of a beginning, no prospect of an end.

There are valid arguments both for and against each of these contradictory theories about the history of the universe. They are to be considered as "working hypotheses" subject to change or discard in the light of new knowledge gained by future research. In the meantime, it should be noted that the scientific appraisal of the future of the earth as an abode for living creatures is not in question. It would be the same, under either of the two hypotheses or any variant of either. The earth has been in existence as a planet in the solar system for four or five billion years. Its future will almost certainly be at least as long as its past. Living creatures of one kind or another have occupied its hospitable environment uninterruptedly for more than a billion years. Although eventually the increasing entropy of the sun will reduce its energy output below the minimum necessary to sustain terrestrial life, that grim stage in the history of the solar system will not be reached for at least another billion years. Now that man has the ability to manufacture nuclear and thermonuclear explosives, it is entirely possible for him to make the earth uninhabitable. It would be quite an undertaking, involving great expenditures of human energy and requiring considerable organizational activity, but the requisite materials, knowledge, and skill are now available. Discounting that utterly insane possibility, astronomers and geologists can assert confidently that the creative evolution of animals and plants will continue here on earth for hundreds of millions of years to come. But it will not continue forever.

That brings us to a consideration of those aspects of the scientists' view of creation which make the most significant impact upon theological concepts and religious doctrines. Like other creatures, man is a product of the process of evolution, subject to its many complicated regulatory principles. He is apparently the latest product of that creative process, but there is no reason to assume that he is the last product. Creation is not finished; it is a continuing operation. As man learns more about the nature of the process and the regulatory principles disclosed by its procedures, he gains the ability to determine, within limits, his own destiny as an inhabitant of the earth. But what he will do with the abundance of time at his disposal in the future cannot be predicted from what he has done in the past. If he is to achieve immortality or gain eternal life, in the actual meaning of those sublime words, it must be in the realm of the spirit, unfettered by the four-dimensional world of space-time. The physical, biological, and social sciences comprise increasing knowledge about human bodies and minds; they can deal only indirectly and tentatively with spiritual entities.

The Theological Point of View

From the theological viewpoint, creation is that which a Creator or a creative power did or does, caused or causes to be, ordained or ordains to come into existence. By some theologians, especially in earlier times, creation has been considered as a single event, completed at some date in the past. By others, especially in more modern times, it is conceived to involve a continuing series of events. Always, however, the emphasis is on the Creator or the creative power rather than the process or processes by and through which the results are accomplished.

Thus, for example, the authors of the two quite different accounts of creation in the first three chapters of Genesis give never a thought to the question, how did "the earth bring forth living creatures according to their kinds" or how "God created man, male and female, in his own image." The one possible exception is in the older of the two stories, which happens to have been placed second in the biblical sequence. This is obviously an allegorical narrative, with its references to a "tree of knowledge of good and evil" and a talkative serpent, whereas the other is a sober, straightforward account reflecting the cosmography of its time. Even so, the fantastic tale of the fashioning of Eve from Adam's rib seems to be a naïve attempt to explain how one of the most engrossing items of creation came into existence. It may be significant that, in his reply to a tricky question about divorce, Jesus referred to the more sophisticated account in Genesis I, rather than to the folklore of Genesis II, even though the latter had been the traditional source of the directive concerning the permanence of marriage.

The theologian's primary concern with the creative power rather than with the creative process necessarily involves him in the problem of the "why and wherefore" of creation. The scientist can do his research successfully by considering only the "how and what" of creation. Morals and ethics come within the ken of both. Each is aware of "values" in his field of inquiry. The difference in viewpoint is, however, an important one. It is essentially the difference between the two questions: why and how.

The emphasis upon purpose in creation impels the theologian to think of man as a creature, in the original etymological meaning of the word. The relation between creature and Creator is explicit in every theological doctrine of creation. This indeed is the central theme of Judeo-Christianity.

Creative Power and Creative Process

From the viewpoint of religion in an age of science, it is surely desirable to seek a rational integration of the concepts of creative power and creative process. In fact, neither concept can be developed very far without giving thought to the other. In the first chapter of Genesis there is explicit recognition of an orderly sequence of creative events. The sequence is different from that discovered by scientific research in recent centuries, even as modern cosmography differs from that of three thousand years ago. It is now known, for example, that there were "swarms of living creatures" in "the waters" long before there were "fruit trees bearing fruit in which is their seed, each according to its kind, upon the earth." And the time-scale for the successive events has been expanded from days to millions of years. Nevertheless, the modern reader of that ancient attempt to deal with the concept of creation is necessarily impressed by its gleam of orderly process.

When a theologian accepts evolution as the process used by the Creator, he must be willing to go all the way with it.

Not only is it an orderly process; it is a continuing one. Nothing was "finished" on any "seventh day"; the process of creation is still going on. The golden age for man—if any—is in the future, not in the past. The fountainhead of Christianity seems to have recognized this when he said "my Father is working still and I am working."

Moreover, the creative process of evolution is not to be interrupted by any supernatural intervention. The evolution of the first living cells from previously existing nonliving materials may represent a "quantum-jump" rather than an infinitesimal step along the path of progress, but it is an entirely natural development. Biochemists are even now on the verge of discovering in great detail precisely how it could have taken place. In similar fashion, the emergence from ancestral anthropoid apes of human beings possessed of spiritual capacities enabling them to display an awareness of aesthetic values and ethical principles is no more miraculous than the emergence of the first air-breathing quadrupeds from their aquatic predecessors. The spiritual aspects of the life of man are just as surely a product of the processes called evolution as are his brain and nervous system.

Whether or not these inferences concerning the creative process are troublesome to the modern theologian, there is at least one allegation formerly attached to evolution which need no longer worry him. In the latter part of the nineteenth century, much of the antagonism to the then new concept was based on moral grounds. Competition in the struggle for existence was alleged to mean that "the law of the jungle" must apply to man as well as to tigers and gazelles. The primacy of "tooth and fang" in promoting evolutionary progress was considered the very antithesis of the Christian directive to love one's neighbor and minister to the less fortunate. Therefore, the whole idea of evolution must be resisted as the work of the devil. Even as late as 1957 this thought was revived in a treatise written by a prominent clergyman of one of the leading Protestant denominations in Australia; "evolution tends to undue harshness and even to brutality and thus it comes in conflict with the Bible teachings in regard to the virtues that should be cultivated." The fact is that biologists and paleontologists have been increasingly impressed by the importance of the role played by mutual aid and co-operation in evolutionary development. There is no space here in which to marshal the evidence, but the conclusion appears to be valid. Especially with respect to man's lineage, evolution tends toward the development of ethical behavior in complete harmony with the high principles of the best religious traditions.

Theologians, however, should carefully examine the process of evolution not merely to ascertain the validity of the charge that it breeds selfishness and brutality. Knowledge about the process and its products provides much valuable information about the nature of the creative power operating through it. Surely this is one way to gain knowledge about the relations between creature and Creator. The study of "the God of history made manifest in his works" is incomplete if "history" is limited to the last few thousand years; it should be the history of all life, indeed of the universe as a whole. Had the knowledge now possessed by nuclear scientists been available two thousand years ago in Palestine, it is likely that Jesus would have advised his disciples to consider the atom and how it is transformed, as well as to "consider the lilies and how they grow."

The responsibility for seeking knowledge about the creative power rests also upon the scientists. A world of law and order is a world obedient to administrative regulations. An orderly, law-abiding and therefore comprehensible process, such as evolution appears to be, demands the recognition of an administration of some kind. Whether science be considered as a quest for knowledge and understanding or as a servant of mankind, the scientist fails to meet in full the challenge of his commitment if he restrains his mind from contemplation about the ultimate nature of the forces and materials with which he deals.

The Administration of the Universe

The rubric, "administration of the universe," may be used as a valid scientific designation. Like many other labels coined by researchers, it is carefully selected to reveal a little knowledge but to conceal a lot of ignorance. It simply asserts that there is something pertaining to the universe which governs the manifold operations under investigation and makes them amenable to intellectual comprehension. Nothing whatsoever is implied concerning the nature of that something. What it may be is left wide open for further study.

Specifically, theologians should note that "administration" is not synonymous with "administrator." The latter term has connotations that are not necessarily ruled out of consideration in connection with the former, but they are definitely not implied when the former term is used in a scientific context. On the other hand, the theologian who truly believes that God is spirit and not a material entity will find a significant similarity between his "God of Law" and the scientists' "administration of the universe."

Certainly, the better we understand the processes of nature, the more we learn about the marching orders of the universe, the truer is our insight concerning the nature of its administration. Thus the record of geologic life development provides some very significant clues to the inherent characteristics of administrative procedures.

The progressive development of plants and animals during geologic time is marked by increasing organization on an expanding scale. Single cells are organized to become multicellular individuals. Internal controls are developed to integrate parts into wholes. Complexly organized individuals are in turn organized in colonies, hives, herds, schools, societies. The administration displays a flair for organization.

But the processes of evolution do not appear to guarantee progress in this or any other direction; they merely provide opportunity for change. Many kinds of living creatures have continued to exist with little or no change throughout hundreds of millions of years. On the other hand, there are unicellular protozoans that have changed noticeably during geologic time but have continued to be unicellular protozoans. Moreover, some creatures have degenerated or retrogressed in the sequence of time but have maintained the existence of their kind of life. Only a few creatures have advanced from simple, "lowly" forms to complex, "higher" forms, and of these still fewer have persisted to the present time. The administration of the universe seems to be permissive rather than coercive.

This, of course, is good Christian doctrine. "Behold, I stand at the door and knock; *if* anyone hears my voice and opens the door, I will come in to him and eat with him, and he with me." The opportunity is offered to everyone to "enter into the Kingdom of God," but no one is forced to accept the invitation. "Whosoever will, *may* come."

The progressive development displayed by individual creatures in successive geologic epochs involved increased awareness of environmental factors. Primitive animals respond only to objects they touch or to chemical or physical changes in the fluids with which they are in contact. More highly organized individuals have organs of sight and hearing which make them aware of objects and events at a distance. Man's awareness of his surroundings, from a purely quantitative appraisal, places him at the present acme of attainment in this regard.

But awareness has qualitative as well as quantitative aspects. Recognition of objects and forces in the surrounding world is a result of interaction between organism and environment. This is just as true of man's response to electromagnetic radiation in his construction of radiotelescopes as it is of his response to the presence of petroleum in the pores of sedimentary rocks. The inference is valid that man's awareness of aesthetic values and ethical principles is likewise a response to spiritual forces in the cosmic environment. There may well be a spiritual field, as well as a gravitational field and an electromagnetic field, to which adjustment may be made in accordance with the regulations of the evolutionary process.

The extent and quality of awareness would seem to be the most appropriate standard by which to rate the evolutionary attainments of any kind of animal life. Judgments made on that basis are not completely objective; they are necessarily anthropocentric. They may, however, be tested by the record of survival and extinction. Anatomical and behavioral responses to environmental conditions have had much to do with success or failure in the struggle for existence.

Purpose in Evolution

The question of the reality and nature of purpose in evolution holds great interest for both scientist and theologian. There is widespread agreement among biologists and paleontologists that it is the purpose of each creature to maintain the continuing existence of its kind of life, but much disagreement as to whether life has a purpose, whether evolution is purposive, and whether the administration of the universe is purposeful. The issue is of critical importance to the basic doctrines of any religion.

The progressive development of terrestrial life through geologic time has been accomplished by a long series of minuscule steps. Each change in anatomy or behavior appears to be designed to improve the adjustment to the total complex of environmental factors at the time and place. Such changes seem to be a result of the application of the method of trial and error—many failures and an occasional success. The procedure is that of experimentation; it often resembles the purposeful activity of the well-qualified scientist in certain phases of his laboratory research and pilot development. Whatever may be the shortcomings of the available raw materials, they are used with apparent cleverness to accomplish each forward step of the procession along the path of life. The transition from paired-fin, gill-breathing, aquatic vertebrates with incipient air bladders to quadrupedal, lung-breathing, terrestrial vertebrates is one of countless examples. To characterize such methods as opportunistic is not in any sense to demean them. "You will know them by their fruits."

The purpose implicit in the evolution of a new species from its antecedent species is short-ranged. One step may lead to another, but no one of them suggests any prevision of the specific demands and adjustments that will occur in the distant future. The geological records afford no suggestion, for example, that a blueprint for man had been drafted on any architect's drawing board a half-billion years ago. Even as late as fifty million years ago, in early Tertiary time, there is no hint of any design to produce a creature precisely in the anatomical mold of man as he has emerged in glacial and postglacial time.

Nevertheless, there are patterns of progress clearly discernible in retrospect as the student of geologic life-development surveys the records of the past. Many lines of sequential "descent with modification" connect primitive ancestral creatures with more highly organized and more diversely capable modern forms. Many of these suggest an aim not only to maintain existence in the midst of changing environments but also to branch out adventurously into previously untried areas of activity. Thus, flying reptiles evolved from one type of terrestrial reptiles, birds from another quite different type, and bats from terrestrial mammals. In each instance, the changes in body form resulted in a new ability—that of long-sustained flight in the lower levels of the atmosphere. Although the achievement thus gained was the same, the means used were different. The wings of pterosaurs, birds, and bats are utterly different in structure. Within administrative regulations there is great flexibility in responses to the general directives, such as "be fruitful and multiply, and fill the earth" (including land and sea and sky).

The evolutionary development of the human species, of which all of us are members, may be traced from generalized Eocene primates, who lived sixty million years ago, to modern man. The pattern of progress is sufficiently known to permit description. The sequence of anatomical changes includes progressive development of bipedal locomotion, erect posture, greater flexibility of hand, a tongue and mouth cavity capable of emitting a greater variety of sounds, and a relatively larger brain and brain case. Especially important was the evolution of the cerebral cortex until it was capable of imaginative reasoning and rational thought. Accompanying these sequential modifications of organic structures were behavioral and cultural changes without which mankind could never have gained the present position of prominence and power. The continuity of existence of this kind of life is much more a result of dependence upon mutual aid and the application of the fine art of co-operation than of agility of body or efficiency of brain. The human spirit became at least as important as the human body in the more recent stages of human evolution.

Each small step in the progress of this particular column in the procession of life may presumably be explained in terms of immediate causes and ephemeral conditions in the local environment. It is only when the over-all pattern is discerned, and the long-range trend is examined in the context of the many other genetic lines developing simultaneously, that any meaningful purpose can be attributed to the creative activity of the administration of the universe. If the trend of the recent past is imaginatively extended into the future, a picture appears to the mind's eye of the goal toward which the evolution of man is directed. Each forward step toward that goal means more complete adjustment to the sum total of the conditions, the forces, and the regulations of the cosmic environment.

On such a basis, the purpose of the administration of the universe would seem to be the creation, through the process of evolution, of an exquisitely functioning organization of creatures possessing such physical, mental, and spiritual attributes that each individual, of his own free will and accord, co-operates intelligently and wholeheartedly with all others of the species in using the available resources for the continuing welfare of all. This is quite different from saying that the purpose of the administration is to produce a biped animal standing erect upon his hind legs, with a vermiform appendix and a cerebral cortex, a four-chambered heart, and dexterous hands. It describes the goal in cultural and spiritual dimensions, not in terms of physical measurements. This, of course, is quite in line with Christian doctrine. If God is spirit and if man is a being created in the image of God, then the goal for man must be the continuing evolution of the human spirit.

But this description of the purpose of the administration does not mention man at all! Man may or may not fulfill it. If man fails, whether he "goes out with a bang or with a whimper," somewhere else, on some other planet among the millions of possible solar systems among the far-flung galaxies of stars, the creative processes may be more successful. The final chapter in cosmic history is not being written by twentieth-century man. On the other hand, if man, with his particular anatomical and spiritual characteristics, fulfills the specifications, all's well and good—for man as well as for the administration. This, I suppose, is what certain theologians mean when they say that "God is involved in the hazard of his own creation."

CHAPTER 4

A Modern Religion

by H. B. PHILLIPS

Massachusetts Institute of Technology

AT A MEETING at Star Island in August, 1955, a committee on Science and Religion, after thorough study, decided that "Religion is man's effort to orient himself in his total environment."

In certain Eastern countries it has long been customary, when locating a house, first to determine the direction of sunrise, the east, and align the building with respect to that direction. Hence our word "orient" for the process of establishing direction.

A building is regarded as fixed. It is oriented in a fixed reference system with respect to a fixed line, west to east. Living things are in process of development. They must therefore be oriented in a moving system, the reference direction being past to future. In the earlier periods of life on earth the process of development was automatic, forms which happened to be better adapted to the environment and better able to utilize the available resources survived, and their qualities were inherited by their descendants.

In man this process has reached a critical stage. Through

increase in mental power he has become able consciously to influence conditions. Thus good and evil and religion have entered the world. Good is anything that promotes advance, evil anything that retards advance, and religion is man's effort to promote advance.

It may seem strange to associate religion with advance or progress. Religion is considered as concerned with ethics, progress mainly with material things. In reality, progress and ethics are closely related. The purpose of ethics should be the promotion of human welfare, and that is one of the effects of progress. This is best shown by a simple example.

In 1929 Dr. Alexander Fleming observed that the growth of staphylococcus colonies had been inhibited in the neighborhood of a speck of mold on the surface of a culture. This led to the development of penicillin and a series of other antibiotics which have revolutionized medicine. This could occur only in a country where not only medicine but biology and chemistry had reached a very advanced stage. And even in such a country it could not have been intentionally accomplished. If in 1928 all the medical research men in the world had concentrated on the discovery of a material that would inhibit the growth of bacteria, it is quite improbable that they would have found penicillin. Such a discovery is a by-product of the general scientific culture and becomes more probable as the culture advances. To increase the probability of such discoveries we are thus under the deepest moral obligation to advance as rapidly as possible.

Admitting this, it still might be claimed that progress is not the only condition influencing human welfare, and that these other conditions should also be considered. A simple answer is that any decrease in human welfare decreases the rate of progress. Thus if progress is most rapid, these other conditions will be automatically satisfied.

The fundamental problem of religion is then how to promote progress. To do this two methods have been tried.

One is by minority or majority action to choose the precise steps to be taken and then go ahead. This has always failed. The reason for this failure is that there is an infinite number of directions to go and no way to predetermine which is correct. The other method is to make no effort to control the direction of advance, but merely to try to establish conditions favorable to advance. This is the method that has succeeded best.

A religion primarily interested in human betterment would then first try to decide what are the conditions under which such betterment is most likely to occur. A simple way to determine these conditions would be to appeal to all the special groups—Christian, Jewish, Moslem, Hindu, Communist, democratic—asking each to make suggestions. It is safe to predict that all the reports would include four features, namely, good morals, freedom, education, and economic well-being. This universal agreement shows that the experience of mankind has everywhere proved the value of these conditions. Their importance is also indicated by direct reasoning.

The case for good morals is simply stated. When people live in close contact, efficient action requires that individual behavior be subject to certain rules or regulations. These rules constitute the morals, or ethics, of the society. They are thus merely a recipe for success in social living.

That these rules have an absolute basis is shown by the fact that they have essentially the same form in all human societies. Even criminals follow many of these rules in dealing with each other. The essential difference is that in the higher religions these rules are considered universal, whereas criminals apply them only in the local group.

In the early stages of human society, knowledge was sufficient only to permit the most limited interference with the processes of nature. Success was then measured almost entirely by social co-operation. Since all important religions date from this early period, they all place principal stress on these social or moral features. In our time other features have become important.

At the head of this list is freedom. Failure to realize its real function is a principal reason for differences in attitude concerning freedom. Liberty is usually pictured as an individual right. According to this notion, restricting the liberty of others merely injures them, and there is only a moral objection to that. In reality we grant liberty to others not for their benefit but for our own, because if allowed to go their own way they will do more for the rest of us, on the average, than under any directions we are able to give. Giving liberty to others is thus merely refraining from killing the geese that are laying golden eggs.

The reason for this is progress. If conditions were practically fixed, as in a hive of bees or a nest of termites, best methods could be found for each particular act and there would be no need for freedom. But in an advancing society the most important feature is advance; for what lies ahead is infinite, whereas what has been done will always remain finite. The problem then is to determine what changes lead to improvement. Since any fundamental change introduces features not previously known, this usually cannot be answered by simple reason. The only other procedure is trial and error. The number of correct methods found will increase with the number of trials, and the number of trials will be greatest when each individual goes his own way. Thus the function of freedom is merely to produce maximum diversity and therefore maximum progress.

For progress to be most rapid the individual must, however, have the opportunity to do his best. This is possible only if he is properly trained. The purpose of education is to supply that training. The greatest genius in history, left entirely alone, could not rise to the level of Archimedes. To do his best now he must start from the level of the present day. Since the period during which he can do anything worth

while is very limited, his education must therefore begin as
early as possible and advance as rapidly as possible. Since no
two people are alike, this requires that the education of each
student be entirely different from that of every other student.

People who have not experimented have little concept of
the learning capacity of the very young child. With fifteen
minutes instruction per day for two or three months, many
children will be reading fluently at the age of three and many
others at four. These children would already have read very
extensively when they formally enter school at six. In school
the grades should be abolished and the schedules so arranged
that each student works in each subject at the highest level
at which he can do good work. Under such a program the
best students in science and mathematics would do graduate
work in these subjects as freshmen in college.

The effect of such a program would be beyond measure
and it need not cost an extra dollar. While good teachers help
they are not essential. With guidance in the choice of texts
and a little encouragement, the best students can educate
themselves under a teacher who knows nothing about the
subject being studied.

Some people object to a program of this kind because it
could result in a narrow professional training and not a broad
liberal education. If started early enough there is no danger
whatever of that effect. Because of their extensive reading
such students obtain a better education not only in professional subjects but also in language and the humanities than is
obtained in the conventional way.

For such a program to succeed there must, however, be
economic well-being. A people lacking the necessities of life
are practically forced to concentrate on immediate needs. Unfortunately, the established religions have inherited their eco-
nomics from a period when world conditions were entirely
different from those existing now. During those earlier periods
wealth consisted entirely of things—mainly food, clothing,

and shelter—and human labor was the only method of producing these things. The main problem was distribution. If one person had more than he could use, the excess should naturally go to others. In our time other methods of production have been devised and these methods are being constantly improved. Wealth is no longer measured by things, but by capacity to produce things. This requires certain concentrations of wealth, and best results are obtained when these concentrations are controlled by those most capable of creating wealth.

Many people think religion should be concerned only with spiritual matters and not with these material activities. In answer it should be noted that there is today a world conflict of ideologies. The decision in that conflict will be determined in accord with natural law. Under that law there is no substitute for success. Whether failure is due to lack of morals, stupidity, or poor business methods makes little difference. The system which results in greatest progress has an advantage which it is impossible to overcome.

Religious organizations cannot, of course, be expected to take direct responsibility for any of these business activities. Theirs is the less spectacular but more fundamental role of creating an atmosphere in which the efforts of others will have greater success.

Pasteur defined democracy as that form of government under which each individual is permitted to do his best for the general welfare. For this certain conditions are needed. Good morals are needed to permit social co-operation. Freedom is needed to permit each individual to do the work he is best fitted to do. Education is needed to permit each generation to start its advance from the level attained by the preceding generation. Material well-being is needed to permit a part, at least, of human effort to be devoted to pursuits unrelated to material ends.

To provide these conditions should be the function of a modern religion.

CHAPTER 5

Notes on the Religious Orientation of Scientists

by GERALD HOLTON

Harvard University

IN THIS INFORMAL communication I have set myself the task of sketching some of the background of the picture of the scientists whose work and interests we are considering in this seminar. In speaking of the religious positions and motivations underlying the work of some scientists, I shall leave out those who have been untypical to a marked degree—either very irreligious or, like Boyle and Pascal, very strongly religiously inclined. Also I shall limit myself mostly to physical scientists. One reason is that I know them best. A better reason is that it was in the physical sciences, and particularly in celestial mechanics, that modern scientists first found themselves in conflict with theologians on a large scale. The case history of that struggle stretches over several hundred years, and it is now happily closed. Therefore one may, I think, seek in it some general guidelines for the resolution of conflicts between scientific and religious positions.

A key figure in the period which saw the beginning of modern physical science was Johannes Kepler, the German astronomer who lived from 1571 to 1630. It was he who provided the link between Copernicus and Newton. Initially trained for the ministry, he wrote in his first book, the *Mysterium Cosmographicum*, "I wanted to become a theologian; for a long time I was restless. Now, however, observe how through my efforts God is being celebrated in astronomy." More than a few times in his later writing, he referred to astronomers as priests of the Deity in the Book of Nature.[1]

From his earliest writings to his last, Kepler maintained the direction and intensity of his religio-philosophical interest. His whole life was one of uncompromising piety; he was incessantly struggling to uphold his strong and often nonconformist convictions in religion as in science. Caught in the turmoil of the Counter Reformation and the beginning of the Thirty Years' War, in the face of bitter difficulties and hardships, he never compromised on issues of belief. Expelled from communion in the Lutheran church for his unyielding individualism in religious matters, expelled from home and position at Graz for refusing to embrace Roman Catholicism, he could truly be believed when he wrote, "I take religion seriously, I do not play with it," or "In all science there is nothing which could prevent me from holding an opinion, nothing which could deter me from acknowledging openly an opinion of mine, except solely the authority of the Holy Bible, which is being twisted badly by many."

But as his work shows us again and again, Kepler's soul bears a dual image on this subject. For next to the Lutheran God, revealed to him directly in the words of the Bible, there stands the Pythagorean God, embodied in the immediacy of observable nature and in the mathematical harmonies of the solar system whose design Kepler himself had traced—a God

[1] Gerald Holton, *American Journal of Physics*, XXIV, No. 5 (May, 1956), p. 351.

whom, he said, "in the contemplation of the universe I can grasp, as it were, with my very hands."

The expression is wonderfully apt: so intense was Kepler's vision that the abstract and concrete merged. Here we find the key to the enigma of Kepler, the explanation for the apparent complexity and disorder in his writings and commitments. In one brilliant image, Kepler saw the three basic cosmological models superposed: *the universe as physical machine, the universe as mathematical harmony, and the universe as central theological order*. And this was the setting in which harmonies were interchangeable with forces—in which a theocentric conception of the universe led to specific results of crucial importance for the rise of modern physics.

Kepler was overjoyed when he found that he could construct a universe in which the life-giving sun rather than the earth was the center. To him, the sun was both the Temple of God and also the seat of that tangential driving force which Kepler still thought was needed to keep the planets moving constantly in their orbits. That the sun and each of the planets were together responsible for the central force that provides stability for the solar system, namely gravitation, was shown later by Newton. To Kepler, his own laws of planetary motion bore out the importance of the sun, for in each of the laws the sun is the body to which the measurements of distance or velocity may be referred. Finally, by regarding the sun as the center of the planetary system, the complex motions of the planets became understandable in terms of simple regularities; and, after all, Kepler reasoned, the uniformity of planetary motion is to be expected if it is caused by a constant never-failing cause such as one may identify with the Deity.

This uniformity of motion is not expressed in constant speed (which is not the characteristic of planetary motion) but in the uniformity of area swept out in units of time by a line imagined to exist between the sun and the planets. This is, of course, the second law of planetary motion. On finding it, Kepler confessed that he was in "sacred ecstasy": "I have stolen the golden vases of the Egyptians and raised a tabernacle for my God, far away from the land of Egypt."

The main importance of Kepler in this discussion is that he is a transition figure. His Pythagorean or neo-Platonic theism foreshadows an important trait in the metaphysics of modern science. Besides his earlier pseudotheological motivation we see in the mature Kepler a motivation akin to that of some modern scientists: An acceptable theory in physical science should, on the basis of the available observations, reveal mathematical order and harmony. Our mind has been so created as to conceive, above all, *quantity* and numerical relations. As Kepler expressed it in an early letter: "Those laws [which govern the material world] lie in the power of the understanding of the human mind; God wanted us to perceive them when he created us in His image in order that we may take part in His own thoughts. . . . Our knowledge [of number and quantity] is of the same kind as God's, at least insofar as we can understand something of it in this mortal life."

To Kepler, and to many scientists following him, the real world is what is quantitatively describable and harmonious. Indeed, perhaps the real world is identifiable with the mathematical harmony connecting experience and fact. We shall speak about the modern counterpart to this position after studying the attitude of the two other physical scientists who, with Kepler, formed the triumvirate of seventeenth-century physics and astronomy.

Galileo Galilei was a contemporary of Kepler. To him, as to Kepler, nature was a simple, orderly system whose working has the inexorable character of mathematical demonstration. The connection between the world of mathematical certainty and of religious belief has, in Galileo's case, been, of course, of enormous historical interest.[2]

In matters of faith, Galileo considered himself to be a devout and sincere Catholic. His defense of the Copernican system and his use of the results of astronomical discovery in support of that system, was in his thought completely congruous with a belief in the teachings of the Bible and of the Church Fathers. To him, there was no conflict. On the contrary, scientific knowledge supplements the knowledge of God obtained through the Scriptures: "As the truth of which mathematical demonstrations give us knowledge, it is the same [knowledge] which the Divine Wisdom knows." Though, of course, God knows infinitely *more* propositions than we can know through mathematical study and physical research, we know those few as certainly as does God himself.

This has two results: It permits us to know God through a channel in addition to that of revelation and prayer—namely through observation and the exercise of the intellect. Secondly, it forces us to adopt some position as to the veracity of literal statements in the Scriptures which are in conflict with the findings of our researches. Galileo's own solution of this problem, which helped to heap so much trouble on him, is best given in his own words, in his letter to Castelli of December, 1613, and to the Grand Duchess Christina in 1615:

> . . . I think that in discussions of physical problems we ought to begin not from the authority of scriptural passages, but from sense-experiences and necessary demonstrations; for the holy Bible and the phenomena of nature proceed alike from the divine Word, the former as the dictate of the Holy Ghost and the latter as the observant executrix of God's commands. . . . For that reason it appears that nothing physical which sense-experience sets before our

[2] For a fine account, see Giorgio de Santillana, *The Crime of Galileo* (Chicago: University of Chicago Press, 1955).

eyes, or which necessary demonstrations prove to us, ought to be called in question (much less condemned) upon the testimony of biblical passages which may have some different meaning beneath their words. For the Bible is not chained in every expression to conditions as strict as those which govern all physical effects; nor is God any less excellently revealed in Nature's actions than in the sacred statements of the Bible. . . .

But I do not feel obliged to believe that that same God who has endowed us with senses, reason, and intellect has intended to forgo their use and by some other means to give us knowledge which we can attain by them. He would not require us to deny sense and reason in physical matters which are set before our eyes and minds by direct experience or necessary demonstrations. This must be especially true in those sciences of which but the faintest trace (and that consisting of conclusions) is to be found in the Bible. . . . I would say here something that was heard from an ecclesiastic of the most eminent degree: "That the intention of the Holy Ghost is to teach us how one goes to heaven, not how heaven goes. . . ."

. . . Hence I should think it would be the part of prudence not to permit anyone to usurp scriptural texts and force them in some way to maintain any physical conclusion to be true, when at some future time the senses and demonstrative or necessary reasons may show the contrary. Who indeed will set bounds to human ingenuity? Who will assert that everything in the universe capable of being perceived is already discovered and known? Let us rather confess quite truly that "Those truths which we know are very few in comparison with those which we do not know." [3]

What is of crucial importance to us is that this position, in a sense, has been completely victorious. Three hundred years after Galileo's condemnation, the Report of the Vati-

[3] Stillman Drake, *Discoveries and Opinions of Galileo* (New York: Doubleday and Company, Inc., 1957), pp. 182–187. Everyone interested in these problems should read both Galileo's letter to the Grand Duchess

can's Biblical Commission, designated to deal with problems relating to Scripture and science teaching, found as follows: "Of those methods which form the primary object of the teaching of natural sciences, God taught nothing to man by the intermediary of the sacred writers, since such instruction would not be of any use for their eternal salvation."

Students of science all too often take the story of Galileo and of his ultimate vindication to mean that the modern scientist does not need to accept the authority of the Bible on any subject. This would have horrified Galileo. The very least that one should stress in this story is Galileo's own position: Science is one of the legitimate ways of reaching out toward God.

Newton, born shortly after Galileo's death in 1642 and living until 1727, differs from Galileo, Kepler, and Descartes in an interesting and important way; although the greatest of mathematical physicists, he does not make the a priori assumption that all of nature is at bottom necessarily mathematical. In his first preface to his great work, *The Mathematical Principles of Natural Philosophy*, he expresses the hope that his work may either show a method of solving all problems in natural philosophy, or else at least show the way to a "truer philosophy." Nor is there among his four Rules of Reason, which are basic to his work, any that direct us to search for mathematical harmony.

As in the case of Galileo, Newton's religious orientation came into the open as the result of an attack after the publication of his scientific works. Only after such attacks as those of Bishop Berkeley did Newton, in the second edition of the *Principia* (1713), add the famous General Scholium, to which we shall turn in a moment. But in the meantime, in 1692–1693,

Christina and Johannes Kepler's preface to his *Astronomia Nova*. It will be noted that the positions of Galileo and Kepler were closely analogous.

he engaged in a significant correspondence with Bentley.[4]

Bentley had been appointed to the Robert Boyle Lectureship; its warrant being "to prove the existence of God by arguments drawn from nature," Bentley's title was "A Confutation of Atheism from the Origin and Frame of the World." In order to be able to use, in his last two lectures, arguments from physics, Bentley turned to Newton himself for advice. Newton replied in four letters, the first of which starts with the sentence: "Sir, When I wrote my Treatise about our System, I had an Eye upon such Principles as might work with considering Men, for the Belief of a Deity; nothing can rejoice me more than to find it useful for that Purpose."

Among the great number of arguments which Newton adduces for the existence of God on the basis of what was then known about the solar system, Newton remarked that if the solar system had been created by a "blind" cause, "without Contrivance or Design," the sun would surely be of the same kind as the planets, i.e., without light and heat. There can be no reason, Newton argued, why only one body in the solar system be qualified to give light and heat to the rest except "because the Author of the System thought it convenient." There being no scientific necessity that the sun gives forth its rays, it must have been designed to do so by a higher intelligence. Similarly, the stability and order of the planetary orbits as compared to the orbits of comets, and the fact that the then known planets and their moons move in nearly the same plane in the same direction "argues that Cause to be not blind and fortuitous, but very well skilled in Mechanicks and Geometry."

[4] The interested reader is directed to the book, E. A. Burtt, *The Metaphysical Foundations of Modern Physical Science* (New York: Doubleday and Company, 1955). See also Perry Miller, "Bentley and Newton," in *Isaac Newton's Papers and Letters on Natural Philosophy*, ed. I. B. Cohen (Cambridge: Harvard University Press, 1958).

I cannot forego a parenthetical remark that forced itself on me as I reread these and the others among Newton's arguments. One by one, science has begun to understand the physical necessity for each of the features of celestial motion which Newton thought were beyond the reach of science and for that reason evidences of the Deity. As science has pushed back the frontiers of the unknown, it has made untenable the position of theologians who argued as Newton did, and has left fewer and fewer chores for the Deity in the everyday functions of the world. In the General Scholium of the *Principia*, Newton wrote later, "This most beautiful system of the sun, planets, and comets could only proceed from the counsel and dominion of an intelligent and powerful Being. . . ." But today one can begin to demonstrate that a solar system such as ours is a consequence of the laws of motion governing the ways in which our solar system probably formed out of a large cloud of particles.

The same thinking as Newton's persisted in connection with the problem of the descent of man before it was explained by evolution, with the surface features of our earth before modern geology, and with many other examples of this kind. Surely we have now learned that it is not only dangerous but blasphemous to let one's belief in the Deity rest on one's estimate of what science cannot do.

Newton's fundamentally theological orientation can be shown to underlie the very basis of his *Principia*, namely the discussion of space, time, and motion. Although it was quite clear to him that absolute space, absolute time, and absolute motion do not impose themselves directly upon our senses, and therefore, from our modern point of view, might be considered as irrelevant and even dangerous conceptions, Newton held that they were needed because they provided a basic connection between God and the world of science. Observable (i.e., relative) aspects of space, time, and motion are founded on their absolute prototypes, and the absolute exists because God exists and God is absolute. Beyond the limit of knowledge attained by science lies the realm of God. In Him resides the "real" nature of things of which science gives only an incomplete rendition. In Newton's philosophy it is He who "constitutes duration and space" . . . "in Him are all things contained and moved . . . [although] in a manner not at all corporeal, in a manner utterly unknown to us."

In contrast with Kepler and Galileo, Newton held the Deity to be essentially unapproachable through science in a direct way; although the intention of the Deity reveals itself in the simplicity of nature, the order of the solar system, et cetera, He allows us at most to *approximate* Him through the study of science. As Newton wrote in Query 28 of the *Opticks,* "And though every true Step made in this Philosophy brings us not immediately to the Knowledge of the first Cause, yet it brings us nearer to it and on that account is to be highly valued." Thus, although Newton's God was less directly graspable than Kepler's and Galileo's, neither was He just an adjutant of science, a handy man behind the scenes who keeps the universe in order. Rather, the case had been made that Newton thought of science as "that part of theology which could be reduced to demonstrative form, the highest form of *reasoning* about God." [5]

It is this view, perhaps, which may be of greater interest when we turn to the contemporary scene. A catalogue of *Religious Beliefs of American Scientists* [6] has been prepared by E. L. Long, Jr. He finds that scientists as a group appear to be not markedly different with respect to the expression of religious affiliation from comparable other professional groups. By and large, the motivation for scientific work no

[5] G. S. Brett, "Newton's Place in the History of Religious Thought." In *Sir Isaac Newton, 1727–1927* (Baltimore: Williams and Wilkins, 1928).
[6] (Philadelphia: Westminster Press, 1952.)

longer contains an avowedly religious component. One may perhaps divide the scientific fraternity of today into six groups. First in number is the group that is frankly pre-occupied with the quest of scientific knowledge for its own sake or the application of science to technology. God is an "optional, peripheral question" and indeed all explicit philosophical questions are likely to be considered unfruitful.

The lack of religious commitment, however, does of course not imply a lack of ethical commitment. No one will be surprised that the widespread secularization of morality has been effective here also. But although the lives of some of the scientists may lack spiritual qualities of the sort that often characterize the life of a member of a worshiping congregation, it has beneficent and chastising influences of its own. The pursuit of science brings with it an optimistic and positive mood and an ethos of work that should not be underestimated. Before castigating a scientist such as this too severely for what some take to be a displacement of ultimate commitment, I would urge that one examine with charity the reason and direction for this displacement. Nothing is more inaccurate and harmful than to conjure up the conception of the scientist as iconoclast.

A second group of scientists is formed by those to whom God appears as he did to Newton: the First Cause, the originator, both of the world of matter and of the laws which control the behavior of matter—even to the extent that matter may aggregate into living beings; a God who does not allow direct access to his true being but rather offers a symbolic and approximate knowledge, for example through exhibiting the unfailing reliability of his natural law through all time.

Thirdly, there is a relatively small group of scientists who belong to liberal religious sects and who indeed have strong religious commitments and motivations. Individual examples are known to all of us, and they include some of the most prominent scientists. In contrast to these, however, there is, or was, an "American Scientific Affiliation," whose new associates sign a statement of belief that God is the author of the Bible as well as the sustainer of the physical world and that there can be no discrepancy between the Bible and the "real facts." The task of the association is specifically to correlate the facts of science and of the Bible. To anyone versed in the history of science, it is no surprise that this group has not drawn forth any significant scientific contributions; for it seems to be an axiom that progress today in science itself depends on one's freedom from explicit doctrinal programs.

A fourth group is also not large. It contains those who are devoted members of an explicitly fundamentalist sect or other religious group with doctrinal positions on matters which most scientists would regard as questions of scientific fact; yet they can attain in their scientific work complete autonomy. From the outside, it is neither proper nor simple to explain this compartmentalization of mind, and one is tempted to compare it with the contradiction between Sunday profession and weekday behavior of many a churchgoing businessman.

The fifth trend is exemplified in Einstein's position as found, for example, in his book, *Cosmic Religion*.[7] Einstein wrote, "The cosmic religious experience is the strongest and noblest driving force behind scientific research. . . . What a deep faith in the rationality of the structure of the world, and what a longing to understand even a small glimpse of the reason revealed in the world, there must have been in Kepler and Newton to enable them to unravel the mechanism of the heavens. . . . The path to genuine religiosity does not lie through . . . blind faith, but through striving after rational knowledge."

From any more sophisticated theological point of view, this religiosity is merely a mystical glow in the experience of order in the cosmos. This sort of reverence, one may object,

[7] (New York: Covici, 1931.)

is not what makes either Church saints or even Spinozas. The God of Einstein is not a God of values, of purpose, of authority, or of love, but one of general sympathy with reason and law. And yet it does inspire in some scientists a noble fervor for their work.

Lastly, the sixth group may perhaps be identified best as complementaristic. They hold, in essence, the modern counterpart of the positions of Kepler and Galileo: God has revealed himself in different ways to the scientist and to the theologian. The Scriptures are not rejected, but are understood as guides to the moral life, set in the language and imagery of antiquity. It is perhaps a triumph both of liberal philosophy and of good common sense that in our time so many scientists have come to accept this position even without being fully aware that they have done so.

At the outset of this talk I hoped I would do no more than provide some neutral remarks on the scientific profession whose impact you have come to examine at these sessions. I now notice that I did not entirely stay on the cold rock of description, but instead have slipped now and then into the turbulent sea of opinion. Perhaps you will let this stand, however, as a token of the fact that I would not wish to claim a firm foothold on such grave matters.

CHAPTER 6

Salvation in the Twentieth Century

by RALPH W. BURHOE

American Academy of Arts and Sciences

WHETHER OR NOT one agrees with the articulate analyses of any of the twentieth-century prophets of doom, such as the treatments by Spengler, Sorokin, or Toynbee; or whether one accepts seriously those vaguer adumbrations of despair, meaninglessness, and confusion being cast up profusely by sensitive artists and literati; there is a very simple bit of logic which lends ominous support to predictions of impending doom. This argument, which is supported by every area of empirical experience, is that when any particular order or arrangement of things is beset suddenly with a radically new set of forces, whether internal or external, that order or arrangement is placed under stresses that threaten its continuation. The more radical the new conditions, the more certain is catastrophe. And it makes no difference whether we are talking about an atom, a star, a prehistoric species, or a human civilization.

By uncorking the magic bottle of science, man has let loose a jinni which probably has more radically altered the

conditions of human existence in the past century than anything that has happened in the past five thousand years;
and it appears to be expanding its power to alter our situation
at a rate which overwhelms our imagination to contemplate.
I am referring now not so much to the releasing in the past
century of a large part of the world's store of fossil solar
energy that it took millions of years to build up, nor to the
potential threats of the unleashing on earth of a vast, atomic
nuclear type of energy like that which fires the sun itself,
catastrophic though these may be; but rather I refer to the
fundamental alteration of the pattern of the forces or conditions of life under which man for millennia has existed. To
prosper under the former set of conditions, man's own internal design and controls have adjusted him, in response to
the processes of natural selection since the beginning of life
on earth. The threat to man is analogous to the threat to a
species of fish occasioned by the drying up of the waters it
had been inhabiting. Unfortunately for the fish, it did not
have time to adapt itself to the ways of life necessary for
survival on dry land, and there was no way it could get back
to the watery circumstances for which it was adapted. It is
very likely that man is not presently organized to survive in
the drastically different environment he has unwittingly provided by his own technological powers.

The changed condition of human life brought about by
science warrants a fresh contemplation of the problem of
perdition or salvation—whether man will be lost or saved.
Many of the traditional programs for human salvation would
seem to be quite inadequate in this unprecedented situation.
Even if we had faith in its efficacy, a prayer to our tribal God
for power to defeat our foes could in fact be a prayer for
self-extermination.

And yet I wish to suggest that our salvation today lies in
religion. This suggestion is preposterous enough; but, when
I add that religion must also be scientific, both the high priests

of the traditional religions and the high priests of science will surely say that this is a mad prophet indeed, for he puts words together that everyone knows cannot be put together—a scientific religion!

Religion's Function in the Total Culture

The seeming madness of saying "scientific religion" can be dispelled only if we are ready to extend the meaning of the term "religion" beyond some of its traditional connotations. I suggest that we would handicap ourselves just as much if we limit our concept of religion today to mean some of its familiar traditions as we would if we limited our concept of geography to a flat earth. We can be as scientific about religion as we can about geography, if we do not arbitrarily exclude the extension of its meaning into modern concepts.

First, then, let us attempt a more generic definition of religion. I submit that religions in whatever culture—and the anthropologists are hardly able to find any culture without one—are the organs or institutions whose function it is to engender attitudes and behavior that tend to adapt man to the conditions of his total environment in such a way as to optimize his prime values. I submit further that these prime values will probably be found to be essentially a continuation of the long-established values of all living creatures: the continuation and advancement of life.

It is necessary here to note that man's behavior differs from that of animal species in that his activities to survive are informed and directed not only by control centers genetically internalized in the physiological organism, like reflexes, hormones, and central nervous systems, but his activities are also directed by sources of control which are transmitted by cultural organs or institutions. The cultural patterns are transmitted by social communication and are picked up by each individual in that culture through learning or education. In the familiar language of Freud these two sources of motivational inheritance may be termed the "id" (related to biogenetic urges and controls) and the "superego" (related to the culturally transmitted urges and controls).

Man knows what is good or bad to eat not only by his animal responses to odors, tastes, etc., but this knowledge is elaborated also by the mores of his tribe. Man's knowledge of how to find food by an elaborate process of agriculture is transmitted to him through his culture and is not genetically instinctive. While agricultural know-how may be accumulated and transmitted biogenetically, as it is in certain species of ants, for instance, the cultural method of accumulating and transmitting, which obtains in the human situation, provides a much more flexible system, one which can evolve at a much more rapid rate and to far higher orders of complexity and effectiveness than the know-how transmitted by the genes. This gift of the capacity to accumulate, improve, and transmit know-how through cultural mechanisms of inheritance (language, tools, etc.) as well as through biological mechanisms of inheritance, is essentially the source of man's uniqueness among all animals thus far developed on earth. By this gift he has in a sense been given lordship over all other life on this planet.

It is necessary also to note, however, that man no longer is an animal which can survive without his culture. Even the most primitive cultures studied by our anthropologists involve a complex system of know-how that is not transmitted through the genes.

To come back to religion, the cultural know-how must be organized to be effective, just as is the biogenetic know-how. For the latter, a portion of the central nervous and endocrine system motivates and properly orders the various operations of the organism. It knows how to evaluate the competing claims from various stimuli. It causes the organism to eat or to stop eating; to breathe or hold its breath; it causes the heart to beat faster or more slowly; a gland to secrete or not; and so on, all in a nicely balanced and integrated rhythm to maintain life. Walter B. Cannon's *The Wisdom of the Body* [1] is a classic account. But, insofar as culture develops to alter and elaborate this biogenetic system of motivations, culture must also provide for complex regulations of behavior in such a way that the first things come first to preserve and strengthen life.

The thesis here presented is that religion is that organ or institution of culture which provides the most all-embracing and fundamental integration of ideas and attitudes that move man to behavior that makes life possible. Religion is to human culture what the neuroendocrine motivational centers are to the animal body.

Religion and Government

Many presume that government is the institution which provides for this co-ordination of behavior and ordering of values at the cultural level. Indeed, it is sometimes difficult to separate government and religion. But in reality government, as compared with religion, is relatively limited and shallow in its power to control and co-ordinate behavior. In the first place, governments generally do not create the moral law and mores which they help to enforce, any more than the schoolteacher creates the languages he helps teach. Secondly, governmental sanctions or enforcements of the moral law are at best gross or crude efforts to create the internal harmony of a society. A government may eliminate or forcibly restrain small minorities of radical offenders. But it cannot very effectively enforce programs that depart radically from the norms widely established in the mores of a popula-

[1] (New York: W. W. Norton & Co., 1939.)

tion, whether concerning alcoholic beverages, chastity, or even tax payments and military service. W. E. Hocking's recent book on *The Coming World Civilization* [2] presents an interesting analysis of the impotence of the state when there is a "failure of the motivation it has hitherto been able to assume in its public."

Moreover, religion not only serves to provide the underlying moral codes and general moral motivation, but it goes beyond anything a government does to provide satisfactory orientations and attitudes to the larger environment and to the inner self.

Man must adjust to tremendous forces against which his own powers, whether as an individual or united in the mightiest empire of the world, are puny. The impact of flood and drought, heat and cold may overwhelm him or his beloved. And from the inside thousands of invisible forces strike him to inflict pain, deformity, and impotence. Governments are powerless to protect the life and welfare of their peoples against certain overwhelming forces, including those which make death inevitable sooner or later for every man. In fact, governments as well as other social agencies contracting to defend a man often specifically exclude themselves from responsibility for "acts of God." The cultural agency to help man adjust to these vast forces is religion.

Then there is the especially tragic case where the very social institutions established to defend and save man turn on him and betray him. We have known or read of the hero or saint who continues faithfully to serve his government and colleagues, family, or friend, even after these have tragically rejected and smitten him. What motivates such nobility? And what will console the recipient of such injustice, whether he becomes a hero or saint or not? Here again is an area of major human concern where religion is the primary cultural instrument of salvation.

[2] (New York: Harper & Brothers, 1956.)

Evolution of the Religious Function

That element of culture which for thousands of years has provided man with an interpretation of things, which enables him to take a constructive and co-operative view under the most extreme threats to his safety, and which gives him faith, hope, and love in relation to the underlying powers of the cosmos as well as to his own social group, is religion. The lower animals have this motivation provided for them genetically. Their "religion" is completely unverbalized; but animals are nevertheless duly motivated to handle themselves with courage and skill so as to survive in the extreme as well as in the routine operations of life. The social animals, like the ants, are also duly motivated to self-sacrifice for the social group. In all animals the genetic code transmits the value system from generation to generation, including the hierarchy or order of primacy of values. Even in man, his courage and social concern are basically instinctual. But in human life, motivation as well as know-how must be provided in part by the culture; and it is this cultural patterning of motivation, of values, especially with regard to the prime necessities, or, as theologian Tillich would say, with regard to the areas of ultimate concern, that we call religion.

How the religions of various cultures have succeeded in performing this function would be an interesting story; but here suffice it to say that it seems to be a reasonable interpretation that religions have evolved like the other elements of culture, such as language or agriculture, largely without any man's premeditated design. Moreover, the complexity and effectiveness of religion, like language or agriculture, are such as to defy any ready and facile rational analysis. They yield only slowly to understanding by a scientific approach. The wisdom of religion and other elements of culture is a cause for man's awe and admiration, like the wisdom of the body accumulated in the genes. Men have accepted the arbitrary features of these products of cultural evolution because in any generation they have not had the wit to create a better language or agriculture or religion. While man's acceptance of the efficient tools and programs evolved by his cultural evolution can never be as complete as the bird's acceptance of the aerodynamic properties of its wings and instinctual mechanisms for operating them, it can be said that, before the age of science, men on the whole accepted the culture of the society into which they were born.

The effectiveness of the various religions in providing their respective cultures with the integrative interpretations above indicated has been pointed out not only by the scholars of religion within existing religious institutions, but also by social scientists. The social anthropologists, in particular, have demonstrated the delicate interrelation of the total culture to the religion. They have also shown how changes in the culture may render the religion ineffective, whereupon the system is either reformed or breaks up. This has often happened when two cultures come in contact. The mutual impact often breaks the religion, the social integrity, and viability of the one society, which then becomes absorbed in the other. The disintegration of primitive cultures on contact with Western civilization is recounted in such books as Abram Kardiner's *Psychological Frontiers of Society*.[3] The formation of new religious institutions, in response to unbearable stresses in societies, is presented in Anton T. Boisen's *Religion in Crisis and Custom*.[4]

However, it is not our purpose to go into detail on the processes whereby religions are evolved by adaptations within societies under the creative forces governing the evolution of life in the universe. The main point here is to note that the religion of each culture provides a dynamic integrating and

[3] (New York: Columbia University Press, 1949.)
[4] (New York: Harper & Brothers, 1955.)

directing pattern of attitudes upon which the survival of the society depends.

The function a religion performs may be vital even when it may appear to an outside observer to be nonsensical and ridiculous in terms of his different cultural background. The sense or nonsense of the rational interpretations of religion, like those of agriculture, do not affect the essential value or necessity of the operations which it performs. If the Plymouth Indians explained to the Pilgrim colonists that they buried a fish in each hill of corn they planted for reasons that seemed farfetched to the Pilgrims, it did not in the slightest alter the effectiveness of this method of fertilizing the soil and providing sustenance for life.

Just as those who fertilize the soil must have some reason or motivation for performing the act, so those who are to behave morally in relation to other men and those who are to behave bravely and usefully in the face of fundamental threats to their safety must have some reason for so behaving, at least insofar as such behavior is not provided for unconsciously in their genes. The religions have provided such reasons through their interpretations of the nature of man and of the nature of the powers outside of human society to which men must adapt. In both cases the religions have established doctrines about entities which are not directly observable—doctrines that are theories or hypotheses if you believe them, myths and legends if you no longer believe them. In short, religions have sought to tell man of the hidden secrets of his salvation, his safety; and to give him reason for faith, hope, and love, in spite of seeming evidence to the contrary.

Concepts about Unseen Realities in Religion and Science

A common belief or theory of the higher religions is that of the immortality of man's soul which they distinguish from his body or more ephemeral nature. One must suppose that such a doctrine was necessary on at least two counts. First, man's rational analysis and prediction of his own death began to provide a rational negation of the genetically provided optimism toward life; for a new attitude of worry, discouragement, and fear of the future was produced by the contemplation of death. Secondly, the religious argument for reward of virtues, particularly for behavior that benefited the group but was detrimental to the individual, could not very well be sustained on the basis of rational contemplation of what nature deals out.

In animal instinctual behavior, provided by the genes, suitable motivation in spite of the ultimate death of every individual was automatically provided for; and motivation for suitable risk and self-sacrifice of the individual in favor of the needs of the society or species was also provided. To a biologist, such provisions for animal species may be seen as very reasonable, sound, and effective for the management of the success of the species.

But men find it hard to take such a view of themselves. Perhaps this is an accidental by-product of the fact that thus far in his evolution man's conscious concerns seem to relate primarily to the regulation of the more immediate skeletal adaptations of his organism to the conditions of the environment. The underlying ends and goals of his life, including procreation and death, are dealt out to him largely from a pile of cards face down on the table of life's game. Only since modern biology has begun to unravel the contents of this pile of genetic cards, which every man is forced to take into his hands and play, have we begun to be able to feed into our brains sufficient detail to become significantly conscious of some of the weightier problems of the goals of life, such as death, to be able to make rational sense of them. The various religions have produced some shrewd and effective stopgap myths or theories. But they are not well enough integrated with the new scientific knowledge to permit contemporary sophisticated men to contemplate seriously their own death and still be of good cheer. Death is only one of many elements of life which are thus rendered confusing, paradoxical, and disruptive for minds which by nature thus far are pretty shallow in their comprehension of the larger mysteries of life.

The biblical Job is a classic argument that it simply is not true, from the point of view of empirical observation, that the man who performs all the moral and other requirements of his religion is invariably rewarded and prospered in terms of the common human values of life, health, wealth, etc. Pestilence and untimely death can hit the perfectly moral man.

In the Judeo-Christian-Moslem religions the theory that resolves this difficulty, if you can believe it, is one that either promises the resurrection of the body ultimately, or the departure of the inner self or soul immediately after death to reward or punishment, which is meted out in accordance with man's success in obeying the religious rules for good behavior. Farther east, the equivalent doctrine of karma provided for the rewards or punishments for good religious or moral behavior by a theory of upgrading or downgrading in future incarnations, since no such rewards and punishments could be relied on to operate consistently or fully in the present incarnation. Many of us have seen people who believe such doctrines and who have consequently behaved morally with courage and confidence, even in a self-sacrificial way, in the midst of circumstances which would otherwise be tragic.

These were bold and imaginative theories, these doctrines of immortality, with little or no empirical evidence to substantiate them. Their acceptance was in large measure supported by the fact that they fitted coherently into the logic of the system of moral requirements for a viable human society, and the psychological or emotional requirements for the individual's sense of worth in the midst of seeming chaos or threat.

But the rise of modern science, besides putting man into the greatest crisis of his existence indirectly by creating an entirely new set of circumstances for his viability because of the new technology, at the same time stripped him of the capacity to believe in such doctrines of eternal life because the religious doctrines could not be made to fit with the newer scientific doctrines about the hidden secrets of reality. Science pushed man over with one hand and pulled the rug out from under him with the other. This happened not only with regard to religious doctrines of immortality, but science disintegrated many other religious beliefs, leaving the intellectuals concerned with defending religion fighting a perpetual logical retreat. An interesting portrayal of this is found in Douglas Bush's *Science and English Poetry* [5] and in many other places. Moreover, the impact of science seems to be doing the same thing in other cultures—Moslem, Hindu, Buddhist, Confucian—first among the intellectuals, and gradually to more and more of the population. This view would seem to justify a widely held notion that science is a deadly enemy of religion and the satanic instrument of human perdition.

This impact of science has led to the feeling that there is perhaps no existing religion—no socially transmitted set of ideas and ideals—adequate for a civilization confronted with the new circumstances, the new human environment, provided by science.

There are powerful and widespread reactions to this apparently intolerable lack of conviction in the values which the traditional religious cultures portray. A number of novel or heretical systems have sprung up in response to the demand for a better integration of modern knowledge with personal and social values. Communism has been said to be the most

[5] (New York: Oxford University Press, 1950.)

flourishing of these; and it is perhaps sounder than some of the narrower national and racial ideals of, for instance, Fascism and Nazism, which grew so rapidly two or three decades ago in Italy and Germany.

An Effort to Integrate Religion and Science

The urgently needed solution to the problem of human salvation, the saving of man, according to a small band of scientists and religious scholars working under the name of the Institute of Religion in an Age of Science, requires a more imaginative effort to "formulate dynamic and positive relationships between the concepts developed by science of the goals and hopes of man expressed through religion."

If theology is a portrayal of the hidden realities about ourselves and about the determiner of our destiny—a portrayal that spells out a program of the right things to do (values) if we are to be saved or to have life more abundantly —then why do we take so long to recognize that the sciences are the most powerful handmaidens theology has ever had? The sciences are building a more honest, more effective, more rich picture of the hidden secrets of our own natures and of the vast reality in which we live and move and have our being than has ever before been built.

Science provides the basis for a new testament, a new scripture of truth about man and his destiny. Even if this revelation should gainsay any of the previous revelations of human destiny, it will be believed anyway. The light is too bright, and the evidence for its rightness is too clear.

But it has been the discovery of several of us that the revelations of science do not basically gainsay traditional religious doctrines; science does not so much destroy as it fulfills the previous testaments. We can hardly more than suggest a dim outline of what the new revelations of science for human salvation may be, because the work has only begun. It will take time to establish some order and attain consensus on what the story is. I have already indicated that we can hardly expect the application of scientific knowledge to religion to alter or improve it any faster than such applications alter or improve agriculture. We are still a long way from synthesizing our food from carbon, oxygen, nitrogen, and a few other elements. The bulk of this chemical wisdom is still a secret in the genetic structure of plants and animals.

Thus the scientific approach to religion will be a humble effort to read the true story of man, his relation to the source of his being, and his consequent duties and privileges. This approach will respect the existing religions in the same way that agricultural scientists respect agricultural traditions. The scientific approach to religion, like all former valid approaches, cannot possibly transgress the sovereign law of the source of being, but can only seek to discover or reveal it.

Tentative Outline of Some Theological Doctrines Reformulated from a Scientific Viewpoint

Although my own efforts to understand religious truth from the perspective of science may be said to have produced only a feeble light in the vast darkness, which I believe will soon be much more powerfully illumined by an untold number of others in scientific theology already at work or soon to join in the task, the urgent need for even a little light emboldens me to give in rough outline some of the major doctrines which I believe will be established and become effective in giving man a proper sense of direction and hope in the age of science. I shall mention in connection with the points below only briefly the names of some of the scientists with whom I have been more closely associated in the institute and from whose lights my own is nourished.

1. *Revelation and Truth.* In the first place, I suggest that religious doctrine formulated in the light of science will not even pretend to be a dogma, fixed and frozen for all time; it will grow and change as the sciences do. Scientists, like the great religious mystics, are impressed with what they do not know about ultimate reality. In fact, during the current century scientists have worked up quite a creed of "ignoramus," something akin to the doctrine of some theologians about the impossibility of man's knowing the ultimate reality of God. The scientists talk about the impossibility of any finite set of neurones establishing an adequate model to explain an infinity of events. What intrigues them is the miracle that we can find the beautiful, simple statements that we do, such as those of Newtonian mechanics which are nearly isomorphic with a vast range of the phenomena of our experience. But in spite of their astounding successes, scientists today are acutely aware of the finiteness and tentativeness of their most powerful theories. Gödel's theorem concerning the impossibility of even asserting the internal logical consistency of a set of propositions is a popular doctrine among them. There is much new insight about human knowledge and its limitations which has evolved in recent science and its philosophy, and many members of our institute have been reviewing this at our Star Island summer conferences and elsewhere, including such scientists and philosophers of science as Ian Barbour,* C. J. Ducasse, Philipp Frank, Gerald Holton,* Edwin C. Kemble,* Henry Margenau,* Harold K. Schilling, P. A. Schilpp, and J. H. Shrader. The newly developed scientific epistemology is of greatest significance for our views of religious knowledge.

2. This scientific confession of ignorance does not mean that a scientifically based religion will lack useful or valid truth, or that there will be little strength in the conviction it elicits. On the contrary, in science man has found the way

* Contributor to this volume.

to build the most reliable and convincing doctrines. Conviction about scientific statements runs so high that men will believe and even stake their lives when a scientist makes such hitherto implausible proposals as that we might jump over the moon, or generate a solar fire on earth, or use an artificial kidney or heart while the surgeon repairs the damaged one. The conviction provided by a scientifically based theology will be more moving perhaps than the best of faiths of the past.

3. *It is the "He Who Hath Made Us" and not "We Ourselves."* The scientific view seems to confirm the ancient religious notion that man did not make himself, but that he is the creature of an infinitely greater power. The creation of man, as the scientific story goes, is the product of a long and complex development under what are presumed to be essentially universal and invariant laws of operation. The rules for stable configurations and for energy transformations have presumably remained the same for billions of years to define the possible forms and actual evolution from molecule to man. Something of the vastness of the view which the sciences provide of this cosmos which gave birth to and nourishes man, is given in Harlow Shapley's* popular book *Of Stars and Men,*[6] a view which involves countless entities ranging from several powers of ten on both sides of the dimensions immediately familiar to our ordinary experience, entities operating in a history so long that it likewise is measured in several powers of tens of years. "The source and ground of our being is infinite, and men are like the grass of the field."

4. Again it seems that the scientific faith is essentially akin to the ancient religous faith in holding that the infinity in which we live and move is in reality one, not many. The scientific faith that all things are variants in a single system, that one law rules the cosmos from end to end, from the biggest to the littlest, is a faith that grows stronger with each

* Contributor to this volume.
[6] (Boston: Beacon Press, 1958.)

succeeding new discovery that shows the relationship between phenomena that previously did not seem to be related. Today this faith is so high that we have little doubt but that there is continuity from man to amoeba to molecule. There is no separation of man from his origin nor from his fellow men. We are indeed all brothers and all children of the same father.

5. This infinite source of our being, which also made heaven and earth and all that is, so runs the faith of the scientists, is not only one, but it is lawful and orderly rather than chaotic, fickle, or unreliable. Its law not only rules every conceivable place in the universe (whither shall I flee?), but it is the same law today as it was in the beginning and ever more shall be. We do not know it fully, and we shall undoubtedly revise our doctrine about the law as new revelations are made; but the faith of science is that the basic law itself changeth not; it is a rock and a secure foundation in the midst of a sea of changing shapes and forms.

6. *God and Man.* In view of the scientifically painted picture of the vastness and pervasiveness of the source and ground of our being, and in view of its orderly design and the immutable law according to which it operates, the only sensible conclusion for man is to recognize it as his "lord and master," and to spend all his days in discovering and applying what it indicates he must do if he is to have life and more abundant life. Since man cannot, on the evidence of science, conceive himself apart from this supreme being or ground of being, and since man is obviously established as a significant although finite agent of it in the history of the solar system, he must view his own true nature and values in terms of this reality. Man can most properly conceive of himself as a local agent and servant of the creative process of the universe. Man is privileged through his continued searching to know ever more of its design and to participate in ever larger measure in the development of its program.

7. In truth man must identify his own meaning and envision his own ultimate significance and being in terms of the program of this ultimate reality rather than in terms of any immediate, transient, or finite elements of it. Man's continuity with the whole is bound by chains of cause and effect permeating all space and time, if we are to believe the scientific picture. He is not a local and transient accident. This statement may be said to be valid not only for man, but for anything in the universe. Every being and event is an inseparable part of the sacred whole. Any notion that man is independent or alienated from the total program of the ultimate reality of the universe is an illusion, so far as the growing faith and evidence of science is concerned. No man is alone, no man is insignificant. As our Canadian biologist, A. G. Huntsman,* keeps reiterating, each man is inextricably bound up in the web of a great whole.

8. *God, Self, and Brotherly Love.* And the first corollary of this first law, man's kinship with his Creator, is man's kinship with all his fellow men, a kinship that is deeper than blood. We are, as I interpret our geneticist, Th. Dobzhansky,* all part of a common genetic pool. The new scientific theologians are elaborating with greater clarity and precision, it seems to me, the doctrine that we heard a couple of thousand years ago in Galilee, that the first law is concern for God and the second is like unto it, concern for fellow man—every fellow being. We participate in a single, sacred whole, from which we are inseparable. Our gravest error is to put self first, to conceive of self in isolation. This inseparableness of man from his group, his species, from all life, from all things and events in the long history of the heavens and the earth has been proclaimed by a succession of scientists at the Star Island conferences of the Institute of Religion in an Age of Science since 1954, including especially the biological scientists Alfred Emerson,* Ralph W. Gerard,* C. Judson Her-

* Contributor to this volume.

rick,* Hudson Hoagland,* Roy G. Hoskins, Ashley Montagu, Oscar Riddle and George Wald; and by some of the physical scientists, particularly Kirtley F. Mather,* H. B. Phillips,* Paul E. Sabine,* and Harlow Shapley.*

9. *Immortality and Divinity of the Basic Self.* I think that the religious doctrine of immortality can now be expressed in terms that are strengthened rather than diminished by our growing body of scientific information. And as the history and analysis of religion might suggest, this is a vital doctrine for motivation and a proper sense of self-dignity and meaning, and one sorely needed as man faces the last part of the twentieth century. The scientific picture says that in reality I am nothing apart from the cosmos and my fellow beings. My own true being lies inextricably bound to the whole. To serve my fellow beings and to serve the program of evolving life is to serve my own deepest and most significant self. This is my "true," my "spiritual" being, or my "soul." It is a more accurate description of my nature, according to modern science, than is the more superficial description in terms of the immediately sensed but relatively transient element that we call the body.

10. This is not to say that the body is evil or illusory. On the contrary, it is an essential part of the system which is I and is equally as divine and sacred as anything. But it must be recognized realistically for what it is, a transient and small portion of the invisible soul or whole which it is created to serve. This core or soul of my being, the sciences reveal, is older than the hills, a growth of hundreds of millions of years, still conserved as living values in my genotype. Another aspect of my enduring soul, against which the transient in my daily experience of myself is to be judged, is revealed in the impossibility of separating me from the cultural types or forms, which take me back thousands of years. Cultural forms are the source of the very words and ideas I am now

* Contributor to this volume.

writing, and through them I shall live for millennia to come. These chains of cause and effect which link me to the evolution of all life on earth, past and future, through the revelation of science, become for me the only rational and emotionally satisfying way for me to understand myself. To serve this deeper self is not to discount the body or the other structures of the more immediate present, for all this is a part of my being. All life is sacred, as Albert Schweitzer says. More than that, all things in the cosmos are sacred, whether we call them living or not. It is this interpretation of the scientifically revealed world as sacred, including my own nature, which I think we need to recognize if we are to get away from our idiotic schizophrenia that spirit and values lie in one world, and matter and knowledge lie separately and independently in another. That is the great lie, the grave error, of our times.

11. *Self Sacrifice and Immortal Reward.* Not only does the scientific view of man engender humility before the vastness and majesty of the source of our being, and engender moral concern for the welfare of all men, but it provides the illumination for faith, confidence, and trust in the continuity and continued growth of the self. Come what may, this grander vision of self as an agent of the ever new and marvelous developments in an ordered cosmic evolution, not only informs me of my duty, purpose, and meaning; but it informs me that this program in which I am privileged to serve is not transient and accidental, but is a design guaranteed in the very nature of the sacred whole. Nothing basic or viable is lost. This is not to deny that what I am now will be replaced by something different in the future. Death is explained by science as a necessary element in the developing of any genotype, including man's. Furthermore, what from the human point of view is called chance, risk, trial and error, is also explained as a part of the mechanism of this scheme of development or evolution. It is in the nature of our being that we are to gamble rather blindly in order to search out new and better patterns

of being. Evolutionary doctrine, like the religious doctrines of self-sacrifice, informs us of the prodigality of the creator or creative process. Risk, repeated trial and error, is the order of the day. "He that gives up his life for my sake [in self-sacrificial attempt to create more viable patterns] shall find it." If we envision ourselves, our true and real being, as basically conserved in such viable products as genotype and cultural form, then the death and the disappearance of transient states of our being lose their sting.

In a basically scientific interpretation we are saying what the Far Eastern religions say when they talk about reincarnation; or what the Near Eastern religions say in using the term immortal soul or spirit. The things to promote and conserve are the immortal and basic elements of the self, and to risk and sacrifice the inherently more temporary and expendable elements of our nature is necessary to this end. The good news, the gospel of the scientific theology that I think is coming, is that my true self is not properly to be identified with what fails and what dies but with the undying elements which continue, elements invisible to common sense and the unaided eye, but more clearly than ever revealed through science.

A Call for Apostles for the New or Scientific Reformation

The above are just some sketchy outlines of speculative transformations of religious doctrines to better fit the realities established by the sciences. I could not elaborate in a short space a full system of doctrine satisfactory to both the scientifically established picture and to the basic religious needs even if well-advanced doctrines had been developed—and what has been done is so woefully inadequate. The main point of this paper is simply to suggest and very roughly outline my interpretation of why some of us think a sound and effective religious doctrine now can be established in the full light of modern science (and probably cannot be without that light). Many seem to feel that the further advance of human civilization, or perhaps even the continuation of life on this planet, urgently requires such a doctrinal system to provide the grounds for a more dynamic and effective morality and morale among enlightened men. We call upon all who can see the problem and who have the background and imagination to join our mission in exploring and developing this new insight into the nature of our being and into the necessities and opportunities provided to us by that reality in which we live, and move, and have our being.

CHAPTER 7

Comments on Religion in an Age of Science*

by R. W. GERARD
University of Michigan

THANK YOU for the welcome to the Isles of Shoals; it is a rewarding experience to participate in this high-minded quest. When I learned of the more recent dedication of these islands to religious conferences, my first thought was, "Why have they not been renamed 'The Isles of Souls'?" And the second, more pertinent query, as I experienced the spirit of this one was, should not the conferences be called: "Souls on the Shoals"? It seems a good title, not only in the geographic sense, but in the metaphoric one. Most of us here, I take it, have had the courage to give up the cradle-of-the-deep belief, of going along comfortably in blind acceptance of those views into which we happened to be born; but most of us, on the other hand, have not yet achieved a satisfactory set of reasoned convictions about it all, the terra firma to which we aspire, and are being buffeted indeed in the emotional shoals of uncertainty and regret. I hope this is not too false a picture of the

* An informal talk given at a meeting of the Institute of Religion in an Age of Science, on Star Island, August, 1957.

conference, and that some things I shall say, which are essentially a distillate of reactions to what I have heard here over a few brief hours, will be neither too repetitious of earlier discussions nor out of the correct spirit.

Some of these comments will not please everybody; so may I take a moment to reintroduce myself, from a different point of view, and show that I am indeed with you in your quest and aspiration. In the first place, I have been on two Unitarian Service Committee missions, to Czechoslovakia and to Greece. The candlelight procession last night carried me back to Easter in Athens, with the candles going up Mt. Lycabettus—a truly impressive experience!

To supplement what Harlow Shapley said about the sympathy of natural scientists for social science: When the natural scientists in this country were polled about the unborn National Science Foundation, four-fifths said they would rather have no Foundation than one that excluded social science! (I was a member of the polling committee.) I have personally moved into the behavioral science and am now a member of a new Mental Health Research Institute. Having worked for over forty years on the nervous system, first on the chemistry of the nerve cells and their electrical activity, then on the waves that interact to form patterns of effective functioning (indeed, on the question of how cells in general interact and get along together—from which I was led to certain ideas about how people might interact and get along together; you will admit the cells do it on the whole a good deal better than people do), and then on the neural mechanisms of behavior, I am now concerned additionally with behavior as such and in the social science area.

It has also been my concern over many years to examine the possibility of extrapolating from science into the problems of ethics and values, and indeed I have been so bold as to present scientific evidence, which carries the weight of scientific conviction, to support the basic religious affirmation of

Jesus, namely that love is a good thing; that altruism and co-operation have real survival value and steadily increase during the evolution of the organic world. Those species which developed more co-operation have tended to be more successful. It has also proven useful to approach the problem of man as a total individual, an entity in his own right, and man as a unit in a larger entity, a superindividual or epiorganism or society—man alone and man as part of a larger totality. All these understandings can come from science itself; and I have been one of those working to show that this is so. Finally, I regard myself as deeply religious. I would agree with many of the things I have heard emphasized here: man must have faith, man must have values, man must have active emotions if he is to do anything—to act at all, and to choose (let us not now get into the question of free will) between alternate actions.

We will agree that a man is first a man, before he becomes, for part of his totality, a scientist, or a preacher, or an artist, or a teacher, or whatever else he may be; and during those actions in which he is functioning as a specialist, as I shall now do as a scientist, certain of his more general values may be important. Perhaps my most precious value, probably that of scientists in general, is a dedication to honest and, if possible, clear thinking. I would echo that famous statement of Huxley: "God give me the courage to face a fact, though it slay me." It would be less than honest of me to fail to indicate to you some of the questions and reservations which have arisen in my mind during these days. It is in that spirit that I advise with you. I certainly warmly congratulate the group for the earnest effort to find a way to eliminate insularity and, I think on the part of most, blind acceptance.

Let me interrupt here to tell a relevant story. The dear old lady in Cook's Travel Agency was being attended by Mr. Finnegan. "I don't want the regular paths but a more exciting jaunt." His eyes lit up, this appealed to him too. "We

have a wonderful safari in Africa." "Not Africa! Wild animals are there, and heathen. I don't want to go to Africa."
"Well, perhaps India?" "Oh no! India is dirty, and with more
heathen." "Maybe you don't want to go quite so far off the
beat, Madam; have you considered Ireland?" "Ireland! That's
cold and wet and full of Catholics!" "Madam, you can go to
Hell! That's hot and dry and full of Protestants!"

I must now take over that dubious role of an expert talking about his technical field. This is in response to some of the
questions raised at the main conference and at various discussions I have heard in one session or another. I speak now
as a neurophysiologist. The question came up as to whether
individual hallucinations and other experiences, produced by
drugs acting on the brain, are or are not comparable to enduring religious experiences, which are universal. Well, many
things done to the nervous system—even the action of drugs
—can produce irreversible changes. I have seen a cat given
one dose of reserpine (Indian snakeroot) over two years
ago, which ever since has had a weekly convulsion. That may
have little to do with personality; but I have also seen psychotic
patients who, given a brief course of tranquilizers—reserpine
or chlorpromazine or another newer one—for a few weeks,
were then able to leave a hospital and, at least for many
months, be rid of the disturbing symptoms. So there can be
enduring changes. Unfortunately, it works the other way
too—LSD, mentioned yesterday, and cortisone, which is now
given for many purposes, have produced what seem to be irreversible psychotic states.

Another question asked was whether one could, with
drugs or in other ways, produce a St. Francis. I'm not sure
what attributes of St. Francis were meant, but I think the
answer is "Yes." A small destruction, symmetrical on both
sides, in the depths of a wildcat's brain can make that animal
completely docile and peaceful, a gentle animal. Conversely,
a worker in my laboratory destroyed a somewhat different
well-defined part of the brains of ordinary tame laboratory

white rats, and now these animals will jump at anyone, biting viciously—as ferocious as any wild animal. One can, comparably, manipulate the brains of animals to make them eat excessively or starve; drink or thirst; experience what look like intense transcendental emotional states. Humans with electrodes placed in different parts of their brains—mostly for legitimate therapeutic reasons—report, when stimulated, subjective experiences of the expected kinds. In fact, animals —even man—with such stimulating electrodes buried under and in different parts of the brain, will either busily stimulate themselves, presumably because some satisfactory experience is produced; or, having tried one stimulus, will carefully avoid a second, presumably because the experience was unpleasant. In schizophrenics having hallucinations, it has been possible actually to find electric waves occurring spontaneously in the same regions in which stimulation produced hallucinations.

The evidence is mounting at a terrific rate that these various experiences with which we are concerned are definitely associated with activity of the brain. I can't take the time to show that animal brains and experiences are essentially like those of humans, but the evidence is strong. Conversely, humans perhaps imprint the way ducklings do; certainly our early prejudices are very hard to change later on. And other animals, rats as well as monkeys, can make abstractions and can reason, can make moral judgments, and can sacrifice themselves for others. You've all seen such behavior in dogs —stop and think about it. Man differs from the other animals, as far as his brain is concerned, only in the number of nerve cells; we have a great many more. So, in degree, there is a tremendous difference; in absolutes, not.

For behavior, or experience, or awareness of any kind, nerve cells must be active—that is the gist of the experimental facts I have cited to you. Now, how do nerve cells become active? Either by nerve messages coming in from the body surface, from the sense organs which pick up the ordinary

events in our environment, or by nerve messages coming to
the correct part of the brain from within the body. And how
do these nerve messages get started? By a stretch somewhere,
a mechanical stimulation, or by chemical stimulation of sense
organs inside the body. Finally, nerve cells in the brain might
be directly stimulated by chemicals in the blood reaching
them, by electrical pulsations, and so on. We are reasonably
certain about these, and this allows no place for extrasensory
perception. If someday facts are established which justify the
conclusion that such exists, I should have to say there is more
in heaven and earth than my present knowledge encompasses.
The present evidence, in my opinion, does not justify it. Perhaps sensory perception extends further in some individuals
than others, as into the ultraviolet range and for polarized
light.

Well, then, this leaves inspiration, or whatever word you
prefer, as a kind of clicking into place of the activities
of groups of nerve cells. We know this happens, and with
it comes insight. If this is what is meant by "revelation," all
right; but I see no other avenue to knowledge, even of God,
or any other path to action. The inspiration of revelation; the
inspiration of the sudden emergence of a magnificent new
scientific idea; the revelation of the artist who suddenly has
a flash, as Mozart did, of an entire symphony, pure and practically fully formed; the revelation to the young child in
school, whose teacher has explained some silly little business
of addition and multiplication, when suddenly his eyes light
up and he can say, "I understand that!"—all these, I think, are
exactly the same kind of thing.

Well, if all this be correct, what about consciousness and
the avenues to it in human experience? So much is really
known about this now that it is painful to make only some
superficial remarks. There is reason to believe that usually,
as environment impinges upon an organism, the neural machinery is adequate to produce a response that eliminates the

disturbance—a reflex would be the simplest kind of behavior —and this does not, need not, involve any kind of awareness. The great bulk of our behavior is completely unconscious. (In earlier forms of life, perhaps all is without consciousness; but with evolution there has appeared subjective awareness. It obviously had some value for survival, although I cannot quite see how it works.) But when messages continue to reach the brain, from inside the body or outside, because the simple response is not sufficient to take care of the whole situation, then there is irradiation and reverberation, and the messages spread further and further. This is associated with increased alertness and eventually with various forms of anxiety.

There are successive levels of awareness; some localized mainly in different parts of the brain. Most action is unconscious; then comes simple awareness, largely unspecified; then —at higher levels of the brain and later in evolution—is awareness with emotion attached, first and mainly pain and then pleasure; and finally, relatively late in evolution, comes that magnificent mantle, the cerebral cortex, which adds, to awareness and feeling, reason and abstraction. Here is collected past experience and current information—a computing machine if you will, although that denigrates the brain—and the best available answer is presented. So Descartes was, of course, far off when he said, "*Cogito, ergo sum*"; you don't prove you exist because you think, that is two steps away. First you exist even without consciousness; then you might say, "I am aware, therefore I exist," then, "I feel, therefore I exist"; finally, "I think, I feel, I am aware, therefore I exist."

The things I have just said about the functioning of the nervous system would be agreed to, I think without exception, by professional colleagues around the world. One active producer in this field happens to be a devout Catholic; most producers are rather uninterested in questions of religion or theology or metaphysics, just in how the brain works. Yet they would agree on these statements—many of which could not have been made a year or two ago, and many of which will have been superseded by more detailed and precise statements in another year or two—and will go along together. That is the important thing.

Now a few comments on the nature of science and religion. In scientific creativity, in artistic creativity, in religious creativity, in any other, one does start with the creative man. Based on experience, immediate or distant, an idea comes which seems to him to be true. Then that man must have faith in the idea, enough faith to bet on it—to bet a good deal of his time and effort, even his standing, on it. This is the kind of faith held by the fellow who bets his stake on a horse. If that is what was meant by faith in the recent discussion, faith certainly is important. In fact, often the most important ingredient in really major scientific creativity is not imagination—one must have that to do anything, of course —but courage. And courage carries the conviction: "What I am doing is right"—which is faith. The great physicist, Clerk Maxwell, truly said that the credit for a new idea does not belong to the first man who has it, but to the first man who takes it seriously.

All right, the scientist gets an idea, it fits into his past experience, either his unstructured experience—usually not this in science—or his scientific background, and he thinks it is a good idea. Then he does something about it. He has faith, he has values, he has emotions, it means something to him; so he goes to work. He will find things, make observations of some kind, which either fit with his idea or do not fit with it. If they do fit, all is fine, he was right, and he is very pleased. If they don't fit, he doesn't like it and may look for an error in his planning or a mistake in his experiment—any loophole, in an all too human desire to save his mental offspring. Now, the great strength of science is that, whatever this first chap does, somebody else will certainly come along and do it all over, or do it differently, or follow up with the next step. And sooner or later, I assure you, the new discovery will *not* fit. This is fine, because by then some other idea will give a better fit—and so on and on.

Next, certain comments on points made in the excellent colloquium, because the treatment left me unsatisfied. One speaker seemed to deny that a fact would destroy a theory. I disagree; many beautiful theories have been slain by ugly facts. That is what I would mean by a "brute fact": one of a validity unquestioned by any qualified person, and with consequences which seem at the time incontrovertible, decisive, and usually uncomfortable to the status quo. I would go further: a negative result is not only as useful as a positive one, mostly it is much more useful. As long as the expected results are found, there is no need for fresh thought; as soon as one doesn't fit, the whole process starts over again, and something new and better comes out. I cannot agree that one does not depend upon logic too much in science, because theories are proved wrong. Obviously that statement invalidates itself; the only way a theory could be *proved* wrong would be by the use of logic.

The origin of the new, whether in science, art, or religion, is basically the same thing neurologically; the same kind of subjective experience is involved. The new idea for the scientist is associated with the same feeling, the same ecstatic mood of artistic fulfillment, of emotional satisfaction, of exaltation that, I am sure, the religious experience brings. The critical difference, the great power of science, is that, after this individual experience, there are means and criteria that allow him and others to make critical tests of it. I remind you of that illuminating story of the physicist, Robert Wood.

On the platform one time the chairman twitted him, "Mr. Wood, please make clear in your talk the difference between a physicist and a metaphysicist." "On this question," Wood said, "I can illustrate the difference by an experience of my own. I was bothered about the meaning of some observations. Tossing in bed one night, suddenly an idea came to me. It seemed like a good idea, but knowing one isn't too critical at such times, I just slept on it. In the morning I thought about it again, marshaled all the facts I had in mind, and they fitted. I thought it was a darn good idea, rushed to the library and read everything relevant, and all this fitted. I thought it was a damn good idea, and tried it out in the laboratory . . . and it didn't work!" "Gentlemen," he concluded, "the metaphysician has no laboratory."

Another speaker suggested the outcome as a test for the effectiveness of faith. "By their fruits thy works shall be known"—or whatever the proper wording is. (I'm not a very good Bible student, but I do remember this kind of scientific testing in the Bible: Did not Moses and Ahab, arguing about the relative power of their respective gods, agree on an empirical test; whichever could do the most marvelous things with his stick had the most powerful god?) Now, this is fine; testing is excellent. But let me assure you, as a veteran hard-working scientist, that just to say "test it" is far easier than it is actually to perform the elaborate, sophisticated, enormously tedious, time-consuming, expensive, and still often uncertain, process of really testing.

I was chairman of a committee concerned with spending millions a year to find out if the new tranquilizers really are effective. So many "cures" of insanity had their successes for a time and then faded; how much do effects depend on beliefs or convictions, on the attitudes of the doctors or the patients, on many other factors?

It is salutary to keep in mind the patient who came to a psychiatrist, continuously snapping his fingers. The psychiatrist, thinking this symptom a good starting point, asked about the snapping. "That's to keep away the wild elephants." "Very interesting. Of course, you know that the nearest wild elephant is seven thousand miles away, don't you?" "Certainly. Effective, ain't it!" Well, when you really have the evidence, your hearer, if he can follow and tries to understand the evidence, *must* agree with you—these are "the truths no mind is free to reject."

I disagree, also, with the statement made at one session that, in order to carry conviction to a class, one needs to indulge in rhetoric and intonation. I remember one of the most magnificent lectures I ever heard, as a student in an advanced course in organic chemistry, about the proof of the structure of certain molecules. Professor Stieglitz, a great teacher, spoke in a slow drawling monotone which would surely put to sleep anyone not attending to the substance of what he said. But those in the class who followed his argument, and there were many, came out of that particular lecture in a mood of aesthetic elation. I actually bumped into a post in the hall, blinded with intellectual beauty.

Finally, a few words on religion in an age of science. Man is impatient. We like certainty, and unfinished business in the mind leads to the anxiety I described. It is not comfortable and we jump ahead to give answers about questions to which we do not have certain answers. Man's collective, logical approach has not yet achieved them. Then we attempt to convince others of our answers, not by the validity of our logic but by invoking the machinery of art and exaltation. This, I submit, is what most of organized religion is doing. The professional voice of the preacher is just as characteristic as the professional voice of the auctioneer; you can tell when he is launching into his role, not to say his "pitch." This is *not* attempting to communicate to the intellect.

It is, of course, important to use all the arts of communication and persuasion—music, candlelight, incense, incantation—if one wants to evoke the emotions and get action; and, since without emotion action is unlikely, this is legitimate. But it is not operating at the level of science or the level of reason. Let's just keep clear which we are doing when we are doing it. One can evoke emotions in a mob that goes to hang a colored man in exactly the same way. Before one goes too vigorously in some direction, it is well to be sure of what one is trying to do or what one is trying to get.

I assure you that, with the advancing knowledge of how

the brain works and how to manipulate it, the techniques of controlling human behavior which the scientist can turn loose (and I tremble for the consequences) will be much more effective than the techniques of art. The advertiser has depended on the artist in the past—he is beginning to go to the scientist now, to the practical psychologist. Brainwashing, brainstorming, drugs, lesions—my goodness, the control of what or how man thinks and feels is potentially very much greater than anything we have dreamed so far. It is vitally important to know where we are going. Let us not emulate the enthusiastic autoist whose wife said, an hour after choosing one fork on the map, "I think we're on the wrong road, dear." "Never mind, we're making wonderful time." Let us remember Coleridge's lovely phrase, "The streamy nature of association, which reason curbs and rudders."

I fear I'm pessimistic about all this. I do not think the great bulk of people will accept the austerity of a rational religion any more than they will accept the austerity of science. This is not the age of science, I'm afraid; it is the age of scientific techniques, of scientific results, but not of scientific attitudes. If any mass religion is likely to displace existing ones, I would say it is something like baseball, with the Red Sox or Tigers as local tribal deities.

Only a few great believers are able to make the creative quest. The question was asked whether religion is the quest or its result. To me, both religion and science are the quests, not the results. The results may change, from year to year or from generation to generation. I still thrill to one of the finest of man's sentences, "Carry from the altar of the past the fire, not the ashes."

In closing, a word about Theodore Green's paper, which I promised to comment on today. I did not feel quite as Mr. Shapley did, because I translated the words I heard into my equivalents. The faith that was described and, I thought, exemplified was the faith of the horse better, or the scientist, or anyone else who decides to do something, based on a greater or lesser intensity of initial conviction and belief. And revelation, to me, was exactly the experience of the high school student who suddenly understands the theorem about the square of the hypotenuse—a terrific experience, but secular. God seemed rather dragged in because, as I understand the paper, the author was asserting that, through our real experience in our world, we can get indications of something beyond our world or immediate experience. And I thought: "Yes, we can see the front of the moon and are perfectly convinced that there is a back of the moon." We have, with our scientific tools and analyses, dissected matter down to the nucleus and subnucleus and seen past the stars; and we assume there are other sub-subparticles of matter and super-supergalaxies of heaven. These are the things Green said to me; hence my comment that bringing in God, in any sense of a capital G, seemed entirely fortuitous and unnecessary. Another story belongs with the one on metaphysicians: at a symposium such as this, the toastmaster, a theologian, introducing the speaker, a philosopher, said, "A philosopher is like a blind man on a dark night in a deep cellar looking for a black cat that isn't there." The speaker conceded, "I think, perhaps, that is a fair characterization of a philosopher; I will only point out that, under exactly the same circumstances, the theologian would produce the cat."

Speaking completely in the role of a scientist, let me tell you now what was told me as a beginning investigator by a great teacher and what I have religiously told my beginning students over the years. I don't think there is a better epitomization of the mood of science, one not to be violated by loose talk, by bandying half-understood words and concepts, by unsupported mystifying conclusions. The advice is simply this: "Young man, take care, lest you find what you're looking for."

CHAPTER 8

Truth in Science and Religion

by HENRY MARGENAU
Yale University

THIS DISCUSSION falls naturally into two sections, the first dealing with matters of science, of which I am reasonably sure,
and the second with problems of religion. That I am not an
expert in theology I need not emphasize, for it will be abundantly evident from what I am about to say. More to the point
is the admission that I have no strong doctrinal views upon
matters of religion, and that the voicing of thoughts in the
second section is essentially indicative of the struggle for enlightenment and truth on my own part.

Some claim that there is no method of science: there are
only sciences, each evolving its own method as it proceeds.
This workaday view of the toiling scientist is a natural reflection of his daily experience. The specialist is concerned
with a multitude of diverse tasks requiring different methods
for their solution. Unless his mind soars above his daily pursuits, it is fairly natural that the working scientist should characterize his business as a welter of different techniques. In the
same spirit the woodsman might claim that there are only
trees but no forests.

Even for the generalist and the philosopher of science,

common features among the various scientific disciplines are not easy to perceive. They will continue to escape one's view so long as it is focused solely upon the substance or the subject matter of the disciplines. The factual field covered by physics is entirely different from that of biology, that of biology entirely different from that to which psychology applies its methods of inquiry, and so forth. So long as *subject matter* is made a principle of classification, there will indeed be only sciences. However, when one asks the more general questions, what is a scientific problem and when does science regard its problems to be solved, certain features common to physics, biology, and psychology spring into view. A measure of unity arises in this *methodological approach* to the meaning of science. It is this approach which I now wish to sketch, an approach that allows science to be seen as a part of our human concern for the validity of knowledge or, some would hold, as that phase of the cognitive process which to date has achieved its highest perfection.

Features Common to All Sciences

Science in its truest sense is precisely what the etymology of its name suggests: it comprises what we know, that is to say, everything we "really" know. How often have we uttered in conversation the simple phrase, "Yes, I know." To lay bare its meaning is our present task, for the meaning of this innocent sentence reveals the method of science.

Since science describes the process of knowing, and since knowing is only part of human experience, science is limited. For our total experience includes, besides knowledge, such components as feeling, judging, willing, and acting as well. To recognize the peculiar relevance of science for knowledge, however, is not tantamount to admitting that science has no application to the fields of feeling, judging, and acting. It may well be that purely affective experiences, insofar as they become objects of knowledge, thus become indirectly tractable by the methods of science. But I wish to ignore this nest of problems at the present time, so that the central features of scientific method shall not be obscured by too much inessential detail.

Let us denote by the term "experience" the broad expanse of all matters that can possibly enter our consciousness. Experience thus means more than it does in the sense of the strict empiricist, who wishes to limit the term to that which is sensorily perceived. Its present usage includes sensing, knowing, reasoning, feeling, judging, acting, and all the rest. From this universe of experience we now select what is known as the *cognitive component*. While it may be difficult to define it clearly (the contents of our experience do not fall into neat pigeonholes, and to define an isolated part of it is always an arbitrary procedure), we all know what is meant by the ingredients of the process of knowing. It involves having some sort of sense impression, remembering similar impressions, interpreting the impression or awareness in terms of some object or objects, relating these objects to other objects of a similar kind, reasoning about that class of objects, etc. In another form, the process of knowledge may start with a question which is heard or read, a question which sets us to thinking, to recalling facts, to analyzing a situation in order to arrive at an answer. Loosely, the faculties which bring about cognition are known as the senses, memory, and reasoning. But these are psychological terms which suggest distinctions that are not altogether clear in the facts of experience.

Two Extreme Types of Knowledge

Among the elements that go into what is called knowledge, two extreme types can be recognized. Representative of one type is a mathematical idea such as that of a *number* or a *function* or a *group*, a pure concept, very abstract and rationally manipulable, whose meaning does not flow from whether or not it "exists." The other type is represented by what is usually known as fact. Pure concepts and pure facts are the names which common language attributed to these two polar types of experience. Yet I hesitate to use these words, pure concepts and facts, because they convey an impression of obviousness and of finality which obscures many of the intricate details and problems of science. This is particularly true about the word "fact," which covers too many sins. At the expense of annoying you, therefore, I shall introduce a different terminology which I will now proceed to explain.

What is factual about a fact is that it is independent of our control: it is simply there; it clamors to be recognized by us as such. A fact is what cannot be denied, what obtrudes itself into the process of knowledge whether we wish it there or not; it is the last instance of our rational or cognitive appeal. A fact is spontaneous in our experience, often unexpected and practically never merely the consequence of some chain of reasoning. It is often in the form of an immediate perception, or a sensory datum, or an observation. At any rate, facts function as protocols [1] against which all other kinds of conjectures are ultimately tested. Let me simply use the letter P (which may stand for perception, or for protocol, if you please) to designate this kind of experience. As examples I offer the seeing of some shape, the hearing of a sound, the awareness of a pain, or indeed that combination of many such immediacies which we call an observation in science.

[1] The word "protocol," despite its current diplomatic usage, is taken here in its original meaning as a "public record or registry," a "first draft" of an experience that later becomes knowledge. It meant literally a leaf glued to a manuscript suggesting or prescribing the contents of the manuscript.

What Are Concepts?

Contrasted with these *P*-elements are thoughts, ideas, mental images, fancies, in general all that goes by the more sober name of concepts. Concepts are the results of human processes of abstraction, sifting, reasoning; they emerge at the end of a long chain of activity in which man feels himself intelligently involved and responsible. Their genesis is perhaps best described by the term "construction." I therefore propose to call them *constructs* in order to indicate the active part which our reason plays in their production. Whether and in what sense they are pure constructs having no relevance at all for more factual types of experience is not of interest at this moment.

The polarity of constructs and *P*-data should not be construed as implying that these two classes of entities never mix. In fact, any cognitive experience involves elements of both

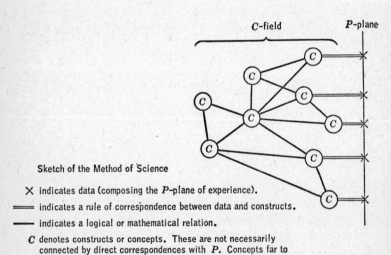

Sketch of the Method of Science

X indicates data (composing the *P*-plane of experience).

=== indicates a rule of correspondence between data and constructs.

—— indicates a logical or mathematical relation.

C denotes constructs or concepts. These are not necessarily connected by direct correspondences with *P*. Concepts far to the left of *P* are "abstract." As science progresses, it introduces more and more *C*'s on the left side of the *C*-field.

classes, but it is only through an effort at methodological reduction that the two ingredients can be separated. Almost
any statement, any sentence about a factual experience, already involves interpretation, conceptualization, and thereby
constructional elements. In fact, the latter abound in our experience, and it is difficult to point to a kind of experience of
which it may be said that it is pure *P*-fact.

There is a sense in which facts are immune to treatment
by reasoning; they are simply there and have to be reckoned
with. Indeed, it is their lack of internal order, their refusal
to follow an obvious rational pattern, which constrains our
mind to engage in the process of constructing rational counterparts for them, counterparts which are manipulable by rational
rules and can be made to fulfill our desire for order and coherence in experience. A heard noise at once suggests the
presence of a sound source somewhere in space; we look for
it, and if this search ends in another *P*-type experience in
which we see the object, our desire for rational coherence
in our experience is satisfied. Coherence has not been established directly between the two *P*-facts; an essential third
element within this coherent scheme is the constructed object.

Necessity of Distinctions

To speak of the intervening object as a construct may be
offensive to many. But it is very important for us to learn
to recognize the germ of the difference between *P*-type
facts or data, and constructs, even in so simple an experience
as this, for if we go blindly ignoring this distinction, we shall
never be able to understand fully the more recondite and involved excursions of science.

If practically any cognitive experience already contains
constructs, what can possibly be meant by a pure *P*-datum?
My answer is it probably does not exist. Yet whenever we

analyze a scientific experience, we sooner or later come to a place where we say: "This we accept," or, "This is incontrovertibly true." Here we have reached the *P*-domain. It forms a sort of limiting plane bounding the unlimited domain of constructional experience. Because of this I like to speak of the *P*-facts as lying on the *P*-plane, and to look upon the *P*-plane as forming a boundary, as it were, of the constructional domain to which I shall henceforth refer as the *C*-field. The latter contains most of the things of which we talk in science, excluding only that "direct appeal to nature" called observation or empirical verification which the scientist uses to validate his notions about the world.

From the point of view of the psychologist, a *P*-plane fact is neither simple nor unanalyzable, but it is a necessity for every science to regard certain data as incontrovertible; if it gives up this premise, every science loses the very basis of its competence. Let us remember, however, that a *P*-fact for one science may not be a *P*-fact for another. The point is that our experience confronts us with a *P*-plane which in its complete lack of organization and coherence defies our understanding. To alleviate our bafflement we set up correspondence between these factual experiences and certain constructs.

Berkeley and "Logical Fertility"

The business of science might be supposed to be the mapping of individual *P*-experiences in a unique and simple way upon the field of constructs, a mapping which is regulated by principles of convenience and of economy of thought. If this were the entire truth, then the simplest and most acceptable scientific theory would probably be one proposed by Berkeley, who believed that every factual experience is but the manifestation of a thought in the mind of God. His thesis creates a simple and indeed convenient correspondence between the points on the *P*-plane and the constructs of the *C*-field. Yet it is unsatisfactory. The reason is not that it is wrong; its fault lies in its very generality. For it lacks a property which I like to call *logical fertility*. The whole scheme is logically sterile, there is nothing which the scientist can derive from it, nor anything which he can test by empirical means. The theory states its case and is done, its acceptance or rejection makes no difference in our experience and our thoughts.

The lesson we may draw from this consideration is that scientific theories must contain constructs which are in some sense logically fertile, and I shall mean by this the deductive quality which the Berkelian theory so obviously lacks. Scientific theories differ in the degree to which they are logically fertile, some having a great deal of logical power, others very little. But in general, scientific constructs strive for a maximum of logical fertility; science avoids the use of ideas leading to sterile situations in which predictions cannot be made.

When the information drawn from many examples is systematized, it entails the following conclusion: Scientific constructs are regarded as valid representations of (*P*-plane) facts if they satisfy two large sets of requirements. The first set may be called methodological, or indeed metaphysical. It has to do with the native fitness of the constructs themselves, with the manner in which they place themselves in formal relations, with their coherence and their logical sweep. It is possible to name the different criteria; I have tried to present a list of them in my book, *The Nature of Physical Reality*.[2] Metaphysical requirements which the constructs of science have to satisfy are: *logical fertility, extensibility, multiple connection, simplicity, elegance,* and several others. This enumeration should not be taken as naming a set of basic axioms, of unchanging categories of thought in the Kantian sense. It is simply an assortment of metaphysical principles of science which has grown through application and use throughout the history of science, principles which have proved their power

[2] (New York: McGraw-Hill, 1950.)

and have now come to be generally accepted by working scientists, who perhaps without knowing it employ them in their researches. They are not *necessary* principles of knowledge, and they may change in time. But a survey of the history of science shows that changes in them proceed very slowly, and that a modification of the metaphysical requirement, when it occurs (e.g., the present changing attitude with respect to the principle called causality), induces profound and extensive changes in the structure of science itself.

Hypothesis Into Theory

A set of constructs which obeys the metaphysical requirement does not for that reason alone become acceptable. Theories, i.e., sets of constructs, must also satisfy the requirement of *empirical verification*. The scientist starts with an observation; this observation is then interpreted in terms of the constructs that are associated with it. These constructs allow him to reason, and he finally emerges with a prediction which says that if the original observation was true, then something else must also be true on the P-plane. This something else can usually be investigated by empirical means. If it is found to be true, the circuit is declared successful. Now the *requirement of empirical verification* demands that a set of constructs be traversable in many ways by circuits of the type I have described. If all these circuits have been found successful, that is to say, if the theory has been tested in many ways, the scientist regards the constructs forming the theory as valid. What was originally an hypothesis has now become a satisfactory theory, the former constructs have transformed themselves into verifacts, and insofar as the constructs had the character of tentative entities, these entities have now become realities, and they are said to exist.

The method of science is nothing more than an elaboration of procedures of common sense. Even the simplest instances of gaining knowledge are examples of the scientific process just described.

The first part of this discussion has concerned itself with some very general features of scientific method, features so general as to be applicable to almost any kind of science, past and present. The treatment, though induced by contemporary developments of physical science, did not take them into explicit consideration. It behooves us, therefore, to comment briefly upon the novel aspects of physical science and upon the way in which they facilitate passage from the strict field of science to the more amorphous domains that lie around science. These include religion.

Common Sense in Error

Fifty years ago a physicist would have been amazed, or shall I say dismayed and shocked, at the remark that the ultimate constituents of the physical world, like electrons, may not have definite positions at all instants of time. How can we conceive of particles that are nowhere in particular? Does not this allegation contradict the most fundamental tenets of common sense? It does indeed, and insofar as it conflicts with common sense, common sense is in error. We have learned with some pain, perhaps, that the ultimates of nature need not have picturable attributes. Common sense once thought that every object, no matter how small, would have to occupy a definite region of space. This insistence was a facile generalization based upon observations in the molar world of ordinary experience. But clearly when an object like an electron is far too small ever to be grasped or be experienced in kinesthetic or tactile fashion, the attribute of localizability may very well disappear. There is no logical difficulty in supposing that something which is too small to be seen may not have a position at all. At this point we simply have to ignore the bidding of common sense, free ourselves of its beguilement, and proceed on the basis of logical and mathematical rules alone. When this is done, we arrive at the science of quantum mechanics, which provides a very successful set of constructs in terms of which atomic experience can be understood.

From many changes in the concepts of modern atomic physics there has resulted a freer and more tolerant view of the requirements of scientific explanation. Science now acknowledges as real a host of entities that cannot be described completely in mechanistic or materialistic terms. For these reasons the demands which science makes upon religion when it examines religion's claims to truth have become distinctly more modest; the conflict between science and religion has become less sharp, and the strain of science upon religion has been greatly relieved. In fact, a situation seems to prevail in which the theologian can seriously listen to a scientist expounding his methodology with some expectation that the latter may ring a sympathetic chord. It is not altogether out of the question that the rules of scientific methodology are now sufficiently wide and flexible to embrace some forms of religion within the scientific domain. At any rate, science has become a wide and open field and, as I see it, there are several ways in which it can adjust itself to the concerns of religion. In the following I shall point to three such ways.

The Scientist Amazed

The open-minded and perceptive scientist, even if he has no desire to ask religious questions, cannot help but marvel at the success of his own method. As he ponders over the infinite and unruly mass of his factual experience, as he contrasts it with the striking simplicity and elegance of the constructional scheme whereby he is able to explain the formidable contingency of P-facts, he succumbs to a feeling of surprise. His amazement concerns the circumstance that it should be possible at all for man to comprehend so vast a domain of unorganized happenings. Scientists feel wonder and awe at the realization that our experiences are not a chaotic welter but display that measure of order and consistency which expresses itself in the use of simple constructs.

Paradoxically such amazement does not spring from the occurrence of breaches in natural order which are often called miracles; on the contrary, it attaches to what seems to be the greatest miracle of all, namely, the lack of interruption of the natural order which expresses itself in the continued and perhaps expanding simplicity of human explanations. The theologian Schleiermacher phrased this sentiment concerning the one supreme miracle, namely, natural order, with unforgetable beauty in his speeches to the German nation. If this sentiment be religious, science does indeed engender it.

Yet I doubt if this form of religion, cosmic religion, if you please, will satisfy the desires of the theologian. He may wish to take it as a basis and go on from there, postulating a cause for order and perhaps a Deity to maintain it. In doing so he goes, of course, beyond the confines of science; his religion becomes what I should like to call a metascience; but I see nothing in the methodology of science which forbids this expansion, this extrapolation upon the method of science. Most scientists readily admit that their methods have limits, and that beyond these limits procedures controlled by other principles may well take hold. It is this transcendence out of the domain of science into a region from which science as a whole can be surveyed that I wish to designate by applying the word metascience.

Freedom and Limitation

Further examination leads to another interesting conjecture. A given *P*-phenomenon can be explained by a series of steps that has apparently no end. Thus, for example, in answering the question why an object falls near the surface of the earth, one may refer to the Galilean theory of free fall which says merely that all bodies fall with equal and constant acceleration. This takes us to a set of constructs not far removed from the *P*-plane. But this law of free fall is nothing more than a special instance of a more general set of constructs known as the theory of universal gravitation, which in our symbolic sense of distance lies further away from the *P*-plane. Again we need not stop there. It is possible to view the theory of universal gravitation as a special case of Einstein's law of general relativity. We have thus taken a third step back to the left away from the *P*-plane. To be sure, at present it is necessary for us to stop at this stage. But there is nothing to block further progress into the more abstract. Indeed, if the past development of science holds a lesson, it is that we shall someday doubtless find an even more general law in terms of which the law of Einstein and others can be jointly comprehended. No limit seems to be set to man's progress to the left in the *C*-field. But as we reverse this procedure, going from the general to the more particular, we end up by saying that the stone simply falls. This is a brute fact, grotesque, final, and meaningless.

Thus arise two questions. The first has often been asked in the history of philosophy as follows: If the *P*-plane limits experience, is there anything beyond experience? If so, and if science is limited to experience, then the affirmative answer transcends science. But I doubt if it is necessarily religion. What lies beyond may be the Kantian thing in itself, that essence which, being no part of experience, is never knowable. Or there may be some mystical kind of nonscientific reality which, lying by definition beyond experience, can never be fathomed. If it is thought that we may encounter the divine in this passage beyond the *P*-plane, that divine, since it excludes the possibility of experience, is not likely to interest the theologian.

The Existentialist View

But the closure of the field of experience raises still another question. Perhaps closure arises from the circumstance that in our entire epistemology we have limited ourselves to vehicles which are rational procedures. We have used induction and deduction in traveling back and forth to examine the *P*-plane. Could it not be that, in order to fathom and probe the fullness of what is actually present on or near the *P*-plane, we are required to abandon reason and to give ourselves to basking without restraint in the sensation of the immediately given? Here we encounter a new emphasis, different from what we call intuition. The fundamental essence of the ebb and flow of sensations, the richness of the immediacy of our direct experience, the metaphysical substance of what assails our being in the act of sensation and affection, may after all escape the net of rational analysis. This is the view of the existentialist, who feels that our representation of the *P*-plane merely as the limiting surface of the scientific domain cannot do it justice, and that much greater emphasis upon the purely existential, upon the contingent and spontaneous features of our total experience are necessary.

There are questions which science with its present methodology will probably never answer; the full drama of existence cannot be enacted on the stage of science with its contemporary setting. Questions like those raised by Kierkegaard and Heidegger—why am I, why is there anything at all, why the phenomenon of experience which science analyzes—questions such as these appear as idle vaporings when viewed as problems of science. Yet they bespeak an intense human concern and contain a powerful appeal that defies the positivistic insistence that they are meaningless or insignificant. If science does not answer them, is it not reasonable that at this point we resign ourselves to other hands? This is indeed affirmed by those who see religion as an extension of experience into the existential domain. They feel that the *P*-plane must somehow be opened up by a new kind of analysis, an analysis not scientific, an analysis for which science offers no help. What happens when this extension is permitted can hardly be predicted in detail. One can go the way of Sartre and dwell in nonreligious fashion upon the nausea of existence. Or one can go the way of Kierkegaard and Gabriel Marcel and couple the existential affirmation with an excursion into the domain of religion. At any rate, the *P*-plane quite obviously is an area of contact between science and religion, as the widespread acceptance of existentialist philosophy today clearly shows. As I see the situation, there appears to be no conflict between science and existentialism; rather, they stand in a relation of complementarity.

A Formal Structure for Theology

My own hope lies in the direction of amalgamating religion with science by an extension of the latter. For it is by no means out of the question that a theory of religion, i.e., theology, when fully developed, may exhibit the same formal structure as science itself.

If such an approach is to be started, the first question to be answered is: What is the *P*-plane of religious experience? A possible and probably correct answer appears to be: The kind of immediate experience which is often regarded as distinctly religious. I mean such things as the feeling of gratitude that springs up in man's heart on a joyous day, the monitoring awareness of a conscience that regulates the lives of most of us, the feeling of awe in the face of overwhelming beauty, the guiltful contrition that follows a sinful experience, the sentiments of misery and abandon at the insufficiency of human power before fate, the longing for grace and for redemption. To say that these are peculiarly religious experiences is not to argue that they are exclusively religious. For they are also P-plane facts for several of the so-called social sciences, and it is far from my intention to suggest that psychology, psychiatry, sociology, and anthropology should not be concerned with them and endeavor to show how they can be organized in the constructional schemes of these sciences. This, however, does not cast out the possibility of an analysis in religious terms, nor does it show it to be illegitimate. For any simple sensation may well be the starting point of an inquiry into a physical or biological or a psychological domain of constructs. The fact that a given experience can be P-datum for a variety of sciences must be very clearly recognized and is no argument against the validity of the various explanatory schemes. And in this sense religion, too, can claim its due.

What follows next in the development of a "science" of religion is a little difficult to predict, though probably not more difficult than it would have been to predict the structure of modern science in Aristotle's day. Sciences grow when people become convinced of their importance and their necessity, and they develop their methodology as they mature. There are those who believe that theology already provides a C-field in terms of which a concatenation and a logical nexus between the experiences I have named can be achieved. If this is to be accepted, the ideas of theology must be subjected to the same metaphysical requirements which we impose on scientific theories. That is to say, they must partake of logical fertility, multiple connection, extensibility, simplicity, etc. Nor is this often denied by workers in the field.

Religion Subjected to Tests

Moreover, if religion is to have the structure of science, it must also expose itself to tests in the manner of our circuits of empirical verification. This forces us to reject at once certain peculiar kinds of theology, such as the deism of the Enlightenment and probably also predetermination of the Calvin type. For these theories could never be tested. Any tests man could devise would be foreordained, would have been included in the Creator's foresight at the very beginning. It would, therefore, be futile to regard the outcome of the tests as significant. But such criticisms do not affect most major theological systems.

It appears that natural science is not wholly without suggestions as to the structure of a religion based on the grounds of its own methodology. But it offers no detailed material aid. Least of all does it require the slavish adherence of theological doctrine to the constructs of physics and chemistry. Not even the social sciences, notably psychology, deem it necessary any longer to ape the physicist. This does not imply contrasts or contradictions—for surely, if a concept applicable in one field has no application in another, it does not contradict it. The notion of temperature is entirely in harmony with that of an atom, although it has no relevance for a single atom. It is the methodological structure of science that might be transferable; I do not advocate "physicalism" in religion.

Whatever else these vague considerations may imply, they are utterly damaging to the tired old slogan that soulless science conflicts with the spirit of religion.

CHAPTER 9

Man Consorting with Things Eternal

by THEODOSIUS DOBZHANSKY
Columbia University

AN EGG CELL, from which every man or woman has developed, weighs approximately one twenty-millionth of an ounce. An adult is roughly fifty billion times heavier. This fifty-billion-fold increase in weight has resulted from the consumption and assimilation of food. It is quite literally true that a man is a conglomeration of transformed groceries. But he is most surely not only that. This pile of groceries perceives, thinks, feels joy and suffering, and accordingly deserves the following description given to it by the author of one of the Dead Sea Scrolls: "So walk I on uplands unbounded, and know that there is hope for that which Thou didst mold out of dust to have consort with things eternal." But how can transformed groceries or dust know anything at all, let alone "consort with things eternal"? Undeniably, some knowledge is possible; one can say with Descartes that we know at least that we think, and, hence, that we exist.

The problem can and should be approached in a variety

117

of ways. My assignment here is to approach it from the biological side. Biology shows that man is not simply a conglomeration of groceries; he is a conglomeration transformed in very particular and special ways, transformed by human heredity. Just how human genes, or genes of other organisms, succeed in this transformation is not known in detail. A plausible guess is that the genes do their job by reproducing themselves. The genes manufacture their own copies from other substances, ultimately from whatever the organism feeds on. One of the by-products, or, if you wish, waste products, of this gene-copying process is the body of the organism which carries these genes.

There is no doubt that genes make more of themselves out of materials that are not genes. Self-reproduction is a fundamental, possibly the fundamental property of the living which distinguishes it from the nonliving. Life carries the potentiality of endless self-replication, but the realization of this potentiality is restricted by the resistance of the environment. Life makes life by imposing its pattern on the susceptible environment, but the supply of such environment is always finite. The genes are powerful, but the environment is niggardly. The environment resists the formative action of the genes, and the encounter between the genes and the environment results in organic evolution.

In this encounter the genes have won, thus far, only a slender victory. Considered on a planetary scale, life is a thin film on the surface of the earth, which is wholly lifeless inside, and which wanders in a wholly lifeless space. On a cosmic scale the conquest of life seems even more pitiful since, for all we definitely know, life exists only on a single second-rate planet revolving around the second-rate sun. And yet, the evolution of life did result in the production of one species which feels that it may "have consort with things eternal," and suggests that some two thousand years ago the Son of God temporarily assumed the form of this species.

The mystery of knowledge resides in the genes. This statement does not mean that there exists a special gene, or genes, in man which distinguish him from the brutes and which confers upon him the ability to think and to know. There are no genes "for" knowledge or "for" anything else in particular. Genes do not work that way. All the genes that an organism has interact with the environment, and this interaction is the process of living. The process of living brings about the development of the body, and this development passes through a sequence of stages, starting with an embryo, then an infant, adolescent, adult, and oldster—ending in a corpse.

Somewhere along this trajectory of living, there appears, grows, and perhaps declines the ability to learn and to know. The interaction of the genes with the environment determines the shape of the trajectory, from its first upswing at fertilization to the final downfall at death. The mystery of knowledge is bound in human genes because it is the whole man who arises from this fateful interplay between the genes and the environment. Please note that the "environment" of which I am reporting here is to be conceived very broadly. It includes not only the physical milieu but also the social, cultural, ethical, and spiritual settings of the human scene. It is a blanket concept which can be stretched to cover almost anything.

Since there is no man either without genes or without environment, the genes and the environment are, in a sense, equally important in the formation of a person. On the other hand, the genes appeared in the Universe later than the environment, and they have caused some rather drastic transformations of the environment in at least one little corner of the Universe. Looked at from the standpoint of a person who contemplates himself and his environment, it is probably justified to hold up the genes as the chief source of our ability to know.

Human genes interact with the environment; the interaction results in a process of development; this process yields, among other things, the potentialities of knowledge and of self-knowledge. To say all this, however, is merely to restate the problem in biological terms, not to solve it. How do the genes accomplish a result so marvelous? Why do human genes confer upon their possessors greater capacities for acquisition of knowledge than do the genes of, say, a mouse or a corn plant?

Satisfactory answers to these questions are not yet available. A biologist is in a position to offer only some tentative answers, or, if you prefer, surmises. These fall in two groups. A majority of biologists conjecture that the process of living represents a highly specialized pattern or sequence of events of the same general sort that occur also in lifeless matter, and which can be adequately described in terms of chemistry and physics. It is not the nature of the events themselves, but the particular arrangements or relative positions of the events which constitute life. This majority surmise is, of course, traditionally associated with mechanistic science and with materialistic philosophy, although it is neither necessitated by this type of philosophy nor inevitably leading to it. This surmise depends for its attractiveness largely on its pragmatic powers. When you swallow an aspirin pill, or take an injection of a sulpha drug, you avail yourself of some of the fruits of mechanistic biology.

The rival surmise postulates that organic activities are directed by forces, powers, or wills which cannot be reduced to, or adequately understood in terms of processes observable in inorganic nature. The variants of this view are so diversified that even a bare mention of all of them is out of the question here. Attempts have been made to project biological and psychic phenomena backwards on inanimate nature. This nonliving matter, down to atoms and electrons, supposedly partakes of vital and volitional powers. In his imposing philosophical system Whitehead has developed this view in some detail. Recently my senior colleague in genetics, E. W. Sinnott, has put forth the speculation that the development of an organism is presided over by an agency called the "psyche." The psyche is a striving or an effort to reach a certain goal, which is, in the first place, a complete and mature organism. The psyche is present in a fertilized egg cell and, presumably, in every living cell. If the psyche really existed, it could perhaps be held responsible for man's capacity to know.

So summary an account as the above inevitably does injustice to the insights of Whitehead and Sinnott. Nevertheless, I must say that in my opinion their views must be rejected both on scientific and on philosophic grounds. What is this psyche which they invoke as a directing force of organic activities? It is a fact not doubted by anyone that the development of an embryo involves sequences of physiological and physicochemical processes. How does the psyche fit in this physiological matrix? It is supposed somehow to canalize the processes which result in organic development. But this externalizes the psyche, makes it a kind of substance or energy, places it squarely among the objects of the material world, and makes it capable of interchange with or transformation into physiological, chemical, and physical processes. The difficulty thus incurred is, as far as I can see, insuperable. It is quite analogous to the dilemma which results from attempts to think of God or of spirit as though they were objects included in the order of existence accessible to our sense organs, albeit objects of a particularly sublime or ethereal sort. An objectified spirit then turns out to be no spirit at all. Whitehead's ascribing vitality and volition to molecules and atoms is a more subtle device than is Sinnott's psyche. It replaces a mechanistic monism by a vitalistic monism, but, to me at least, it does not make an understanding of the workings of vital and psychic processes even a trifle easier.

We must look for a solution of our problem elsewhere. Even the "simplest" organism, microbes, and indeed viruses, turn out to be staggeringly complex when we begin to study how they are built and how they function. When it comes to man, the complexity is overpowering. Can a complexity so great, and yet so orderly, arise by mere rearrangement of atoms in the materials which are kept on the shelves of grocery stores? This seems an impossible flight of fancy. In exasperation we are tempted to look for a psyche, which could be charged with doing what mere physical processes seem unable to accomplish.

But there is an error in this reasoning. It overlooks the basic fact that life has had history; life has evolved. Organic development has two dimensions: an individual and an evolutionary one. Any day we can observe that living things grow and multiply; therefore, living protoplasm, with all its complexity, constantly arises from relatively simple nutrients. But this miracle does not occur except in the presence of a seed of the living protoplasm of the same species. In other words, life does not arise spontaneously, it only reproduces itself. Moreover, this self-reproduction has been going on for an unbelievably long time. The history of life on earth extends for an estimated two billion years. We seldom stop to consider the very remarkable fact that our own life, and the life of any other creature, is a direct lineal descendant of primordial life. Those who take pride in the antiquity of their family lineage should not forget that everyone else is also a direct descendant of the primordial protoplasm itself. The history of life has been composed of a long succession of cycles of births, growths, reproductions, and deaths. But this is not simply endless recurrence of the same eternal form, as visualized in some oriental philosophies. Darwin has shown that the history of life has consisted of more than futile repetitions. The individual life cycles are seen in the perspective of time to be linked into spirals; the history of life has involved changes, and these changes have been on the whole progressive. The immense complexity and the marvelous organization and design of a living body have not arisen in their present perfection all at once from inanimate matter. They have evolved, and their evolution has consumed an interval of time amounting to perhaps as much as a quarter of the age of the Cosmos itself.

Furthermore, and this is the cornerstone of modern evolutionary thinking in biology, most of the evolutionary changes occurred because they served to maintain or to improve the adaptedness of life to its environment. Life did not change merely for the sake of changing. It was not the kind of change to which the French saying applies that "the more it changes the more it remains the same thing." Life is at present a very different thing from the primordial life. It has endured in the world for as long as it has, exactly because it has been capable of changing to keep itself attuned to the demands of its environment. And at its summit, in man, life has become able to some extent to dominate its environment.

Biological evolution has been, on the whole, utilitarian. It is utilitarian because it is steered by natural selection. The workings of the mechanism of natural selection are remarkable and fascinating, but we cannot stop to consider them here. Suffice it to say that because of natural selection organisms change in response to and in accordance with the demands of their environments. Furthermore, the changes usually make sense, meaning by this that the changes usually help the creatures to stay alive. An environment may change in the course of time; the organisms which depend on it may then become altered in such ways that their fitness in the new environment remains as high as that of their ancestors in the old environment.

However, environments change not only in time; they change also in space. On our planet there exists a great variety of opportunities for different modes of living. Some evolutionary changes result in organisms becoming able to adopt new ways of life. Thus, aquatic animals have repeatedly evolved terrestrial descendants. Some of these terrestrial forms have become aquatic again, but it may be noted that the secondarily aquatic forms are more or less radically different from their original aquatic ancestors. This does not mean that a terrestrial form is necessarily better off in its sphere than the aquatic is in its province, or vice versa. The utilitarian nature of biological evolution means that different organisms are fitted for different modes of life, and that each of them is at least tolerably competent in its own sphere.

Perhaps a million years ago, at the close of the Tertiary or at the beginning of the Pleistocene period, there appeared a biological species in which biological evolution transcended itself. This species, man, differs from all others by its ability to maintain and develop a body of learned tradition called culture. Whereas all organisms inherit by way of biological heredity the structures and functions of their bodies, man acquires also a store of knowledge, beliefs, and rules of behavior. Biological heredity is transmitted through the sex cells in the direct line of descent; culture is passed chiefly by way of language between members of a society, who are not necessarily close biological relatives.

Biological heredity and culture are interrelated. The possibility of the latter is conditioned by the former. Culture can originate, endure, and grow only in possessors of human genes. This simple fact is important, and its consequences must be appreciated. The fountainhead of the ability to gain and transmit knowledge lies in human genes. But human genes are a product of biological evolution. Biological evolution is fundamentally a utilitarian process. The genetic equipment of the human species is what it is because it proved useful. Indeed, biologically considered, man is by far the most successful species. He has spread all over the world, learned to control and utilize some of the forces of nature, and forced other species to serve his needs. This biological success became possible not because of any particular strength or prowess of the human body, but because of the might of the human intellect. Man's ascendancy is the fruit of his genetically conditioned powers of knowledge and understanding. It must be stressed that the biological success of a species is often due to its excellence in some one or a few respects. In a bird of prey this is keen eyesight and powerful flight; in the prey it is concealment and escape; in many parasites it is tremendous fecundity; in man it is the ability to know.

The evolutionary origin of man's ability to know tends, however, to limit and circumscribe this ability. To oversimplify the issue, man can know chiefly what is useful for him to know. Natural selection has adapted man to his environments; it has done so by fostering the growth of a mental equipment serviceable for the control of these particular environments. The undying merit of Kant is that he was the first to state clearly the relations between knowability and knowing. The existence which man perceives is colored by the activity of his own mind. We construct a world in part in our own image, and accept it for true being. It is unfortunate that Kant lived more than a century before the philosophical implications of biological evolutionism could profitably be discussed. Bergson attempted to take up the task, but his effort was vitiated by his adoption of Lamarckism as the basic evolutionary hypothesis. The issue stands as a challenge to modern philosophical thought. For the time being one can do no more in this field than to try to ask intelligent questions.

The adaptive nature of biological evolution seems, at first sight, to favor a crudely pragmatic epistemology. Natural selection should have sharpened those and only those mental abilities which assist man in the control of the environment. It would seem that man needs to know nothing but what assists him to survive and to reproduce. This would, in turn, seem to favor the development of only the most empirical and matter-of-fact kind of knowledge. A financial tycoon, a general, or a politician is more powerful than a poet, a philosopher, or a scientist. Socrates had to take poison, and Nietzsche died in misery and abandonment; but Babbitts are usually respected and successful. All this would seem to lead to the ethic of "eat or be eaten." Such a conclusion was actually drawn by the so-called social Darwinists, and T. H. Huxley recoiled from it with horror in his famous lectures of nearly a century ago.

The problem of the origin of human understanding has, it must be admitted, thus far eluded a satisfactory and satisfying solution in evolutionary terms. Empirical knowledge is clearly useful for survival. But it is hard to see what biological utility could be ascribed to theoretical knowledge. Perhaps a solution lies in the deeper meaning which "utility" acquires in human affairs. Man is not a solitary animal but a social one. His survival does not depend solely on his having enough to eat and on avoiding physical hazards of the environment. It depends also on man's ability to arrive at a mutual accommodation with his neighbors. Interpersonal relations are facilitated by the use of language. So are the processes of instruction and learning. The biologically adaptive function of communication by means of language is beyond question. Now, the establishment of language depends upon the ability to form and to deal with generalizations, symbols, and abstractions. The word "stone" or "water" does not refer to just one particular object, but to classes of objects having in common the property of stoniness or of wateriness. The so-called languages of animals do not involve the use of such generalizing or abstract thought, or at most involve the barest rudiments of it. The human kind of language is a phenomenon which has little precedent on the subhuman level.

Without doubt, natural selection has favored the development and strengthening of the capacity for symbolic and abstract thought. This capacity, so foreign to the animal world at large, has set man apart as a biologically unique species, equipped to pursue a novel way of life. There is no need to stress the importance of this ability to social man; its loss owing to injury or to inherited defects makes a human being an idiot, helpless in a human community.

However, the ability to form symbols, generalizations, and abstract ideas is not subservient to linguistic needs alone. A basic ability of this sort opens up avenues of cognition foreign to the animal world, and inaugurates a variety of new possibilities of further evolutionary development. Here must be mentioned a property of the process of natural selection which is relevant to the problem under consideration. It has been pointed out above that natural selection is opportunistic. This means that selection favors properties which are useful at the time and in the place of their establishment, regardless of whether those properties will be useful or harmful in the future. Extinction of biological species is the price which life often pays for this opportunism. The extinct forms are those which were driven by natural selection into blind alleys of adaptation to environments which subsequently ceased to exist.

But there is another side to the opportunism of selection. Once in a while it endows an organism with novel abilities. The house mouse, the rat, the house fly, the common cockroach were probably only moderately successful species before the advent of man and his civilization. Yet they happened to fit snugly into certain adaptive avenues inadvertently created by man. The same was probably true of the ancestors of most animals and plants that man has domesticated.

Such accidental emergence of qualities which become useful only in environments which the species encounters in the future is referred to as preadaptation. Preadaptation does not mean that the evolutionary process somehow has a pre-science of the future. It means simply that evolution is a creative process which may lead to the appearance of completely new qualities, some of them potentially useful and others devoid of utility or even injurious to their possessors. Human evolution involved occurrences of this sort. Natural selection has endowed man with a genetic equipment which opened up the possibilities of symbolic abstract, and generalizing thought. This novel ability has been highly adaptive, for it resulted in the emergence of language. But it brought with it also other developments which proved even more crucial for man. The capacity for abstract thought had as its corollary or by-product the inception of self-awareness. Man tasted the forbidden fruit. He became conscious of himself and his environment. He attained the status of a person in the existential sense. This was, as we see it in retrospect, the closing of the prehuman and the opening of human evolution.

Biblical symbolism describes this crucial event of evolutionary development as the Fall. The passing of the happy state of a simple child of nature brought heavy penalties. Man became, and he still remains, a creature rent by internal contradictions. He stands with one foot in his biological past and with the other in his divine future. He is a paradoxical being, capable of unspeakable egotism and cruelty, but also of love, abnegation, and self-sacrifice. The subconscious life of man is replete with queer sexual urges and traumas, and his conscious activity is often guided by desires of economic gain or by an appetite to dominate others. But man is also ashamed of his defects and suffers from his depravity. He is able to construct in his imagination worlds different from the actual one, and can visualize himself in these imaginary worlds. His imagination tells him that he is not what he ought to be. Biologists have been afraid to probe the terrifying depths of human nature. These depths have been explored by thinkers such as Plato, Dostoevsky, Kierkegaard, Nietzsche, and more recently, and in only quasi-biological and quasi-scientific terms, by Freud. But the riddle of man is in part a biological riddle. Man, the whole man and not merely his bodily frame, has biological components. Man's spiritual evolution has taken shape in the setting of biological evolution.

Whether man's self-awareness is adaptive in the biological meaning of the term may well be questioned. It does not seem to help man to harmonize his existence with his environment. It may even be disadvantageous under many conditions. Among the consequences of self-awareness are a thirst for freedom and aspirations of self-transcendence. But willing slaves and complacent mediocrities are favored in most human societies. In a sense, human self-awareness and consciousness are not legitimate products of adaptive evolution. They came, as it were, through a back door of the evolutionary process. The hypothesis that they are products of biological evolution may easily be challenged, and it is incumbent upon us to consider whether this hypothesis can be sustained on purely biological grounds. I believe that it can; it is not an *ad hoc* hypothesis, but an application to man of a reasonably well known biological principle.

Establishment in organic evolution of adaptively useless and even harmful traits is not an infrequent occurrence. This does not contradict the principle of utilitarianism of natural selection. The proviso necessary for such an occurrence is that useless traits must be by-products of the same genetic constitution which yields also traits of overriding usefulness. Examples are not hard to find either in human or in animal or plant evolution. Thus, the erect body posture of man has become established in human evolution because it freed the hands from walking duties, and thus permitted their employment for delicate manual operations. The adaptive value for the human species of the possession of well-developed hands is sufficiently obvious. But the erect body posture in man entails disharmonies in several bodily functions. The difficulty of childbirth is perhaps the most evident of these disharmonies, and it is clearly disadvantageous from the standpoint of natural selection.

Why, then, has the erect posture become a fixed trait in the human species? In a sense, this is just another manifestation of the opportunism of natural selection. We often speak of natural selection as favoring this and discriminating against that trait. But, in reality, what is selected is not traits, but genetic constitutions. It is the organism as a whole that survives and reproduces, or remains childless and dies. Therefore, possession of a very useful quality may compensate for some concomitant weakness.

Our species is a biological success because of its intellectual capacity. Man is biologically specialized to control his environment by the force of his powerful brain, not by his relatively weak body. Self-awareness is, biologically, an adjunct of this powerful brain. Man's biological success became a reality despite the tragic discords within his soul.

It may seem odd that the genetic equipments of so many living organisms, both lower and higher ones, show obvious, and even glaring imperfections. This is not what romantics generally expect to find in nature's products. But this is what might be anticipated among the products of a natural creative process. Organic evolution is such a process. It lacks foresight and the ability to construct things according to a predetermined plan. I like to illustrate the principle that the organization of living beings is not free from shortcomings by the example of the man-o'-war bird. This is a superb flier commonly observed along tropical seacoasts. It is evidently a highly successful form of life, judging by how common and widespread it is. And yet, although it gets its food from or near water, its plumage is not water-repellent and easily becomes waterlogged. The legs of the man-o'-war bird are so weak that the bird is unable to get into the air except from an elevated perch.

Man's genetic equipment is responsible for the biological success of our species, and yet it is not the acme of perfection. Like the man-o'-war bird, man has his strength in his spiritual flight and his weakness in his spiritual legs. Man is able to form mental images of things and of situations which do not yet exist but which may be found, brought about, or constructed by his efforts. Man is endowed with foresight. His powers of cognition enable him to plan for the future. He can build objects and devise acts which he has not observed or committed previously. The adaptive potency of foresight and of creative imagery in the biological success of man is too obvious to need emphasis. Although his genes failed to provide him with wings, he has become a flier far more powerful than the man-o'-war bird.

Foresight is an adaptive trait of commanding significance. However, the possession of this trait has as its adjunct another property of man's nature, the adaptive value of which is more questionable. This is the basic existential experience of freedom. Man can not only contrive new objects and actions, he also feels free to execute some of his plans and leave others in abeyance. Human freedom is adaptively double-edged. The experience of freedom gives man a supremely poignant feeling of being the master, rather than a slave, of his own nature and of the external world. But it also burdens him with a crushing sense of responsibility. Man knows that he is accountable for his acts. He should be able to foresee the consequences of his plans, and accordingly should either pursue or avoid a given course of action. This is a dreadfully heavy load to carry.

Man's genes fail to tell him which things are good and

which are bad, or which acts are right and which are wrong. The knowledge of good and evil is gained only through the experience of freedom. A cat, a mouse, a bird, or an insect meets with no such knotty problems. Their actions are forced upon them by their genes and by their environments, including their previous experiences. All this is much more difficult and complicated in man. Freedom is an awesome gift. Man's reactions to freedom are contradictory and conflicting. He strives for freedom, and may even be ready to pay for it with his life. And yet, he may not only sacrifice his freedom for apparently trivial gains, but often enjoys the absence of freedom. The most extreme slavery is one which makes the slave unaware of his bondage.

To become a slave is easy, to remain free is difficult. Slavery is compatible with, and indeed requires passivity. It is restful. Freedom requires activity. It is creative and restless, because it involves a sense of responsibility. Man cannot rely on his genes to choose the direction of his activities. These genes give rise to human beings who carry internal contradictions in their innermost souls. The soul is lacerated by the dilemma of good and evil. Some persons break down under the weight of their internal disharmonies, and the breakdowns are liable to occur in all environments in which human life is possible, ranging from the most primitive to those created by advanced technology. But the knowledge gained through the experience of freedom is a precious form of knowledge which is made possible only by the human genetic equipment. Freedom is the source of knowledge which is alone capable of yielding answers to many questions of profound importance to mankind.

I am, of course, fully aware that the foregoing attempt to visualize the development of human knowledge in terms of man's biological, as well as of his cultural evolution, will be regarded by many as an unwarranted intrusion into a field usually pre-empted by philosophers and theologians. The *National Review* has published an unsigned comment on my little book, *The Biological Basis of Human Freedom* [1] in which the reviewer does me the honor of describing my effort in the following terms: "It is good to see a sensitive man struggling to emancipate himself from the shackles of scientific superstition, even when—although with evident regret —he stops short of a positive acceptance of absolute transcendent values and takes refuge in vague talk of 'cultural development' and 'human responsibility' as a foundation for ethics." I am afraid that what I have tried to do here is to give another boost to the "scientific superstition." I contend that the absolute transcendent values become such only through the experiences of self-awareness and of freedom, possibly only on the foundation of the human genetic equipment, which is a product of the process of evolution.

The issue here involved is really that of the relation between the Creator and His creation. The Creator is often thought of as quite separate and distinct from His creation, a spectator rather than a participant in the events of the created world, once the act of creation was completed some six thousand, or some five billion years ago—depending upon whether you choose Bishop Ussher's or a modern astrophysicist's chronology. Or else, the creation may be thought of as a process rather than an act, the Creator being constantly involved in his creation, which is dependent upon and is inseparable from Him. According to this second view, evolution is God's method of creation. The cosmic, biological, and cultural evolutions are ultimately parts of a single creative process. If so, man is a witness of the process of creation. He may be called upon to be more than a witness—a participant, a collaborator, and a companion.

According to the first view, whatever we may learn about the created world through scientific investigation has

[1] (New York: Columbia University Press, 1956.)

really no relevance to our understanding of the Creator, which can be gained solely through revelation. This view has been recently and most ably defended by Brunner, in his book, *The Christian Doctrine of Creation and Redemption*.[2] But if the second view is correct, then, as L. C. Birch rightly states in his critique of Brunner's work, ". . . the sacred and the secular, the natural and the divine, are not uniquely separate divisions of reality, desirable though it may be at times to separate them for didactic or analytical purposes." We nurture "the hope of attaining some sort of synthesis of religion and the rest of culture, while preserving the most precious insights of both."

A common foible of scientists is to suppose that the little truths which they discover explain everything rather than only something. The kindest way to regard this foible is to say that scientists are only human. A less kind way is to suspect that a fondness for explaining highly complex situations by one simple cause is an earmark of a mediocre mind. This is, however, beside the point, since believing that the evolution of the Cosmos is the method whereby the Creator actuates His idea of creation has neither the defects nor the virtues of simplicity. Some philosophers have rejected such a view because they supposed that evolution can be nothing more than the mechanical unfolding of something performed at the start, a kind of a gradual release of a spring wound up on the day of creation. If this were true, then the entire history of the Cosmos would, indeed, be rather pointless, although no more so than it appears to any world view which embraces the notion of predetermination. But modern evolutionary thought does not hold biological and human evolution to be the mere unfolding of pre-existing rudiments, something like the opening up of a bud disclosing a flower. Evolution has creative components. Moreover, the creativity has grown as

[2] H. E. Brunner, *Dogmatics* (Vol. II, Philadelphia: Westminster Press, 1952).

the evolution of the living world progressed, and has reached its peak, so far, in man with his existential experience of freedom.

It is really strange that so many religious thinkers wish to confine God only to the gaps left in the series of natural events. This makes the whole of nature as completely godless as the crudest materialists ever pictured it. This is perhaps a consequence of the old ascetic view, which held that the natural world is evil and corrupt, and that natural man is depraved by Original Sin. But Christianity is a religion of redemption. Christianity does not reject or condemn the creative diversity of nature or the variety and multiformity of the human intellect. It rejects only the infirmity and the imperfection of the world and of the old Adam, and calls for their deliverance and reformation by love. The old ascetic view becomes less tenable with every advance of human understanding. Scientific knowledge is cumulative; the breaches between natural events become fewer and narrower. This diminishes a God who stands apart from the created world; not so the God who includes the Creation in His divine being.

CHAPTER 10

The Impact of the Theory of Evolution on Religion

by ALFRED E. EMERSON
University of Chicago

SELF-CORRECTING KNOWLEDGE of the universe and of our earthly habitat has been growing since antiquity. Science came into conflict with religious dogma in early times, but during the Renaissance of the fourteenth century with the flowering of all branches of learning, many discrepancies were revealed between traditional religious beliefs and the growing knowledge of the physical universe. Biology, because of its relative complexity, did not have much effect upon religious concepts until the eighteenth century, and the most dramatic impact awaited the work of Darwin in the mid-nineteenth century. Darwin's *Origin of Species* was published in 1859. Probably no other book has so stirred the thoughts of men on all aspects of life, nor so comprehensively substantiated the integration of the human species with the natural world.

Darwin was preceded by many others who had fairly clear ideas of the evolution of life and the guiding principle of natural selection, but Darwin's great contribution was the accumulation of evidence from a variety of sciences sufficient to convince a large number of his contemporary biologists and gradually to impress much of the lay public with the scientific truth of his most important conclusions. Darwin's explanation of the origin of species came into direct conflict with the literal interpretation of the Babylonian myth of the creation of life incorporated into the Book of Genesis. All educated persons are aware of the tremendous effect this controversy had on religious philosophy and belief.

Darwin himself stayed pretty much behind the scenes during the ensuing debates and left the waging of battle largely to his able colleague, Thomas Henry Huxley. Darwin's wife seems to have maintained a rather orthodox religious viewpoint throughout her life, and we have some reason to believe that Darwin never tried to persuade his wife away from her traditional religious beliefs. In his writings he often tried to harmonize religion and science, but never at the sacrifice of his faith in scientific logic based upon accumulated sensory experience and the relations of multitudinous sensory facts. He was the leading biologist among many who gradually showed the time dimensions of existing species of plants and animals. He produced a testable hypothesis to account for the processes of evolutionary change and increasing adaptive adjustment to the environment. Without a great deal of philosophical penetration or argument, Darwin postulated a progressive direction of change. He did not discuss Aristotelian teleology or final causes, but he assumed that adaptive evolution showed a *purpose* for each species population, and that purpose was the survival of the species, often by the elimination of competitors.

Man had already been treated as a part of nature with relations to other animals. Linnaeus had given man a Latin name a hundred years before Darwin, and had included the human species in the mammalian order Primata. Darwin carried this idea much further and convinced the scientific world of man's common origin with the old-world monkeys and apes.

In summary, Darwin established man as a natural, not a supernatural, creation, and indicated the effectiveness of scientific inquiry in understanding the natural principles of creation. He also suggested that his theory could be used as a basis for the ethical nature of man. In *The Descent of Man and Selection in Relation to Sex* (1871), Darwin says: ". . . it seems more appropriate to speak of their [lower animals] social instincts, as having developed for the general good rather than for the general happiness of the species. The term general good, may be defined as the rearing of the greatest number of individuals in full vigour and health, with all their faculties perfect, under the conditions to which they are subjected." It "would be advisable . . . to take as the standard of morality, the general good or welfare of the community, rather than the general happiness." Thus Darwin should be placed as a great pioneer in the development of "naturalistic ethics" in the last half of the nineteenth century and continuing to the present day.

Darwin's studies not only had a profound effect upon religious concepts and institutions, but greatly encouraged researches in biology and the social sciences. His interpretations stimulated the gathering of tremendous amounts of further pertinent information about natural populations and, since 1930, we may say that Darwin's main thesis has been substantiated—namely, that natural selection is the guiding principle of progressive genetic change in evolutionary time. How has the developing knowledge of organic evolution influenced the thinking of man since the time of Darwin, and what is the impact of evolutionary thought on religion today?

First, let us consider the negative aspects. What traditional religious beliefs must we relinquish if we are to find consistent compatibility of our scientific knowledge with our fundamental emotional needs?

1. We have to accept the origin of man, including his nature, his mind, and even his "spirit," from animal ancestors by means of natural rather than supernatural causes.

2. We have to recognize that pain, discomfort, illness, disease, suffering, and death are the products of nature along with pleasure, vigor, health, and well-being. We may reduce pain and disease and prolong health and individual life by scientific knowledge, compassion, and social co-operation, but we cannot avoid all physical and emotional suffering nor the inevitability of personal death.

3. We have to accept change toward a better existence rather than a deterioration from a golden age or from a perfect life in a Garden of Eden.

4. We have to give up our belief in anthropomorphic spirits and gods with evil or beneficent attitudes toward individuals, together with the necessity of special rituals for their propitiation.

5. We have to become more self-reliant on human nature and intellect, both as individuals and in social organizations, for the amelioration of our woes and the enhancement of our existence.

6. We have to give up our belief in a dualistic separation of our minds and our bodies. This means giving up the concept of an individually conscious personal immortality and a personal life after death either in a heaven or a hell.

7. We have to give up defeatist philosophies that attempt to separate portions of human nature into unrelated compartments. One such philosophy besides dualism is the belief that man's social nature is separated from his sensory nature, and that empirical natural sciences are totally dissociated from the normative sciences that deal with values, ethics, and morals.

Some would feel that the abrogation of such traditional religious beliefs means the giving up of religion itself. This, of course, depends upon the definition of the basic religious concepts and attitudes.

I make no claim to be either a philosopher or an historian of religions. And my biological colleagues not only tend to avoid crossing the boundaries from traditional science to traditional religion, but they often express disapproval or even consternation when I venture into this "no man's land." However, I personally find fascination and an inward necessity in attempting to bridge the gap—what I consider to be an artificial gap—between scientific knowledge and deeply emotional religious attitudes. I shall attempt to show how one biologist who considers himself religious tries to bring his intellect and his feelings into harmonious balance. But please do not assume that I speak for other scientists or other biologists.

To me, religion is not a set of dogmatic assertions of truths assembled from revelations by a supernatural God and incorporated into sacred texts. There is great beauty in the early myths that symbolize the wonders and aspirations of man. I do not disparage the wisdom of the ages nor the exacting study of origins and meanings of religious books. To me, the attempt to view these myths and statements of early prophets at their superficial and literal face value is the antithesis of fundamental religion, even though such adherence to oversimplified interpretations is sometimes referred to as fundamental religion.

Modern scientists stand in awe of and reverence for the physical and living universe which they study. They are aware of their great ignorance and lack of full understanding of nature, including human nature. They are aware of the fact that they are part of a much larger whole and are dependent upon the natural environment and the rest of humanity for their existence and the fulfillment of their highest desires. They are aware that within each individual is incorporated the time dimensions of life back to the origin of life itself some three thousand millions of years ago. Within each person is a participation and continuity with the past, and a projection into the future. Scientists know that each individual belongs to a population system with emergent properties that transcend the summation of the attributes of all included persons. They know that the human species is related to all other life on the planet, both genetically and functionally. They find that their intellectual powers enable them to penetrate the unknown and to improve rapidly their understanding of themselves and their environment. They are motivated by emotions of aesthetic beauty as they become sensitive to the harmonious relations of both the outside universe and their internal consciousness. They are aware that love of others and co-operative work with others enhance their own individual satisfactions and well-being, both emotional and physical. They develop loyalties, identifications, and responsibilities toward other persons and organized groups. Each scientist becomes humble in the face of the infinite immensity, infinite minuteness, and infinite complexity of the physical universe, of the plant and animal life of his earthly habitat, and the social relations between fellow human beings, particularly between mates, between parents and children, and between immediate and distant associates.

These attitudes are religious, are the basis of human values, and form the foundation of a moral consciousness and practice. The scientific man and the religious man cannot be separated without a destructive schizophrenic conflict and inconsistency within the individual personality. The emotional, intellectual, mental, and physical nature of man have evolved over long periods of time, and they are still evolving and improving. The individual has an orderly unity and belongs to more inclusive unitary systems.

To what extent can modern scientific knowledge and attitudes contribute constructively to religious progress? We have seen that science has rendered obsolete some of the old false beliefs that were associated with religious sects, but that this weeding out of ancient superstitions and authoritarian dogmas has not destroyed the religious nature of man. The continuous addition of scientific truth and the interpretation of the universe and of man have enlarged our religious perspective. We have increased our sensitivity to our responsibilities toward mankind and to our living and physical environment. We have a greater awesome regard for the order of the universe of which we are an intimate part. Science is augmenting and developing religion in a better balanced relationship to our evolving culture and civilization.

What are some of the positive influences that modern science, and particularly our modern understanding of evolutionary directions and processes, brings to bear on present and future religious attitudes? To what extent can the integration of the intellectual and emotional aspects of human personality contribute to a more profound wisdom?

1. We now know that life and humanity are not static, but that progressive change is inherent in existence. Religion and science must change along with other aspects of human culture, and cannot rely upon traditional beliefs and authoritarian statements of past ages. At the same time there is a great need to study the history and development of religions and sciences, for we cannot adequately comprehend the modern viewpoint without understanding the foundations upon which we are building.

2. We must understand the conservative and relatively unchanging aspects of both individuals and social institutions, and discover some of the reasons why persistence of old elements occurs alongside of the new and rapidly changing elements. In other words, we need a respect for the past as well as a respect for innovation and novelty. Too rapid change results in chaos. Too little change arrests progress.

3. We need to recognize that relations are as important as the things that are related, and that new properties emerge from new associations. In other words, creativity and en-

tirely new events and concepts arise before our eyes in both the world of nature and the segment of nature that we call the world of man.

4. Cause and effect are not linear in time, but may be circular with feedbacks from effects to causes. The order of nature shows that causes are continuous or repeated and may therefore come after preceding effects. This fact has profound significance in evolution and enables organisms to react to the statistically probable future. There is an end-directedness in living organisms, and man, by understanding this principle, to some extent can control his own destiny.

5. Life in general, and human life in particular, is infinitely complex. There is a danger in the oversimplifications of science and philosophy. We shall never have complete knowledge or understanding. We must forego the absolute, the perfect, and the final, and learn to adjust to the relative, the incompatible, the conflicting, the imperfect, and the partial. Neither science nor religion will ever lead man to perfect knowledge or complete comprehension. We should make our goals realistic if we aim to move toward them efficiently.

6. Relative progress is not only possible but occurred long before man appeared on the earth. We can understand what we mean by progress and the principles underlying both progressive organic and cultural evolution. We can apply these principles in assisting the advance of civilization and humanity. Homeostasis, defined as the development and advance of self-regulation of optimal conditions for existence and survival, is the direction of organic evolution, and seems to be the direction of cultural evolution as well. This is the meaning of life processes in the individual and in the various integrated groups of individuals. Homeostasis is a term originally used for physiological regulation within the plant or animal body by means of feedback mechanisms, but the concept is measurable and allows cross-comparisons between individual, social, and ecological systems. The improvement of

homeostasis is the fitness that has survival value which results in natural selection. Natural selection guides the direction of progressive organic evolution. Conscious selection by man can play an ever increasing role in guiding the direction of progressive cultural evolution of man and civilization.

7. Neither analysis nor synthesis alone leads to adequate comprehension. We must use both in reaching wisdom and perspective. Because of feedbacks and emergent relationships, information about mechanisms is insufficient for an understanding of any whole unit, particularly of even the simplest of living units. Sufficient knowledge of the origin of mechanisms depends upon an understanding of the evolutionary time dimensions of each whole organized living system. Natural selection is one principle that illustrates the dependence of mechanistic causes upon functional effects. Here we have an example of the use of both analysis and synthesis in science, and there are many others.

8. Intellect and emotion must be accepted and joined in the balanced personality. The avoidance and fear of emotional reactions by many scientists are not to be condoned. Personally, I have yet to meet a so-called cold-blooded scientist. Emotions have evolved because they contributed to homeostasis as did also the physiological body and the mentality of man. Religion is possibly more emotional than is science, but I see every reason for co-ordinating emotion and intelligence in religion as I think they should be integrated in science.

9. The aesthetic values in every form of beauty need to be incorporated with the intellectual and emotional nature of man. There is great aesthetic beauty in science, although some scientists do not fully recognize it, and few artists are even dimly aware of it. Artistic expression has also evolved and is obviously an important part of progressing civilization. Religionists have fostered the arts more than have scientists. I suggest that the aesthetic arts contribute to individual and

social homeostasis, but much inquiry and investigation is needed before this meaning of the creative arts is substantiated.

10. In all aspects of human nature and personality, the individual is in part the product of the social system to which he belongs and owes his origin, and each person can contribute to the larger entity of which he forms a part. Through co-operation, love, self-sacrifice, example, inspiration, and accomplishment in the arts, sciences, and human relationships, each individual has worth, dignity, and immortality. Because the individual is part of a higher unity than himself alone, selfish individualistic philosophy is insufficient, short-sighted, and vicious. Through the function of the individual within a more inclusive system, one may come to an understanding of both life and death. Innate death mechanisms have evolved for the benefit of the group. So the age-old preoccupation of religion with the problem of death may be emotionally and intellectually resolved on realistic grounds without recourse to a false dualism.

11. Cultural evolution is based upon somewhat different mechanisms than organic evolution, but significant functional analogy exists. Organic evolution has been explained much better since the discovery of the gene units of heredity. Cultural evolution can be understood far better when the units of social heredity are recognized and analyzed. I suggest that the symbol is such a unit, and that the gene and symbol have parallel effects in organic and cultural evolution. Both progressively evolve complex patterns and co-ordination that function toward improved homeostasis.

What action can we take to achieve a comprehensive understanding of the relations of religion and science? How can we improve our attitudes and perspectives toward the deepest concerns of man? How can such discussions as these have a dynamic influence toward progressive advancement?

1. Let us vastly increase our information of facts, the

relations between facts, and the interpretive meanings of the facts and their relationships. Interpretations should be based upon verifiable evidence in psychology, the social sciences, and the humanities, as well as in the natural sciences. Let us support and encourage many thousands of talented individuals in creative research, scholarship, and attainment in all fields of inquiry, including religion.

2. Let us gain perspective on the importance of detailed minutiae of information and experience. Science has shown that no observable fact is without importance and without meaning. Other fields of knowledge should follow the lead of the natural and social sciences in this discovery.

3. Let us recognize the values of both analysis and synthesis in all investigations.

4. Let us recognize that no aspect of existence—physical, living, or human—is beyond the scope of scientific inquiry. Let us recognize that we can correct past errors, discover new knowledge, and arrive at solutions of many problems that have often been thought to be beyond the scope of human wisdom.

5. Let us recognize that no single individual can encompass all aspects of reality, but that we each belong to a much larger entity (humanity) that will continue to investigate and interpret ourselves and our environment in the past, present, and future. This is necessary for the improvement of social homeostasis and is in conformity with the direction and meaning of the evolution of life.

6. Let us seek means by which our religion can make more of an appeal to our intelligence, and our science more of an appeal to our emotions.

7. Let us recognize and improve our wise understanding of the unity of the human personality, humanity as a whole, and the species of man within animate and inanimate nature.

CHAPTER 11

Two Versions of Man

by HENRY A. MURRAY

Harvard University

SINCE I AM NOT ASKED to report as an official or even unofficial representative of my profession, I assume that I am free to set forth whatever biological and psychological propositions and hypotheses seem to me both tenable and pertinent to our topic, whether the majority of my colleagues would agree with me or not. Also, I am trusting that you will tolerate the frank avowal, here and there, of certain beliefs of mine respecting science and religion, some of which are very questionable value judgments that may singe your ears or even upset your livers, but not seriously, I hope.

"Religion in the age of science." It should be opposite. Our topic states correctly the existing relationships of the two domains. But, as I see it, this relationship is the reverse of what it should be. That is to say, in my hierarchy of valued ends, the sphere of religion is *super*ordinate to that of science. Strange thing for a scientist to confess. But, let me add, I am not thinking of the Christianity that persecuted scientists, of Judaism, or of any other great religion, as it now stands. I am but dreaming of certain dawning possibilities, of a religion that is compatible with science and understands its aim and destiny.

147

Why do I believe that the sphere of religion should be *super*ordinate to the sphere of science? Because, as defined by men whose judgment in this matter I respect, the sphere of religion is the sphere of ultimate concern. That is, religion is, or should be, devoted to final values, beyond which no other values can exist. It is not hard to see what this means in the frame of the once-dominant Christian myth. A man's ultimate concern is whether he spends an eternity of years in the best place imaginable or in the worst place imaginable. Seventy multipleasured years on earth are of little worth when weighed against an endless age of sizzling in the underground; and a lifetime of vexation, misery, and woe are tolerable if after the fever of life is over one is destined to enjoy a trillion years of bliss.

But if one cannot believe this, apprehending the whole scheme as an effective stratagem of priests in suppressing misbehavior, useful as well to rulers and to parents, if one cannot accept the Heaven-and-Hell alternative as a matter of ultimate concern, what can replace them? What is there in this world on earth of comparable value to the promise of another world? As you know, numerous answers to this question have been given, by ancient and by European authors, especially since the eighteenth-century Enlightenment. I suppose a portion of the answer I would give dates from the saying attributed to Protagoras: "Man is the measure of all things." Certainly in my scales the ultimate concern of man is man himself, the development toward perfection of his inner being, the development toward perfection of his interpersonal relationships, the development toward perfection of his societies, and eventually the creation and maintenance of a harmonious world community, in short, better personalities for a better life for a better world, the highest spiritual good of all men and women of this earth. This view accords with two of Alfred North Whitehead's memorable statements, first: "What should emerge from religion is individual worth of character," and second: "Religion is world loyalty." To put *in a nutshell* the science-religion relationship as I order it: It is the development of science for the development of man, rather than the development of man for the development of science.

I am suggesting here that religion should be defined, not so much in terms of beliefs as in terms of aims.

Another way of defining its relative position is to say that science itself does not determine the ends to which its products will be used. The aim of science is valid knowledge, a theoretical system in terms of which events may be perceived, analyzed, formulated, explained, predicted within limits, and, as far as possible, controlled. Such knowledge is often a tremendous source of power, power to harm or power to benefit mankind. But which of these alternatives will be chosen? All scientists agree that the answer to this question lies outside their proper sphere; and because it does, the role of science, great as it surely is, will never be more than a subordinate or instrumental one in the enterprises of men and of societies.

If this is true, we are left with the question: In what sphere is it decided how scientific knowledge should be utilized? The down-to-earth answer is that scientific knowledge and techniques are utilized by those who want them and can afford to pay for them. There are countless individual decisions by the public as well as institutional decisions in the spheres of industry and of government. In the last analysis, of course, it is the government that decides. In Russia, for example, the government regulates to some extent which scientific theories will be announced and taught and which refused and suppressed. Happily, there are no crass interventions of this sort in these United States. But the influence of our government on the course of science—no doubt a necessary and proper influence within limits—is nonetheless enormous. With dazzling research grants as bait, it has hooked and landed a great number of physical, biological, and social scientists, and directed their imaginations and talents toward the solution of problems relevant to the successful prosecution of a global war, a war, the expert tells us, in which all we cherish might be shattered, might crumble and dissolve like Shakespeare's "insubstantial pageant faded, and leave not a wrack behind." I am not in any way condemning these practices of our nation, world conditions being as they are. I am merely pointing out that a large proportion of our scientists are being subsidized by the government in the name of might, and none, to my knowledge, in the name of right. Here we have science in an age of rampant nationalism and materialism.

But what is superordinate to nationalism and materialism? Nothing really influential so far as one can see. A widespread but vaguely apprehended moral standard, a diffuse yet fickle and unreliable goodwill, a great craving for security and peace; but as yet no clear vision of world unity, of the highest good for all men and women of this earth. Is it not apparent that this highest good is, or should be, a matter of ultimate concern to everyone? I would say, yes; and repeat that the sphere of ultimate concern is one definition, a fitting definition, of the sphere of religion. A multiplicity of militant nationalisms requires an inviting and evolutionary ideal of mutual embracement to subdue and unify them, the moral persuasion of a universal world religion. Today we have many religions in an age of science, science in an age of nationalisms, and nationalisms in an age of nothing, or nearly nothing, nothing in the West. Beyond the Iron Curtain, to be sure, there is the powerful ideology, the tremendous mental force, of Communism, like that of Islam in its day of vaunting strength; but in opposing Communism, we, unhappily, have no equally enthralling vision. There is no center of gravity that attracts, binds, and unifies the peoples of the free world, or even of the Western world. In the much quoted words of the poet Yeats:

> Things fall apart; the center cannot hold;
> Mere anarchy is loosed upon the world . . .
> The best lack all conviction, while the worst
> Are full of passionate intensity.

According to my dream, a transformed religion, a new religion, will ultimately occupy that center and hold the world together. Whatever may be the nature of this religion of the future, a good many of us believe that it will have to be compatible with science.

When people speak of the conflict between religion and science, they usually have in mind the Christian religion and the physical sciences: the Christian religion, because no other religion has so mightily and persistently gathered up its powers to oppose and suppress science on fundamental issues, and the physical sciences, because astronomy and physics were the first to collide with religion, and because these were the first to develop in a great way and today represent science at its best. But now the crucial conflict is not between Christianity and physics, or even between Christianity and biology; it is between religion and psychology. Here I am using the term "psychology" in a general sense to include all the young, groping, would-be sciences of man—academic psychology, clinical and social, psychiatry and psychoanalysis, and, in addition to these, whatever facts and theories from cultural anthropology and sociology are relevant to an understanding of the emotional experiences, mental processes, and overt behaviors of human beings.

I am saying that the crucial conflict is between religion and psychology, because the focus of both of these disciplines is the same, namely, the nature and transformation of human feelings, evaluations, needs, beliefs, purposes, and actions. The Church can graciously withdraw from the domains of astronomy, physics, chemistry, and biology, without seriously weakening its foundations or its standing in the minds of men. It can readily give way to new scientific discoveries about the revolutions of galaxies, about the nucleoproteins of the living cell, or about bees, ants, and reptiles. But it can never abandon its concern with the vicissitudes of human personality, can never withdraw from the sphere of psychology, because *this* is its

hereditary station. The Church Fathers were in no sense astronomers or biologists, but some of them—St. Augustine, for
example—were eminent psychologists in their day, and during
the succeeding centuries the Catholic Church accumulated—
in large measure from intimate confessions—more knowledge
about the tribulations of the human spirit than is dreamed of
by academics of our day. And so, when Christianity is confronted, as it is today, by the findings and speculations of
anthropologists and psychologists, there is trouble—not yet to
any marked degree, but in the offing. Not yet, because nowadays the two disciplines are functionally separate, their currents of thought being almost wholly dissociated, neither of
them knowing at what conclusion the other is arriving. Their
social interactions are exceedingly amicable, but these rarely
include intellectual communictions on basic issues. The prevalent condition, as I see it, is one of peaceful, if not oblivious,
coexistence, or, in some quarters, friendly collaboration in
various practical endeavors. It's as if the members of both
professions had tacitly agreed to put aside their differences in
the name of sociability and composure.

In this genial company of compatible men and women, on
this quiet island, in this mild weather, it seems that the part of
decency and tact would be to tiptoe round the sleeping incon-
gruities of faith and of aim between religionists and psychologists, and concentrate on what they have in common. Were I
to choose this more agreeable and ingratiating policy, we
might advance together smoothly and serenely to a happy
ending, but we would have to leave several provoking problems in our rear, and these, sooner or later, would steal up on
us and shatter our peace of innocence.

It is because I strongly feel that religion and psychology
should and *will* eventually embrace each other, that I am
adopting the opposite policy—disquieting today but sound-
est in the long run—of examining points of disagreement first,
and later, if there is time, the broader area of agreement.

My plan is to submit to you a brief account of one version, one aspect or potentiality, of man's nature, a version, based on the theory of creative evolution, which is not without relevance to religion. At certain points I shall contrast this view with the traditional Christian view, and thereby call attention to certain differences between current assumptions of psychology and the age-old assumptions of this religion. Because differences on these issues constitute the present grounds for the functional separation of the two disciplines, these are the issues which must be settled if reconciliation is our serious and sincere intent.

Since I cleave to the principle that an adequate understanding of any living creature depends on the possession of sufficient knowledge of its history—its genesis, its past encounters with the environment, and its serial developments—since the truth of this principle has been verified over and over again in my experience, I shall start my characterization of man by considering the question of his origin. First, let us recall the biblical picture of the facts.

According to the Babylonian-Hebraic-Christian story, the first man was made by *the* supreme parent, the sovereign of the universe, in a single day and in his likeness. Then from this man's rib a woman was fashioned, and the pair, complete in mind and body, were assigned the selectest place in which to dwell in uninterrupted harmony and joy. Unhappily there was a flaw in each, an importunate and irrepressible need for freedom, freedom to explore and to experiment, to taste the never tasted and forbidden. The result was exile and a curse: from then on, life for the human race would be a load of pain, sweat, and grief, with perfection, paradise, and the tree of eternal life —the golden age of man—forever in the past.

Many centuries passed before another testament proclaimed that a new dispensation was forthcoming, and in due course it was concluded that paradise and the tree of eternal life had been transferred from earth to sky and the long-standing ban of exile was no longer absolute and unconditional. Thenceforth, the kingdom of heaven would be open to a number of elected people. As most authentically set forth by St. Augustine, confirmed by Calvin, and unanimously acccepted in colonial New England, this revised conception states that all men, being inheritors of Adam's guilt, are born in sin and in the wrath, but that God has mercifully chosen some of them to be recipients of his indispensable, prevenient, irresistible, and indefectible grace, and by the operation of this grace—not at all by their own efforts—these will be saved from their depravity, redeemed, and so made fit for blissful living in the heavenly company of saints and angels. Down the centuries of Western history this still current view of the inherent nature of man, and of his possible mysterious transformation, has been tremendously influential in shaping the deep thoughts of men.

The points to be specially noted in this version are eleven in number: (1) the supreme male parentage of man; (2) man's creation in the image of God; (3) the omission, if not the denial, of sexual conjugation and the female's function—the absence of a Goddess, the procreation of life accomplished without her participation, the first woman being taken out of man; (4) creativity credited to the transcendent being outside of nature; (5) the great speed of creation; (6) the source of original sin—intellectual curiosity, the desire for wisdom, knowledge of good and evil; (7) the fall of man from an initial state of bliss; (8) a God-made perfect world, established in the past and then held up as the ultimate goal to be reached, if reached at all, in the far future, after death; (9) the depravity of human nature due to the inheritance of Adam's sin; (10) the possibility of transformation by the saving grace of God; and (11) the dictation of these statements by God and hence their absolute and undeniable truthfulness.

According to a more recent version of himself—the version I shall put before you—man is descended from the very humblest of parents, a purely fortuitous combination of chemical elements—such low-caste stuff as hydrogen, oxygen, carbon, and nitrogen. Instead of a day, it took two billion years or more to shape him. And instead of falling from his primordial state of being, he has risen—increasing his powers by periodic leaps as well as by more gradual acquisitions. Also noteworthy is the evidence that this wondrous evolution from the simple to the complex may be credited, in large measure, to the very propensity which in the Garden of Eden drama led to man's disgrace and fall, that is, the propensity of all organisms to explore and to experiment.

In the panorama presented to us by the theory of evolution, a better world—and we must avow that most religions are devoted to the idea of a better world, in one sense or another—a better world is neither a premade perfection that existed on this globe in pristine times, nor a premade perfection in the sky awaiting the elected few, but a condition that might, by concordant creative efforts, be achieved on earth in the very distant future.

Darwin's formula for the evolution of fishes, reptiles, birds, and mammals, man included, stresses two chief factors: (1) countless slight variations of structure, and (2) the survival of those organisms with variations that operated beneficially, concurrent with the elimination of those with variations which proved injurious.

When presented in the mid-nineteenth century, this conception of man's ascending career on earth was shocking to his self-esteem. The notion that he had moved up from the status of a monkey was somehow less congenial to his soul than the thought that he had backslid from the original gracefulness of Adam. The new theory was equally shocking to his intellect, in its abandonment of two long-cherished concepts: that of God's design—the operation of an unseen hand in the determination of events—and that of Aristotle's final cause or goal —something in Nature comparable to human purpose. According to Darwin, all the millions of variations which marked the path of evolution might be accounted for by purely accidental (and hence purposeless) physical changes.

When *we* do something accidentally, we commonly call it a mistake, or slip, and say that we are sorry. Could man, the paragon of animals, have been no more than a mistake, the end result of countless sorry slips? Not possibly, our pride assures us. Man is admirable, and when *we* do something admirable, we are apt to feel we purposed it, to claim we had the deed in mind before we acted, and to take full credit. God or Nature, therefore, must have planned for *Homo sapiens*. The advent of our breed must have been intended from the start. But, unhappily for vanity, the experts have repeatedly assured us there is no evidence of consciousness of goal in any of the structurations which led to the human species. At first blush, it looks as if the facts constrained us to the view that pure chance was the author of every variety of organisms, even of so complex and remarkable an organism as that of the erect, tool-using, tribal dreamer that we call man.

Despite Darwin's emphasis on accident, or chance, the theory of evolution was understood by some scientists as an encouragement to their faith that all biological phenomena, including human conduct, would eventually be understandable in terms of the physical and chemical properties of matter. The word they chose to symbolize their faith was "mechanism": human nature is nothing else than a machine of great complexity. This view of man is at the limit of self-depreciation, far more crippling to our aspirations than the theological assertion that man is born depraved. For, according to the mechanistic model, we humans do not even have the powers that might expose us to moralistic judgments: we are automata, first and last. And as mere automata we are unspeakably inferior to the best gadgets of today. Though savory to some tongues, this thesis has been rather hard to cram against the stomach of our knowledge that machines do not grow by feeding on their surroundings and constantly restructuring themselves, and do not habitually converse, embrace each other, multiply, nurse their young, and institute societies. But it did not become obvious that the word "mechanism" was a poor choice to designate this model of man's nature until classical mechanics was abandoned as a foundation for the sciences of physics and chemistry.

The error of supposing that the procession of organic variations could be represented in purely mechanistic terms might never have been launched had Darwin's terminology not concealed the crucial fact of creativity in nature, irreversible and hence unmechanical creativity. His theory, as we have seen, depends on the occurrence of variations of form; and what is a variation of form but a new configuration of elements, a unique pattern, that retains its structure for a while? And by these very words creativity is defined.

The original outline of the theory of creative evolution was Bergson's seminal contribution; but since its publication many profound thinkers have, in different and more or less radical ways, expanded and revised it.

Briefly, and most generally, this thesis states that the processes of nature have been constantly, though often very slowly and imperceptibly, formative and transformative. The transformations have been both integrative and disintegrative, evolutionary and involutionary; but the former have predominated, and among these—these products of integrative energy—some have been veritable creations, unparalleled in history. This applies on the chemical level to the compounding of new and more complex atoms, molecules, and crystals, and *hypothetically*, to the much later emergence of a living organism, say a few genes in an envelope of protoplasm; and then, on this supervenient biological level, to variant conjugations and permutations of genes, resulting in the development, through interactions with environment, of unexampled living forms, dispositions and abilities, of brains and animal intelligences. It applies with equal cogency, on the social level, to the establishment of groups and of exceptional systems of co-ordination among its members, and, on the symbolic-cultural level, to the creation of words, concepts, and germinal ideas eventuating through numberless expressions in collectively valued myths, beliefs, art forms, moral and legal codes, plans of action, technical designs.

This view of the natural course of events in no wise contradicts Darwin's formulation. In fact, it supplements it by pointing to those properties of things which might account for stable variations, not only as he described them on the biological and social levels, but on the chemical and ideological as well. We have only to conceive of the *movement* and hence inevitable approximation of different entities which are inherently attractive to each other—*attraction* being one of the great and constant forces in the universe—and then conceive of these attractions resulting in a multiplicity of structural *combinations* new to this planet, and, most importantly, conceive of the *coherence*, the sticking and staying power, and hence the relative stability and longevity of many of these unprecedented forms —organic compounds, genetic clusters, family relationships, governmental laws, religious creeds and rites. Since individual organisms are mortal, another power must be present on the biological, social, and symbolic levels, namely, the power of *propagation*, the ability to implant in others and hence to transmit and multiply the new variations from generation to generation. Furthermore, to survive in a competitive and dangerous environment, most entities must possess *combative strength*, defensive and offensive force. "Vary, multiply, and be strong," was one of the several pithy precepts drawn from Darwin's theory. Finally, one more property is required if an established form is to have further evolutionary value, namely, a certain *plasticity*, or flexibility, the capacity, that is, to play a part or to become involved in subsequent *transformations* or reconstructions. The picture is one of continuity through change. Only by losing its particular identity, by perishing as such, can a variation become a link, stage, or episode, in an evolutionary sequence, such as the one and only sequence that led to the human species.

Can we find evidence of purpose in all this?

For the production of chemical and biological variations no credit goes to purpose, or consciousness of goal. The creative transformations of nature, according to this theory, occurred blindly, without foresight of their ends. Furthermore, they were not necessarily, or even predominantly, beneficent: enormous numbers of them were useless or disadvantageous to the species in which they occurred, rendering its members more vulnerable to injury, less capable of resisting, circumventing, or coping with destructive forces from without. Thus, deleterious variations of form or behavior were, for the most part, extinguished and only those variations which happened to serve a vital purpose have survived. Consequently, almost all biological processes that are observable today are in the long run sustaining to the majority of individuals or to the race in which they occcur, and so have a purposeful appearance. Without any consciousness of goals, they nonetheless attain them. For example, males and females of prehuman species may have been aware, in some fashion, of each other's fascinating qualities, but no members of a conjugating pair, we can be sure, were ever directed in their activities by the conscious aim of producing a variant that would advance the cause of evolution, and yet, in countless cases this was precisely what resulted from their unreasoning embraces.

Must all variations be attributed to accident?

Although no credit for these advances can be ascribed to purpose, only a portion of it, according to this theory, belongs to acccident. We all agree that it is impossible to predict precisely which entities at precisely which stages of their careers will meet each other, or precisely which rearrangement of their components will occur at precisely what hour. Such synchronicities among events are affairs of chance and beyond our reckoning. For all we know, evolution might have taken a very different course and come out with a more amiable species than our own. But the occurrence of *some* form of evolution, the movement and mingling of different entities, magnetic and affectional, the enduring units that result—cohesive, cooperative, logical—and the reconstruction of these into larger and more accomplished units—events of this general character are no accidents but have been fated from the beginning by the inherent potencies of the universe. For us the crux of this version is the observation that the most outstanding heroes, or demigods, of the long epic of this earth—*movement, chance, attraction, combination, coherence, propagation, combative strength,* and *transformation*—are playing no less important parts today in the development of societies, of ideologies, and of personalities.

Such is the bare skeleton of a very general view respecting the more strategic component processes of evolutionary transformations. For the sake of brevity, several components have been omitted, as well as *all* details. Last year Professor Wald gave a beautifully ordered account of what facts and current suppositions are relevant to an understanding of evolution on the physicochemical and biological levels. This year Professor Emerson is certain to contribute a great deal to our knowledge of analogous processes on other levels. Last night we were informed by Professor Huntsman's admirable address. These disciplined observers of nature, these gifted theorists, I trust, will be my saviors, give meaning to the vagueness and diffuseness of my notions, by providing whatever substantial facts, whatever specificities and particularities, are essential to even a provisional acceptance of the view I am expounding. For better or for worse, I must confine myself to generalities, taking it for granted that you fully realize the tentative and hypothetical status of these concepts.

Now, assuming that the theory I have outlined is roughly

consonant with the known facts, what additional conclusions pertinent to our topic can be drawn from it? At the moment, I shall restrict myself to four:

1. Creativity, the power to construct new and coherent forms, is a property of nature, of human nature especially, as I shall suggest later, of the deeper strata of the mind. This conclusion is contrary to the orthodox belief that creation is a special power and prerogative of a transcendent personality who like a master artisan manipulates natural objects from the outside. But it is not discordant with pantheism, the belief that God and nature are identical, or with the not uncommon inclination to deify creativeness in general or beneficent creativeness in particular.

2. Most of the more fundamental evolutionary processes occur so slowly—taking, in some cases, many thousands of years to run their course—that a Methuselah would be incapable of recording them. This is one of the major reasons why scientists for centuries, attracted first of all to the more static and stable aspects of nature, overlooked the crucial question of the *formation of the forms* they chose to study. Anyhow, we must confess that the biblical report of the creation of the universe in six days is a little out of line with the evidence that is now at hand.

3. The theory of creative evolution stresses the importance of the female role in sexual conjugation, reproduction, and child-rearing, as well as in other varieties of interpersonal relations, and by so doing, opens our eyes, if by any chance they are still shut, to the several evidences of pathological prejudice toward women and toward sexuality in the Hebraic-Christian story of creation and in its story of man's first surrender to temptation. This prejudice was outspoken in the writings of the Church Fathers, and its virulence was contagious to subsequent generations, one result being that no spiritual form of erotic love has ever been offered us by Christianity.

4. Finally, the theory of creative evolution is death to the

hope that any entity, any pattern, any production of the mind, can remain for very long both fixed and dominant. Infallibility is impossible in nature.

At this point, a few comments pertinent to evolution on the social level might serve to elucidate the view of human nature I am submitting to your judgment.

Surveying the evidences of man's development on earth, Darwin concluded: first, that the survival of the fittest is a principle which applies decisively *not* to individuals, but to rival groups—tribes, states, or nations—and second, that mutual sympathy, aid, and collaboration among members of a group are conducive to its solidarity, and hence to its combative power and survival. To put it another way, one of the critical variations established long ago was a clannish combination of families more powerful than any single person, a flexible yet stable social system with some differentiation of functions and consequently with an enhanced capacity to cope with various tasks and crises.

From the beginning, if we follow Sir Arthur Keith's composition of the evidence, every successful group has adhered to a double code of conduct, a Janus-faced morality: one face preaching submission to authority, reverence, cooperation, loyalty, good will, and generosity within the group; and the other more contorted face shouting with rage and murderous aggression toward members of opposing groups. Other things being equal, it must have been the clans or tribes which embodied this dual standard to the highest degree that triumphed and endured, and passed on to their descendants down to the present day the dispositions which sustained it.

This theory of group evolution helps us to understand why man is a social, rather than a solitary, self-sufficient creature, and why, as a social creature, he is both humane and brutal. Illustrative of his *social* properties are such familiar facts as these: that the vast majority of men are reared in one particular society, a society that is prejudiced in its own favor, and are satisfied to be lifelong interdependent members of this society; that the bulk of their enjoyments come from interacting with its members; that they are at peace with themselves only when they feel and act in accord with its customs and ideals, and that, even in their furthest reaches of self-forwarding ambition, they choose for their most delectable final prize the applause of their fellow beings, and, after death, fame— "that last infirmity of noble mind." The dual morality of groups—tribes and nations—accounts, in some measure, for the failure, the halfheartedness and insincerity, of all attempts to abolish war, and for the fact that human beings have been generally so willing, even eager, to suppress their fears of self-extinction and fight for their country to the tragic end, as well as for the fact that a man who kills a hundred members of an enemy society is declared glorious, but is condemned to the severest punishment if he stops the life of a single fellow citizen.

It is supposed that the generally victorious groups were those which most fully incorporated and exploited the vaingloriousness and pride, the greed and will-to-power of their individual members. But what is the significance of the will to power? Power, intoxicating as it may be to some men and to some nations, is a *means* to something, not an end. Power for what? To this question the response of a creative evolutionist might be: power to construct ever larger and less vulnerable social units controlling ever larger areas of the earth's resources, or, in other words, power, spurred on by greed, to grow and to develop, by invading, conquering, subjugating, and assimilating weaker units, or, more peacefully and happily in some cases, by federating with other units. History reports a great number of such sequences: the integration of primal groups into clans, and of clans into tribes, and of tribes into small nations, and the integration of small nations into great nations that subsequently broke apart, the rise and decline, the evolution and involution, of mighty civilizations, as Toynbee has shown us, but as yet, unfortunately, no orchestration of state sovereignties into a world order, no political embodiment of that dream of universal fellowship which centuries of religious men have recommended to our hearts.

This curtailed abstract of evolutionary processes on the social and political level is clearly inadequate. Something should be said about the determining importance, first, of the family structure—the interrelations of father, mother, and offspring—and, second, of the total social structure, or form of government, of a group. Also necessary is some account of the role of religious beliefs and practices in the achievement and preservation of tribal and national unity. But the time allotted me does not permit even a brief discussion of these matters. Furthermore, this is not the place for it, since the evolution of human societies and religions has depended on the capacity for speech, and speech belongs to the symbolic-ideational level of creativeness, with which we have yet to cope.

Before proceeding, however, it might be stated that the theory I have been expounding gives comfort neither to the Augustinian judgment of total depravity at birth, nor to the judgment, most often attributed to Rousseau, that newborn babes are springs of sympathy and love. In my opinion, human infants are an aggregate of potentialities, potential drives to action and potential abilities, those which in the past have been most generally conducive to the evolution and survival of the social unit. Most of the potential drives, or dispositions, are in readiness to propel actions which aim at self-preservation and enjoyment, neither good nor evil in intent, and associated with these are dispositions conducive to the joy and well-being of other people as well as dispositions to fury and destructiveness. A sufficient study of the dreams and fantasies of little children, say four to six years old, will convince the most adoring mother that the human psyche, at this age at least, is predominantly and most excitedly engaged in inventing scenes of violence, death, and mutilation. But at present most psychologists believe that except for the instincts of the body, the bulk of the child's dispositions are no more than potentialities, and it largely depends on chance and the social environment —the parents and the surrounding culture—which among these various potentialities get stimulated, encouraged, and rewarded, and thus established as enduring components of the personality, and which *do not*. The theory of creative evolution draws special attention to the rhythms and stages of transformation which the structure of personality undergoes from birth to maturity, sometimes very slowly by imperceptible gradations and occasionally with striking rapidity; and also to the fact that the formative processes responsible for these changes go on unconsciously, for the most part, and, in their depths are scarcely more subject than the grace of God to man's deliberate direction. I assume that it is these transforming processes in human nature and their determinants which constitute the major focus of concern for the majority of religious men. But I shall say no more about them until I have discussed the top and last level of human evolution.

Consideration of the very earliest social systems—small colonies, let us say, of prehuman anthropoids—suggests another emergent variation in the course of man's genesis and development, this variation being one of the chief products of social life as well as the chief means of ordering and sustaining it. I am referring to symbolic language and to the mental capacity from which this kind of language stems, namely, the capacity to form concepts combined with some awareness of their meanings. It is the power of imagination and conceptualization linked with the power of symbolic representation and expression which distinguishes man most saliently from all preceding species. In the beginning was the Image and the Word.

This enormous step brought man to the ideational, the symbolic-cultural level of evolution. For the first time, the mind of a living creature could dissociate itself to a significant

degree for a significant length of time from its immediate surroundings and conceive of things that were not then present
to its senses, and even more, conceive of arrangements of
things that had never been present to its senses. But this gift of
abundant and far-ranging imagination had dangerous as well
as fruitful possibilities. Spelled by its productions, on the one
hand, and fearful of the external environment, on the other, a
child might far prefer his inner world, come to live in it entirely, and remain an idle dreamer, or become a senseless visionary or victim of insanity. In short, lunacy is the dreaded peril
and genius the coveted prize of this new power of thought and
of verbalization, the power that lifted man out of the class of
primates.

It is not without significance that the advent of this mental
capacity was accompanied, on the one hand, by an unprecedented degree and duration of helplessness and dependency in
the offspring, and on the other, by a corresponding increase of
enduring maternal aid, devotion, and concern. Here, in this
intimate symbiosis of primitive human mother and primitive
human child, we might look for the first germ of religious
compassion, the *agape* of Christianity, as well as for the first
germ of ideational creativity.

Look at the human infant—of all creatures, objectively
speaking, the most unfit to live, the most incompetent, endowed with no resources save the voice to cry for help. But
there, encased within this body, as correlate of its complete
impractibility, resides a mind, an imagination that is a veritable
hive of promising possibilities to be realized in their season if
chance consents—perhaps in middle-age or later—provided
the child receives, during his good-for-nothing years, a due
degree of maternal warmth and care.

If you insist on immediate efficiency and quick results, turn
to the practical progeny of your animal neighbors, but if you
require more efficiency than this and can check your impor-
tunity, turn to the impractical human infant, because this one

is capable not only of learning a much wider variety of more efficient tricks, but forming theories, theories which can be converted into actions of extraordinary practicality. Here is a truth this hasting world has not yet got hold of and digested. There is nothing so practical as a good theory.

Then look at the human mother, or mother surrogate, in close and constant proximity to her playfully dreaming child, teaching him to speak and applauding his every effort, encouraging his expanding spirit like a patroness of some unadjusted would-be artist, prophet, or philosopher.

The thesis I am submitting here is that the creativity of nature in general is manifested most clearly and most saliently by the creativity of human nature, by the formative mental processes of man; that novel ideas, charismatic ideas are the mutant genes of cultural evolution. Like countless wanton and wasteful experiments of nature, man's imaginings may run off the beam of progressive and beneficial developments and produce one or another variety of deformation—criminality, neurosis, or psychosis. But creative imagination at its best, cheered by sight of an ideal or valued end, and checked by rationality, is the fountain from which all inventive and regenerative currents flow. The ancients missed the point. Only recently, since the beginnings of romanticism in Europe, less than two hundred years ago, has the role of creativity in man become apparent to some people. Even now its role is not widely and sufficiently acknowledged, certainly not in the United States. It is not fully appreciated, to take one example, that our cherished democratic system, for the preservation of which so many men have lived and died, was derived from a formation of ideas that once took place in the heads of John Locke and of Rousseau. Nor is it fully appreciated in this country that all the fundamental hypotheses and theories relative to the atomic energy on which some think our mightiness depends came from minds in England, Germany, France, Denmark, Italy, Poland, and Australia. That the superior striking power, if not the continued existence, of an entire nation may hang on the unimpeded imaginations of a few theoretical scientists is today only too appallingly apparent.

But let us return for a moment to primitive man and the practical significance to him of his newborn power of imagination. When governed wholly by instinct, an organism can learn the specific ways and instrumental means to its goal only by overt trials, their failures and their successes, at the time the instinct is operating. But man, gaining a little liberty from instinct, became capable, by the mere play of fantasy, of conducting countless behavioral experiments in his head, conceiving of numerous alternative paths and tactics, evaluating them in his mind's eye, discarding the apparent worst and selecting the apparent best—all very much more rapidly than would be possible if every idea had to be successively acted out and tested by experience. And then, with the invention of language, consciousness of goal, or purpose, began to play an increasingly important role in social evolution. For language enables people to submit to each other's inner sight word-images of desirable ends, alternative strategies and rules, and through discussion to arrive at enough agreement to permit the execution of long-range collective enterprises. For these a consciously shared objective is indispensable. Language, furthermore, is the best means of introducing variations, since it empowers a person with a new idea, a new hope for the future, a new plan or tactic, or a new ethical conviction, to start it in the thoughts of others and keep it rolling there until familiarity argues for its acceptance.

In all likelihood, primitive man's creativeness was oriented almost entirely toward contriving means of physical survival—exploring for edible plants, for a suitable territory to occupy, building shelters, inventing pots and tools, and fashioning weapons for hunting and for war. Along the way, momentous discoveries were made: fire, agriculture, irrigation, the domestication and breeding of animals, stone, bronze, and iron. In the judgment of numerous historians, technical inventions have resulted in more drastic transformations of human behavior than any other kind of variation: a proposition that is verified most strikingly by the changes of habits that have occurred within our own lifetime.

Most relevant to the topic of this conference is the fact that as technology has advanced, first in this and then in that area of activity, religious beliefs and rituals have receded. Being largely dependent on the fertility of the earth, and hence concerned with the succession of the seasons, the heat of the sun, rainfall and the rising of their rivers, primitive man engaged in all manner of supposedly influential practices—sympathetic magic, supplications, propitiations, glorifications—directed toward the personified powers that were, in their beliefs, responsible for the required processes of nature. But in the West today such practices are almost obsolete. Christianity is to no extent preocccupied with the promotion of the crops. The same withdrawal has occurred in other fields, indeed to every field which the physical and biological sciences have invaded—medicine, for example, most people having come to the conclusion that the methods of trained physicians and surgeons are more generally efficacious than the ceremonies of the Church.

I have been talking about the creative processes of the mind operating in the service of physical well-being and survival, the well-being of individuals and, more often among primitives, the well-being of the whole society. Some of these imaginations, these novel ideas, have taken the form of purely physical or technological procedures, whereas others have been psychological in nature, symbolic postures, acts, words, and dramas, which might well have proved efficient if the forces of nature were veritable gods, such as Baal, Adonis, or Asclepius, with receptive psyches that were in sympathy with men's wants. A little while back, I also mentioned in passing the role of mental creativity in the development of effective governmental forms and the office of religion in maintaining the sanctity of the kingship and its code of morals, and thereby the solidarity and continuation of the social system.

The words "creation," "create," "creative," were limited at first to the operations of a divine agent. As Davies wrote in 1592, "To create, to God alone pertains." But as time went on, the usage of these terms expanded, and by the beginning of the nineteenth century they were being widely used to describe the mental processes and productions of poets, artists, and musicians, especially the works of romantic genius. Somewhat later people began speaking of eminent scientists as creative, those who had proposed and at least partially verified some all-embracing theory of great explanatory value. It is now allowed that some applied scientists and inventors are creative. Creativity in these two spheres, that of art and science, is at present generally acknowledged, and nothing I could say in a paragraph or two could be of service to us. Strangely enough the word "creative" is seldom applied to the mental processes of religionists. Why is that? As a psychologist apprehends it, man's imagination has gone to greater lengths, greater depths and heights, under the name of religion than under any other name. Think of the galaxy of primitive religions with their multiplicity of gods, myths, legends, beliefs, passions, solemn and wild rituals and orgies, bloody sacrifices, temples, idols, and sacraments. Whence all this, if not from the endless fecundity and spontaneity of man's mind?

Pertinent to this problem are two characteristics of creative processes: (1) their goal does not exist at first and hence cannot be visualized, and (2) they operate involuntarily and, to a large extent, unconsciously. The goal-object, let us say, of the need for acquisition—be it food, a house, or some utility —is known to you: it exists somewhere in the environment and you must take it as it is. But the aim of creativity—say, a symphony, or a novel, or a scientific theory to explain a peculiar sequence of events, or a more effective foreign policy,

or a better way of life—has no existence anywhere. It is necessary, first of all, to get a satisfying image or conception of it
and, if fortune favors you with this, it is then necessary to em-
body your vision in a written work or course of conduct. A
man may rack his brains throughout a lifetime without receiv-
ing the vision or idea for which he longs—say, a better form
of architecture, a better theory, a better constitution for the
United Nations—or, if he has the general idea in mind, he may
labor for years without finding the way to expound it in a
persuasive manner. That is to say, we are dealing here with
energies of the human mind that do not respond directly to
voluntary efforts. Voluntary efforts can influence their direction, defining, so far as possible, the target of their endeavor,
but they cannot force them to render up the wanted form.
Today it is pretty generally agreed that imaginations of any
real consequence are generated outside or below the stream of
awareness, during a more or less prolonged period of incuba-
tion, and they are apt to leap to consciousness abruptly at the
most unexpected moments. Sometimes, like a dream, they seem
to come from *without* rather than from *within* the mind. A
vision is called a vision because it is a presentation, a present, a
gift, to the inner eye, just as the heavenly constellations at night
are a presentation, or gift, to the outer eye. We cannot *will* the
rise of Sirius on the horizon, or the voyage of Jupiter across the
sky. Nor can we dictate the emergence of an idea of great import to us or to society. These are extremely rare, and when
they do come, they do not come from the conscious "I" in us,
but from a deeper layer of nature.

The point I am getting at is that visions which appear as
promised or possible fulfillments of a great craving, visions that
hint of the resolution of a protracted conflict, visions of extraordinary beauty, visions that come—as did St. Paul's on the
road to Damascus and St. Joan's at her home in Domremy—as
a challenging invocation to one's innermost being, seemingly
beneficent or coercive—spirit-lifting visions of this sort were

for centuries attributed to superhuman force, to the gods, or to *the* God. And why not? Did the visionary consciously and deliberately compose this vision? No, it was engendered by autonomous forces, natural forces, a psychologist would say, yet forces which one might well call supernatural insofar as their product is an unexampled creation, a never yet conceived form or goal, something that was unpredictable by scientific laws, laws which announce only that which is statistically most probable as determined by recordings of past events. Since the vision does not conform to the regular laws of human nature, it is, by this criterion, unnatural, and since, in addition, the kind of vision we have in mind strikes the visionary as something of supreme worth, the most desirable, the most valuable thing he has ever contemplated, it is, in his estimation, not only unnatural, but supernatural, a veritable miracle.

We are all familiar with the passage in *Phaedrus* in which Socrates describes the four types of divine madness, "the source," he affirms, " of the chiefest blessings granted to man." Sustained by an array of evidence, he insists that inspired madness is a noble thing, that madness, being of divine origin, is superior to common sanity. The first kind of providential madness is associated with prophecy and the second with spiritual healing, a vision of deliverance from woe. The third kind is the madness of those who are possessed by the Muses, and the last the madness of erotic love. We hear an echo of this passage in Shakespeare's saying that "The lunatic, the lover, and the poet, Are of imagination all compact . . ." Shakespeare, however, does not ascribe the "fine frenzy" of his poet to a god, and Socrates, though sincere in his reference to the gods, does not insist that everything they tell him is absolute and incontestable truth for all men for all time.

Perhaps the most famous recent description of the state of creative possession is Nietzsche's account of how his *Zarathustra* was composed.

Can anyone at the end of this nineteenth century possibly have any distinct notion of what poets of a more vigorous period meant by inspiration? If not, I should like to describe it. Provided one has the slightest remnant of superstition left, one can hardly reject completely the idea that one is the mere incarnation, or mouthpiece, or medium of some almighty power. The notion of revelation describes the condition quite simply; by which I mean that something profoundly convulsive and disturbing suddenly becomes visible and audible with indescribable definiteness and exactness. One hears—one does not seek; one takes—one does not ask who gives: a thought flashes out like lightning, inevitably without hesitation—I have never had any choice about it. There is an ecstasy whose terrific tension is sometimes released by a flood of tears, during which one's progress varies from involuntary impetuosity to involuntary slowness. There is the feeling that one is utterly out of hand, with the most distinct consciousness of an infinitude of shuddering thrills that pass through one from head to foot:—there is a profound happiness in which the most painful and gloomy feelings are not discordant in effect, but are required as necessary colors in this overflow of light. There is an instinct for rhythmic relations which embraces an entire world of forms . . . Everything occurs quite without volition, as if in an eruption of freedom, independence, power and divinity. The spontaneity of the images and similes is most remarkable; one loses all perception of what is imagery and simile; everything offers itself as the most immediate, exact, and simple means of expression.

Note that even Nietzsche—who had recently announced with certainty that God was dead—could not completely reject the idea that he was the mere incarnation or medium of some almighty power. He does not intimate that this almighty power has a separate existence outside of him, and we can safely infer that he would have identified the creative force of which he, in his own proper person, was the instrument with a natural force, a force which happened to vent itself more powerfully in him than it did in other men. If this was his opinion, there would be few dissenting voices from the ranks of today's psychologists. It is the grandiose assertion that the source of such unleashed energy is an all-knowing and utterly truthful being in the sky which provokes dissent among my colleagues.

For the origin of historic and long-surviving assertions of this sort—dogmatic and unequivocal assertions of infallibility —one must turn to the Hebrew prophets, each of whom claimed to be in his day the one appointed mouthpiece of the omniscient Yahweh. Apparently, the imagination was not in any way involved. The prophet merely opened his ears and spoke the words of the Lord as they came down to him. The proud and vaunting certitude of these devout and dedicated men was, so far as I can see, the prime source of centuries of anguish. To speak as they did was no doubt natural to them and sanctioned, even demanded, by their society. In the light of a remark made by the eminent Jewish philosopher, Spinoza, it was hardly more than a habit of speech. If Jews "desire anything," he tells us, "they say God has disposed their hearts towards it; and if they think anything, they say God has told them." This way of talking, of course, was carried to much greater lengths by the prophets, whose frantic utterances inevitably gave rise to the bitterest disputes. What could be said when scores of visionaries were in the streets, each insisting that his revelation was the sole authentic one? At one such time, the word of the Lord came unto Ezekiel saying: "Son of man, prophesy against the prophets of Israel that prophesy . . . out of their own hearts." That is to say, prophecies from a man's heart and mind are false and evil; all true revelations come from above, from the creative being who stands outside the order of nature. This conviction was fully accepted by the Church Fathers and passed down from generation to generation, the result being that no truly religious man, none of the great visionaries of Christianity, ever claimed to be, was ever officially thought to be, or allowed to be, creative. In short, the great religionists of the past reserved for themselves a separate category beyond the processes of nature.

Just here—if you will pardon a personal evaluation not flattering to the Church—just here is where religion eventually got stuck, in this blind alley, in this prison house which it invented and masoned for itself. The prison was built, it seems to me, by vanity and pride—ironically enough, the Christian Church's deadliest sin to be—the very human and understandable vanity and pride of those who insisted that they were the only selected spokesmen, the only genuine vehicles of the one and only God, that they had heard exactly what the omniscient Lord had said, remembered it and recorded it—"thus spake Yahweh"—without a flaw, and consequently everything that they wrote down was truth, absolute, infallible, and everlasting. Having compiled the writings of the chosen authors and bound them in a book, the high priests announced that *there*, between those covers, was the one sure repository of uncontradictable sacred truths. Later on, the Protestants were to agree with them completely, and so to become, in their turn, the "People of the Book." The Holy Bible is without doubt the most majestic creation of our literature, the greatest spiritual treasure that the West inherited from the East. But the nemesis of its majesty was this: Deity was imprisoned there and silenced. From then on, God could only repeat with minor variations or in different keys what he had said in Palestine, hundreds of years ago. He was not permitted to go further, to reveal more, to present men with any unprecedented vision, fitting and timely to their current situation.

In other words, the creative imagination was excommunicated, and beginning with the Renaissance, found in art, science, and public affairs far broader, freer, and happier domains for its exuberant and effective exercise. My thesis is that enchantment always keeps company with creative imagination, and what results from their combined play is evolution. Reli-

gion, by sitting pat in its citadel of solidified infallibilities, re-
pelled the lovely goose that lays the golden eggs—the creativity
in man—and thereby lost its charm, its lure, its magnetism, its
spring of inspiration and renewal—the only source of veritable
progress.

This is the rudest and crudest thing I have in my heart and
mind to say about religion. Forgive me if you can.

Another important fact not generally acknowledged is
that the Bible is poetry, in its best parts, magnificent and edifying poetry, and that without this poetic essence its spiritual
efficacy would be negligible. Some devout Christians overlook
the fact that the stirring and and sustaining power of the Book
they live by depends on the wondrous emotive language, the
vivid imagery and figures of speech, with which its wisdom is
transmitted. This is one of the major qualities by which a religion can be distinguished from a moral philosophy or system
of ethics. If the New Testament, for example, had been written by a modern social scientist in the jargon of his profession,
it would have died at birth, and Mithraism or Manichaeanism
or Mohammedanism would have taken possession of the European mind. A religion is propagated by the aid of the aesthetic
imagination, that is, in striking parables and metaphors that
kindle or console our profoundest feelings. A code of morals,
on the other hand, can appeal only to our intellects and to a
few of our more superficial sentiments. This is but one reason
why my discourse, couched as it is in commonplace referential
language, cannot possibly touch your vital centers.

The playing down of the crucial import of the Bible's
poetry has gone hand in hand with the playing up of its factual
dependability, its historicity. The great fallacy of Christianity,
Santayana has suggested, was:

> The natural but hopeless misunderstanding of imagining
> that poetry in order to be religion, in order to be the in-
> spiration of life, must first deny that it is poetry and deceive
> us about the facts with which we have to deal—this mis-

understanding has marred the work of the Christian imagination and condemned it, if we may trust appearances, to be transitory. For by this misunderstanding Christian doctrine was brought into conflict with reality, of which it pretends to prejudge the character. . . . Human life is always essentially the same, and therefore a religion which, like Christianity, seizes the essence of that life, ought to be an eternal religion. But it may forfeit that privilege by entangling itself with a particular account of matters of fact, matters irrelevant to its ideal significance.

I have been assuming, all along, rightly or wrongly, that the focus of religious concern is the transformation, the conversion, of the personality at its very center. Something was said, a little while back, of its social development, from birth to maturity, the successful outcome of which is a well-adjusted person equal to the functions of the role he has elected. Religion is not uninterested in this process; but socialization does no more than fit a person for a particular society, in a particular place, during a particular period of history, and this requires the adoption of a great aggregate of conforming beliefs, sentiments, and tastes which are local and transient and, from a larger viewpoint, mere prejudices, restrictive of spiritual freedom. Furthermore, there are always countless individuals who have become alienated from their society—either by feelings of guilt, inferiority, and resentment, or by repulsion, a profound aversion to the values of the great majority. All such people—those who are stifled in the strait jacket of convention, those who are afflicted by neurotic symptoms, and those with superpersonal hopes and aspirations—all such people will be in need of some healing vision, of transformation and renewal. It is just here where religion, with its profound intuitive understanding of the tormented human soul, and psychology, with its new methods of investigation and of therapy, might most beneficently collaborate, provided they can come to some agreement respecting the aim of their endeavors.

Now it is time for a last reckoning, a summary of the story I have told so hurriedly, a final comparison of my short abstract of the once authentic Christian view of man's origin and destiny, and my abstract of the theory of creative evolution. To repeat what I have said before: According to the latter view, man was not made from without and from above, like a pot of clay by a master workman, but from within and from below. The great God of creativity has been from the start and is today immanent in nature and immanent in us.

Second, the creation of natural forms was not achieved all of a sudden, as the image of a tree, an animal, or a man can be instantly called to mind by an act of will, but it proceeded gradually step by step over millions of years. During the last centuries, however, it has been progressing very much more rapidly on the symbolic-cultural level than it ever did on the physical-biological level.

Third, perfect chastity does not stand out as the highest ideal for our time. On the contrary, sexual love, sexual conjugation, pregnancy, and deliverance is the epitome, the very best paradigm, on the biological level of the creative process. It proceeds like the Hegelian dialectic: the male thesis embraces the female antithesis, and the result is a genetic synthesis and the development of a new and unique being. Mutual erotic love, erotic adoration, is the most natural religion, far stronger and more natural than a son's adoration for his father, the father-son relationship (with mother and daughter omitted) having been from the beginning the mythic paradigm of Christianity.

Fourth, the newborn child is neither soaking in original sin nor beaming with benevolence for all mankind. He or she is a composite of manifold potentialities for promoting its own good, promoting the good of others, or harming others.

Fifth, the course of a single life from its genesis, through its intra-uterine existence, through childhood, adolescence, and its adult years is marked by a continuity of formative and transformative processes, rapid at first, on the physical level, and, with the passage of time, slowing down and eventually coming to a stop, but advancing, in many persons, on the dispositional and mental level until the age of maturity and beyond. The theory of creative evolution stresses the fact that most of the formative processes engaged in the development, the transformation and conversions of personality, are not directly subject to the will, though the will can indirectly influence their course; these divine creative processes of nature occur autonomously, for the most part out of consciousness, and chance plays a large part in determining their fortunes. This is roughly comparable to the Catholic doctrine that the realization, or rather the partial realization, of the ideal self-image is something that exceeds man's voluntary powers and only through the operation of God's grace, with the acceptance and co-operation of the will, can an individual approach it.

Sixth, the conversion of personality from the old self to the new self is only temporarily facilitated by forceful repression, say, the repression of hatred, lust, greed, envy, and vanity. Harmful egocentric dispositions of this sort must be transmuted and made to serve a nobler purpose. A mass of evidence from the case histories of psychoanalysts goes to show that strong instinctual tendencies do not atrophy and die out when subjected to repression, but, living on in some subterranean region of the mind, are capable of no end of mischief. The puritan's sharp dichotomy of good and evil, of pure white and pure black, the obligatory *expression* of the white and the obligatory *suppression* of the black, is one of the major determinants of obsessional neurosis.

Seventh, Christianity's traditional method of dealing with evil *within* oneself by forceful repression is comparable to its traditional method of dealing with evil on the outside: evil persons, especially persons with deviant heretical beliefs, must be ostracized, persecuted, tortured, or burned at the stake, and, whatever may be their punishments on earth, committed after death to the most painful torments the imagination can contrive. The nearest approach to this in modern times are the gas chambers and lethal concentration camps of the Nazis. Such are the solutions of impatient adolescent sadists. The method of dealing with evil that is derivable from the theory of creative evolution is the exact opposite of this. It has never been more succinctly revealed, so far as I know, than by Henry James, senior. These are his words: "It is no doubt very tolerable finite or creaturely love to love one's own in another, to love another for his conformity to one's self: but nothing can be in more flagrant contrast with the creative Love, all whose tenderness *ex vi termini* must be reserved only for what intrinsically is most bitterly hostile and negative to itself." In the mind of America's most profound philosopher, Charles S. Peirce, this sublime sentence "discloses for the problem of evil its everlasting solution." Here is another way of putting it: Embrace the opposite. This applies, I would say, to opposing groups and nations, and to opposing theories and ideologies, just as well as to opposing individuals. This is evolutionary love, and its ideal products are deep, beneficent, and mutually creative harmonies, enduring continuities of relationship through change.

Eighth, a better world calls for the active imaginations and dedicated endeavors of peoples on this earth here and now and throughout many future generations. Transformations of personalities are certainly of prime importance, but these can be going on concurrently with efforts to improve society, to lure—shall we say?—this modern world out of the hollowness and dreariness of crass materialism.

Ninth, the Christian religion was not handed down from above in a perfect and unalterable form; but was produced, as art and science are produced, by the procreative powers of the unconscious mind of man, directed by the will to goodness and ordered by the powers of reason.

Tenth, the effective core of a religion is not historic facts, or theoretical speculations, or ethical propositions, but wondrous and awesome, comforting or inciting, edifying and transforming myths, legends, rituals, and precepts, poetically set forth. In its apprehension and utterance of the essence of a moral apperception, a religious parable or story, at its best, is a good deal nearer the wanted truth and surely far more efficacious than a matter-of-fact account of any historic episode, no matter how dramatic.

The moral of this tale, as I read it, is that the requirement of this dire moment in man's history is the religious imagination, the realization by religious men that the creativity of nature is within them, and, perhaps for the first time, with the assent and aid of a greater consciousness, free to stretch itself, to break the strangling bonds of an ancient allegiance, and bring forth the seeds of a new emergence of the spirit. If the religious imagination fails, where shall we be? Santayana suggests a gruesome possibility which I find challenging, and so with this in our mind's sight, I shall bring this discourse to a close.

"The greatest calamity," he writes, "would be that which seems, alas! not unlikely to befall our immediate posterity, namely, that while Christianity should be discredited no other religion, more disillusioned and not less inspired, would rise to take its place. Until the imagination should have time to recover and to reassert its legitimate and kindly power, the European races would then be reduced to confessing that while they had mastered the mechanical forces of Nature, both by science and by the arts, they had become incapable of mastering or understanding themselves, and that, bewildered like the beasts by the revolutions of the heavens and by their own irrational passions, they could find no way of uttering the ideal meaning of their life."

CHAPTER 12

Poised between the Dictates of Nature and a Peculiar Freedom

by A. G. HUNTSMAN

University of Toronto

BY OVERESTIMATING our knowledge, we often make things drab and of no account. But an increase in knowledge and experience need not make our lives boring or disgusting. Science is one branch of knowledge which has been spectacularly successful in many directions in predicting the future. Yet for each one of us it can have no firmer basis than our awareness of our surroundings through sight, hearing, and our other senses. We should not confuse such knowledge or awareness of things with their being or reality, since it is not possible for us to be other than ourselves. Humility may permit wisdom in appreciating the significance of things.

Let us turn from our habitual obsession with the seemingly infinite and hopelessly puzzling complexities of everyday human affairs, and consider man's situation as a very small part of a tremendous whole, which, try as he may, he can only vaguely appreciate. The paradox of one whole being many parts is resolved by the relations between the parts that make them a whole. But the relations remain an enigma.

In considering man's situation, it may be of some help to indicate what we mean by some of the words we shall use, particularly for different kinds of being or existence. In this life of change, *mere being* is merely changing. The simplest change is a rearrangement of parts, and in final analysis a complex change seems to be the same. An *enduring* or lasting *being* is a continuing change. The circular movement of one part around another is a change in arrangement that can continue indefinitely, that is, can be most enduring being, as in the cases of an electron revolving around the nucleus of an atom and of the earth revolving around the sun. A *living being* is an extremely complex one, involving continual interchange of parts with the surroundings. A *moving living being* is one that moves of itself in relation to its surroundings, as an animal does in comparison with a plant. *Knowing* is being conscious or aware of one's surroundings through sight, hearing, feeling, and otherwise. It is a very transient or fleeting matter. Consciousness, which is the basis of the knowledge or science of which we proudly boast, is thus a decidedly impermanent kind of being. But associated with it is *memory*, which is enduring being. To *create* is to bring into being. New arrangements of parts can be created. What is eternal, that is, what always has been and always will be, cannot be created. In this life of change the eternal seems beyond comprehension.

Science Can Be One with Religion

It should be understood that consciousness and knowledge do not enable us to appreciate other aspects of our whole being except through imagination. Still less can they be expected to reveal anything beyond this life of ceaseless change on earth in time. Since science cannot deny any more than it can affirm possibilities of other existences, it is not in conflict with belief in another life. Science can be one with religion to make this life better.

Man is far more wonderful than we can ever conceive. Even more wonderful must be his Creator. It is quite evident that we are merely small parts of a tremendous and continuously changing whole. We should strive to learn how best to play our roles in this whole, with the firm assurance that they are significant and that if, in the ceaseless change that forms time, we seem to pass away from this life just as we came into it, we will nevertheless in some forms or ways share in the eternal future even as we are products of the eternal past. We have been created by the whole and we share in future creation.

What has science revealed concerning ourselves? Of what is mankind now aware through accumulated experience, from careful and repeated observation, experiment, and thought of countless individuals of many generations through recent centuries? Where does man live? How does he live? What is his nature? Whence has he come? These questions can be answered by the simpler and basic facts, although complete answers are and probably always will be out of the question owing to the excessive complexity of man and his surroundings.

Man's Living Area Limited

Man lives on the earth, and with our present knowledge it is very doubtful that he could live on any of the other planets in our solar system. They do not seem to provide the conditions that are necessary for his existence. Even on the earth, man can live only in very restricted situations. Life is practically confined to places where solid earth or land, liquid water, and gaseous air come together either directly or indirectly. The waters that cover almost three-quarters of the earth's surface have life throughout, but man and many other kinds of life cannot live in them. He does not inhabit all of the land above water. The highest mountains and much of the polar regions, such as the Antarctic continent, with their low temperatures are uninhabitable, and the waterless deserts are not much more suitable.

White or north European man is more limited in his distribution than man in general. On this continent, as elsewhere, he lives best in the intermediate or temperate zone between tropic and polar zones, or, if in the tropics, at intermediate levels between the edge of the ocean and the mountaintops. He is to be contrasted on the one hand with the Negro who lives near sea level in the tropics, and on the other with the Eskimo who lives near the North Pole. Whatever may be the reasons, man is more abundant in the temperate zone of the Northern Hemisphere. While assessment of life presents great difficulties, there are indications that life in general is more abundant there than elsewhere.

Necessities of Inhabitable Area

The space that can be inhabited by life in general must have solids from the land, water from the ocean, and gas from the air. Man's living depends upon all three. His dependence upon air is evident from the rapidity with which his living ceases when he is unable to breathe. The oxygen that forms about 20 per cent of the air needs to be available in his lungs, whence it is carried to the various tissues of the body in the blood stream in combination with hemoglobin, a characteristic constituent that gives the red blood cells their color. Another gas, carbon dioxide, and water are produced in the tissues by the combination of the oxygen with carbon and hydrogen, which are in sugars and starches (carbohydrates) and in fats. The carbon dioxide needs to be removed, and the blood stream carries it in the reverse direction, from the tissues to the lungs, and thence it is expired. Life activities are dependent upon such steady interchange of gases between the body tissues and the air.

Man's tissues consist largely of water, without which their characteristic activities are impossible. Water must be obtained from some source. Water that is lost from the tissues, by evaporation into the air in the lungs or otherwise, must be replaced. Water to drink becomes as vital a need as air to breathe. The "breath of life" and the "water of life" are comparable. The importance of water in life activities depends upon its permitting greatly varied chemical processes. Many substances dissolve in water, where many of them split up into simpler and more active parts, the ions. Interaction between ions as dispersed in water has indeed been considered to characterize the living of organisms.

The Land's Contribution

That man needs solids is shown by his regular consumption of food. Fat in his tissues is the most evident form in which food is stored for future use. But food consists largely of substances formed by other living creatures. That he requires substances from the land is shown by his bones, which are hard by virtue of their content of lime or calcium and phosphorus. Solids which dissolve in water, such as common salt, are needed in living activities, usually in small amounts. Man forms more or less peculiar substances of his own, but, like other animals, he must depend upon plants, either directly or through other animals, for relatively simple organic substances, which when combined with oxygen provide the energy for his activities—substances which he cannot make himself from the still simpler substances that are in air, water, and earth. The plants alone can make these, but only by getting energy from the sun's rays when exposed to its light.

These interchanges between man and his surroundings

form only part of his living, but they reveal his dependence, not only upon air, water, and land, but also upon other living organisms and through the plants upon the sun. Throughout he is of the earth earthy, peculiar as are some of the substances of which he is composed.

Ordinarily our main concern is with our conscious living, which we are wont to consider higher than the interchanges of substances with our surroundings. But the mind, that is, the brain, cannot properly say of the rest of man "I have no need of thee." Consciousness, indeed, high as it is placed in our scale of values, promptly goes when its supply of oxygen through the blood fails.

Man's conscious living is even more intimately related to his surroundings than it is indirectly through breath, drink, and food. Like the animals that most resemble him, man responds promptly to some of the extremely rapid waves through space, such as those emitted by the sun, when they reach his eyes, and also to some of the much slower waves through air, water, and earth when they reach his ears. The former give him sight and the latter hearing. He also responds to changes in pressure acting through the skin (touch), to changes in temperature acting through the skin (heat), to changes in concentration of certain substances in the air acting through the nose (smell), and to changes in concentration of certain substances in water acting through the mouth (taste). In these ways man is conscious or aware of his surroundings and acts accordingly.

Sight a Key to Consciousness

Sight is the principal way in which man is conscious or aware of his surroundings, and thus by which he has been able to accumulate knowledge and develop science. The waves which give light are called light rays, and they travel in straight lines unless deflected or reflected by substances. The very great intensity of the light rays from the sun, together with the rotation of the earth on its axis, gives us the striking alternation of bright day with dark night. This is the basis for an alternation between consciousness as wakefulness during the day and unconsciousness as sleep during the night. Consciousness is most evident in man through his moving as a whole or in part, and it may be inferred in animals when they move similarly in response to the stimuli of light, sound, pressure, etc. The simplest stage in an animal or the simplest animal shows the most definite relation between activity (and thus presumably consciousness) and light. For example, streaming movements in the protoplasm of a simple, one-celled amoeba have been found to cease and to begin anew when the light reaching it drops below and rises above a certain intensity. Again, young salmon stop swimming, rest at the bottom, and soon fail to respond to stimuli when it becomes quite dark, but they resume activities gradually when illuminated by a flashlight. Conscious living is thus more or less definitely dependent upon sensitive relations with one's surroundings, particularly through sight and with high light intensity. By far the greatest part of our conscious living is made up of such relations.

At whatever level we may consider it, man's living is not an independent affair, but is largely a part of a very much larger whole. It is a mistake to think that one has a separate existence, strong as is the feeling of personal individuality. It is true that we live and move separately, but life and movement are relations with other parts of the whole.

Man's Peculiar Nature

How different in nature is man from other parts of the large whole? He is more like plants than he is like air, water, and earth. He is more like simple, minute, one-celled animals, the protozoa, than he is like plants. He is more like the fishes of the sea, than he is like the protozoa. He is more like the whale, the seal, the bat, the mouse, the horse, the cow, the dog, and the cat, than he is like the fishes. And he is more like the lemur, the monkey, the chimpanzee, and the gorilla, than he is like the other mammals that have just been mentioned. He differs from other living things as they differ from each other. He has a peculiar nature, but indeed each of the various kinds of man, such as white, Negro, and Eskimo has a peculiar nature. In fact, each human individual has a more or less peculiar nature through peculiar experience if not through peculiar inheritance.

On analysis, man in common with other living creatures is found to be a peculiar and extremely complex combination of various elements that are in land, water, and air, such as carbon, hydrogen, oxygen, nitrogen, calcium, phosphorus, sulphur, iron, and iodine. The essential structure of any of the vast number of cells, of which man consists, is so extremely complex as to be much beyond elucidation by the chemist who works out the arrangements of the elementary atoms in compound substances or molecules. In addition to its essential structure, the cell contains a certain amount of water with various substances dissolved in it, as well as solid substances, such as fat. Materials produced by the cells, such as cartilage and bone, may be between them. In passages or vessels between the cells, such as those of the blood and lymph systems, water circulates with various substances in solution. Floating in the water separately are special cells, the red ones with hemoglobin being quite passive, and the white or transparent ones being able to work their ways out between the cells of the wall of the vessel. Air moves into and out of the lungs. Food and drink enter the digestive canal, and the residue with some additions leaves it. Various glands produce material that may or may not leave the body.

Man's nature is thus excessively complex and peculiar, but he is made of elementary substances that are to be found in his inanimate surroundings. He is peculiar only in the particular arrangement of these elements. Man consists merely of elements which the earth affords him, arranging them to suit himself.

Protozoan Superior to Man?

Each person begins his more or less separate existence as a minute, microscopic cell, the result of the union of a sperm from his father with an egg from his mother. At this stage he is somewhat comparable in simplicity of structure and living with one of the simplest of animals, the one-celled protozoan, and comparable with the beginning of a fish, which is like him in being an oösperm or fertilized egg. But he and the fish oösperm are more comparable with the protozoan when it starts its life with the union of two antecedent cells, and before it develops the structure and ability to cope with changing surroundings, responding, no doubt consciously, to the stimuli of the changes. At the beginning in all three, the protozoan, the fish, and the man, conscious living, although doubtless represented, is clearly very slight, particularly in the man with uniform conditions surrounding him in his mother's womb. The fully developed protozoan may even be considered superior to the fish and the man in their initial stages; it is able to survive without the shell that protects the fish, or the womb that protects the man.

In his mother's womb, the man develops much more rapidly and further than the fish, just as in its shell the fish develops much more rapidly and further than the unsheltered protozoan, or even than the protozoan when similarly sheltered, as a parasite, to fish or man. At one stage in his development, the man is somewhat comparable in structure with the adult fish. But he must be considered as being then inferior to the fish on two counts. He gives no evidence of the well-developed consciousness that the fish shows in responding by movement to light and to other changes in its surroundings, nor is he able to survive if removed from his shelter and exposed to such stimuli.

Man Made by His Surroundings

Man's living is at first as simple as that of the simplest living creatures. He is wholly dependent upon his surroundings to keep him alive and to make him develop into an adult. His own part in this, his peculiar nature or structure, is significant, but minute in comparison with what his surroundings provide. He is made by his surroundings rather than by himself. He owes his simple beginning to his parents, who in their turn were almost wholly the products of the things around them.

Man prides himself on his peculiar nature, which makes him "the Lord of Creation." What is the origin of that nature? The deposits of the ages on the surface of the earth reveal that peculiar nature only in a very thin layer on the top of the deposits. The deeper we go in them, the less do the remains of living creatures resemble man and the more they are restricted to the simpler kinds of life. There has thus clearly been a development through the ages of man's peculiar nature, just as he himself developed as an individual from a very simple kind of living.

Genes Make the Man

What has brought about the development or evolution of man's peculiar nature? We are still far from having a satisfactory answer to this question. We know much about the way in which an individual man gets his peculiar nature by the shuffling or rearrangement of the hereditary genes in the reproductive cells of his parents. But to discover how a new gene is brought into being is a most difficult matter. A gene is excessively complex and cannot be isolated for analysis. Recognition of its newness comes only through its effects on the adult, which are very remote both in time and in number of intervening processes. Nevertheless, experiments show that the surroundings may change the genes and thus make new ones, since they sometimes bring about changes in the adult living creature that are inherited. It may be concluded that the earth has brought about the evolution of man's peculiar nature, even though we are still far from knowing in detail either how the earth itself has developed through the ages or how the successive conditions it presented acted upon the line of living creatures antecedent to man.

The Creation of Man

It may thus be affirmed with confidence that man has been created by the earth, which forms his immediate environment. But the earth has been what it has been only by virtue of its relations with the sun. Practically all the energy for the living of man and of his antecedents has come from the sun. The earth provides the materials for his structure, but the energy for building and operating the structure comes from the sun. Plants alone can use the energy in the sun's rays to form man's food, in which the energy he uses has been stored. Without the sun's rays, the earth would be too cold for man as for any other kind of life. Without the sun's rays there would be no daylight to develop the very high level of consciousness that we enjoy. While near approach to the sun makes an end of all life, the earth by virtue of its enduring relations with the sun has created living things, among which latterly has come man.

To create is to bring into being. Each person at his beginning is created by his parents. As a newborn baby he has been created further by his mother. As an adult he has been created still further by his varied surroundings. It is a mistake to consider the development of a person as being merely the elaboration of what is already there. At his beginning as an oösperm, he has neither the adult consciousness nor the adult structure. To ignore the major effect of the surroundings in bringing the adult into being is to ignore the vast differences between the oösperm and the adult. To think only of the individual as determining what he does and becomes is to deny his being but a small part of a great whole, his having been created by something vastly greater than himself.

If he has been created by his surroundings, how can man appreciate his surroundings? His knowledge or science has no better basis than his consciousness or awareness of the things around him, that is, his sensitive relations with them. He knows these relations, that is, how they affect his consciousness, but not what they are in themselves. His science, for accurate prediction of what will happen, does reveal changes in the arrangements of parts of his surroundings, but not what they are otherwise. To him, therefore, the universe seems to be only a mechanism.

How far science is from revealing anything more than mechanical rearrangement of parts becomes evident when science deals with man himself. It finds a most wonderful mechanism, vastly more complicated than can ever be elucidated. But it fails to find the realities of sight, hearing, touch, taste, smell, will, joy, and sorrow. These realities may all have mechanical aspects, as is to some extent evident, but they are much more than mechanisms.

Can We Appreciate Ourselves?

Man is indeed so excessively complex and varied from part to part that he can appreciate himself to but a slight extent. His consciousness seems to be but a passing aspect of his conscious self, which is perhaps the reticular structure of the brain stem, a small part of the whole man. This self in being conscious seems unable to appreciate even memory, only the remembering; and memory is perhaps another aspect of its being, namely enduring being rather than the merely transient being that consciousness is.

How can conscious man hope to appreciate his Creator? He finds in his science that the universe is mechanical, but what it really is he can only vaguely infer from resemblances to himself. His consciousness is perhaps represented mechanically in science by the changes of the chemical processes in the brain, or in their electrical concomitants. These chemical processes are rearrangements of various kinds of atoms. The atoms themselves are more lasting arrangements of parts, the electrons and nuclei, with great energy involved that gives no threat to stability. Like one's brain, both earth and sun consist of different kinds of atoms variously arranged. The realities of the earth and the sun are, therefore, basically the same as the reality of one's self that is conscious. In having continuing stable arrangements of most of its atoms, as in the complex substances that constitute rock and earth, the earth is largely enduring being, like one's memory. The sun is at the other extreme in being. It seems that not only do its atoms largely fail to maintain stable arrangements at the excessively high temperatures that exist, but also many of them break down with release of tremendous energy. The sun has being that is much more active than our consciousness, the most active part of our being. As conscious beings, we can but vaguely appreciate either the main being of the earth that is more enduring than our memory, or the main being of the sun that has explosive release of energy from atomic disintegration, in comparison with the slight release of energy with chemical change in our being conscious.

"Torn Between Two Ideals"

We have been brought into being, created by what is like ourselves basically, but immensely greater, and which shows more extreme conditions in stability and activity. We are not independent, but each person has independence in some measure and can have a fuller, greater life by taking responsibility. What should be our ideal to guide action? We are constantly torn between two ideals that are opposed to each other. One ideal, typified by the hard, cold, and solid earth without the sun's influence, is enduring being or stability. The tremendous energy that exists is locked up in past arrangements of parts. The other ideal, typified by the sun, is evanescent being or activity, with energy liberated that passes elsewhere. In this one, past arrangements are disrupted.

As a creature of the earth, under the sun's influence, man pursues a somewhat middle course between these two ideals. In his nature he has a measure of stability, and in his living he has a measure of activity. Even in his thinking he wavers between the stability of keeping the old order and the activity of making progress with new order or arrangement.

Back of stability is firm unity, close and strong relations of parts giving endurance. The outcome of activity is diversity, disruption of close and strong relations that permit independence and freedom. In his middle position, man attempts to strike a balance between stability and activity, between unity and diversity. His goal seems to be to combine unity, which depends upon the closeness and strength with which parts are related, with diversity, which depends upon the arrangement of the parts. In this he is carrying out the will of his Creator as shown in the myriads of living creatures that people the earth.

CHAPTER 13

The Methods of Science and Religion

by IAN G. BARBOUR

Carleton College

"When we consider what religion is for mankind, and what science is, it is no exaggeration to say that the future course of history depends upon the decision of this generation as to the relations between them."

ALFRED NORTH WHITEHEAD's words of thirty years ago find new urgency in the age of nuclear fission and the Sputniks. What factors today hinder the co-operation of science and religion on which the future course of Western civilization may depend? Thirty years ago literalistic interpretations of symbolic narratives in the Bible conflicted with scientific discoveries in the controversy over evolution. Today it is not the *content* of specific scientific theories but the relation of the *methods* of science to religious beliefs which is likely to trouble the thoughtful man. Are the methods of science the only avenue to knowledge, requiring religion to follow scientific methods if it is to make any claims concerning truth? Or are science and religion such radically different enterprises that their ways of understanding have nothing in common?

Contemporary scientists hold a view of their own methods and the status of their theories different both from the views of earlier scientists and from the popular misconceptions of today. Contemporary theologians have also approached the problem of methodology and the basis of religious belief in new ways. But before comparing these developments we must note a new attitude among scientists concerning metaphysics, that is, their view of the nature of reality.

I. INTRODUCTION: PHYSICS AND METAPHYSICS

1. Classical Physics and Mechanistic Philosophy

Galileo and Newton were the first men in history to practice systematically the combination of experimentation and deductive reasoning characteristic of scientific methodology. But they were also the perpetrators of metaphysical distinctions that had far-reaching influence on man's view of the world. Galileo divided the attributes of perceived objects into two classes: the "primary qualities" of mass and extension, which he believed to be properties of objects themselves; and all other "secondary qualities," such as color, taste, smell, hotness, which he believed to be merely subjective sensations in the observer's mind produced by the atomic particles constituting the real world. On what basis did Galileo make this distinction? The basis he himself gave for speaking of primary qualities was their permanence. But it is clear that he was actually attributing to external reality only those properties, namely mass and velocity, with which he as a physicist had been able to deal successfully. E. A. Burtt refers to this process as constructing a metaphysics out of a method: "It was easier to get ahead in the reduction of nature to a system of mathematical equations by supposing that nothing existed outside the human mind not so reducible." External reality was construed to be matter in motion, a cold and impersonal machine; and the very qualities that seem most real to us, such as color and sound, were said to have no existence outside our minds. All causality was said to lie in the forces between atoms. To explain anything meant to reduce it to its elementary parts.

The development of this viewpoint in the complete dualism of Descartes and the total materialism of Hobbes is well known. In the French Enlightenment it became the basis of a thoroughgoing naturalism and mechanism. The categories of physics, which had proved so tremendously powerful, were believed to be adequate to describe every aspect of man. Laplace claimed that if he knew the position and velocity of every particle in the universe he could predict all their future positions and hence all future events, governed by inexorable causal laws. This mechanical conception of nature dominated nineteenth-century physics. Lord Kelvin stated that we do not really understand something until we can make a mechanical model of it. An example of mechanistic thinking seventy-five years ago can be seen in the fantastic models of "ether molecules" devised to account for the properties of light transmission.

2. *The Contemporary Situation*

Twentieth century physics has shown the inadequacy of these earlier perspectives. Mechanical models have been replaced by abstract mathematical representations. In Einstein's relativity, mass and length and time are no longer unchanging properties of objects in themselves; mass is a temporary manifestation of energy and vice versa. In quantum mechanics we have had to abandon continuous paths and perhaps the very concept of position as a property of atomic particles. The Heisenberg Uncertainty Principle has refuted Laplace's claim concerning the universal predictability of the future. Analysis of systems into their smallest parts is no longer the exclusive mode of explanation. The atom must be considered as a whole;

for example, the wave-function of a two-electron atom is not the superposition of two wave-functions, and even the separate identity of the orbital electrons has had to be abandoned. At higher levels of life, behavior must be analyzed in terms of patterns rather than as aggregates of parts.

The most radical change has been in the physicist's understanding of the nature of any *scientific theory* and its relation to reality. Previously, scientific knowledge was thought of as a literal description of reality, a sort of exact reproduction, a replica or photograph of nature as it is in itself. Today we recognize that our theories are much more indirect and symbolic representations of the particular aspects of nature which we are studying. They are like the image of a countryside, viewed at night on a radar screen, in which we have to try to reconstruct the characteristics of the countryside as best we can from the way in which it reflects our radar signals and our experimental probings. In the case of atomic physics the relation of the scientific representation to the reality represented is particularly indirect. The atom is "described" by an abstract mathematical equation (psi-function) which essentially tells us the probability that a given experimental result will be found when a given operation is performed on an atom.

Now, these changes have in themselves no religious significance. Despite the triumphant idealists who claim that materialism is disproved, there is surely nothing more spiritual about energy or wave-equations than about the old ping-pong-ball atoms which seemed more substantial. The fourth dimension may seem to the layman to be out of this world, but it is no steppingstone to heaven. The Uncertainty Principle gives no final solution to the human freedom. But there is today a significantly changed attitude toward the relation between science and metaphysics. The downfall of mechanism makes us more aware of the danger of *reductionism;* for example, the implication that psychology is basically biology, and biology is really chemistry, which is just complicated physics. Scientists are today more willing to uphold the validity of various levels of explanation, and to talk about factors occurring in higher levels of life and in human existence. The contemporary climate of opinion in the scientific world is more flexible and open-minded.

The downfall of the earlier mechanism also shows the dangers in using too limited an area of experience as a basis for a total world view. We are more aware today of the way in which our metaphysical assumptions influence our methodology, and vice versa. To be sure, *naturalism* is still a live option, but it is clear that it must be defended as a philosophical viewpoint and not as a conclusion of science. For if science deliberately limits itself to certain aspects of experience, then it cannot itself decide whether its description of reality is complete. The point is illustrated by Eddington's parable about the man studying deep-sea life by means of a net of ropes of a two-inch mesh. After many expeditions he concluded that there are no fish smaller than two inches in the sea! So also science selects one type of variable from the wide spectrum of human experience. Thus the debate between naturalism and theism is not a conflict between science and religion, but a conflict between two metaphysical interpretations of the nature of reality and the significance of human life.

Metaphysical constructions are not just scientific theories of wide generality, since (1) metaphysical theories suggest patterns of co-ordination between widely diverse types of experience and are thus totality-assertions, and (2) they involve judgments of significance and importance. Experience does not come to us already organized. Every philosophy of life selects some aspect of experience as the key organizing principle, as the most significant category of interpretation. Though every such world view is in part a venture of faith not deducible from science alone, it need not be an irrational choice unsupported by evidence. We will examine a particular metaphysical perspective, that of theism. Among the many aspects of religion, we are concerned with those most closely connected with its theistic belief.

II. Science and Religion: Similarities in Method

1. The Interaction of Experience and Interpretation

Both science and religion involve these two basic factors. In science, experience takes the form of observation or experiment, and the interpretive aspect is called hypothesis or theory. Science is often misunderstood as being just a matter of precise observation. But no one has seen an atom. Scientific concepts are symbolic mental constructs by which we try to organize and correlate complex laboratory experiences. Concepts such as acceleration or valence are not given to us ready-made by nature, but are abstract interpretive constructions which enable us to see coherent patterns of relationship among experimental data. Science requires the creative activity of the human mind in inventing new categories and concepts. Imagination and ingenuity are important aspects of scientific discovery. Men watched apples fall for centuries before Newton had the flash of insight from which he developed the law of universal gravitation. There is, then, a continual interaction between experience and interpretation. Initial hypotheses determine the design of an experiment, whose results suggest several possible theories, from each of which deductions can be made and experimentally investigated.

Turning to religion, we find the same basic components: experience and interpretation. Man's *religious experience* includes his wonder and gratitude at creation, his response of reverence before what is to him holy and sacred, his sense of dependence and finitude and contingency. It includes prayer and worship, as well as moral experience, the obligation he acknowledges to choose good rather than evil, his guilt when he falls short. It includes his reflection on the basic structures and conditions of existence. Biblical religion in particular does not focus on some ethereal other-worldly sphere, but on man's life in the present. The God of the Bible acts in concrete historical events, in human communities, through individual persons—the prophets, Jesus and his disciples, men and women down through the ages. The men who wrote the Bible were writing of what had happened to them, attempting to interpret their own experience. So, too, the early Church was not speculating about theological ideas in the abstract; it was trying to understand what had occurred in its life. Men have spoken of the reorientation of their lives in what they understood to be a new relationship to God—a reorientation in which a person can be freed from oppressive guilt in the experience of forgiveness, can be freed from anxiety about the meaning of life in the security of this new relationship, can be freed from excessive concern about himself so that he is able to be concerned about others. All of these descriptions involve experience and interpretation.

2. The Role of Community and Analogy

As a second point of similarity, both science and religion depend not only on individual experience, but on the experience of communities. On the one hand, the role of the scientific community is seldom appreciated by the layman. There is no one-man science, for science is a social enterprise, a co-operative venture. A physicist is dependent on his predecessors, and on the whole group of physicists, which has its own institutions and journals and meetings. The physics community has its own jargon, its own norms and loyalties. Similarly the religious community is central. Religious experience has its corporate aspects, a group that worships and acts together, bound by common loyalty to God, attempting to be a community of love and forgiveness. The religious community, too, draws upon the past experience of its historical life.

Moreover each community has its own *symbolic language* in terms of which it interprets its experience, and these symbols have little meaning for the outsider until he enters into the life of the community. We have mentioned how mechanical models seen as literal representations of nature have been replaced in modern physics by abstract mathematical symbolisms which could never be visualized. These are symbolic representations whose function is to allow us to co-ordinate experimental relationships. But note that the community itself is not consciously aware that its language is symbolic. Both science and religion arise as unreflective and spontaneous responses—a response of curiosity about nature on the one hand, and of worship of God on the other, or in the case of the Christian community, response to the events surrounding the life of Christ. There is an assumed realism on the part of the working scientist or the worshiper. In practical operation they use language as if it were a literal description of reality, and only in their more reflective moments is its symbolic and interpretive character recognized.

It is instructive to analyze the role of *analogy* in both fields. Analogy can be defined as the extension of concepts drawn from some relation within experience to suggest a possible mode of co-ordinating other experiences, that is, the suggestion of similar patterns or structures of relationship in different contexts. Thus Maxwell's theory of electromagnetic transmission was conceived by analogy with waves in solids (a very fruitful analogy, though, like all analogies, one with limitations, for it seemed to imply a medium, the hypothetical ether). So also in religion man uses analogies from other areas of experience to describe the responses through which he conceives his relation to the transcendent. Perhaps the universal nature of such ultimate response is the reason for the frequency of analogies of Father and King, or symbols such as light and height. Dorothy Emmet suggests, for example, that the awe and sublimity experienced in looking up at a height is transferred by analogy as an appropriate expression for man's response to God. If the symbolic character of such language is ignored, it runs the risk of making God too "human"; but impersonal analogies fail to do justice to the characteristics of the experience itself. One of the central modes of biblical communication is the parable, whose analogical character is always clear.

3. The Primacy of Relationships Rather than Objects

If the model of the atom which scientists used until about 1920 were enlarged a trillion times, it would become an empty sphere a hundred yards across with basketball-size electrons whirling in definite orbits around a central nucleus the size of a pinhead. But today the physicist represents the atom by a complex pattern of waves which cannot be visualized at all. If one imagined oneself inside such at atom, the whole sphere would be filled by waves, in harmonic relationships which we might compare with a sort of three-dimensional symphony of musical tones of incredible complexity. Matter consists not of little particles, but of probability waves in harmonic ratios. We describe matter not as a collection of objects, but in terms of forms and relationships. In biology, too, relationships are central. The very concept of organism implies an entity which must be considered as a whole, not just as a sum of separate parts. This viewpoint prevails in many fields today, from Gestalt psychology to the philosophy of Whitehead. Reality is constituted by processes and relationships.

Now, in biblical religion there is a similar emphasis on the primacy of relationships. Man is man, not as an individual alone, but in a fabric of social relationships. He is constituted by his various roles—he is who he is, not as an isolated ego, but as father, brother, and member of a nation. So, too, the biblical tradition does not talk about God as a separate object, does not try to describe him as if he were a thing in itself. The important questions are about God's relation to man, and man's relation to God. Sin means man's violation of his true relationships, means being alienated from God and one's neighbor; love means reunion, overcoming these divisions. In both science and religion, then, we are interpreting experiences of relationships.

4. *The Testing of Interpretations*

In both areas testing requires the full use of reason, applying criteria of consistency and comprehensiveness. Yet in neither area is final and complete certainty possible. In science certainty is never achieved, and no formulation is final and irrevocable. The chemist Arrhenius received the Nobel prize for his electrolytic theory of dissociation; the same prize was given later to Debye for showing that the Arrhenius Theory was inadequate. In modern physics texts you will find the concept of parity or symmetry presented as one of the fundamental principles of nuclear structure; I will long remember the 1956 meeting in New York at which three Chinese physicists showed the falsity of this long-accepted principle. A scientific theory is never proven true; at best it is seen to be more fruitful, consistent, comprehensive, and simple than the alternative theories currently available.

In religion, too, we cannot claim certainty. We must test our interpretations, for we are all prone to wishful thinking. St. Paul wrote to the Thessalonians: "Test everything; hold fast what is good." Protestantism in particular has stressed the principle of self-criticism; no human institution or theological system can claim finality. Our religious beliefs must reflect the most adequate, consistent, and comprehensive interpretation of all human experience.

Now, in this approach there is a significant place for the concept of *revelation*. In interpreting our total experience we need clues, crucial ideas, and categories of interpretation. A nation interprets its present experience in terms of key events in its past. America sees the meaning of its life today in the light of the Declaration of Independence. For the Christian community the life of Christ is such a key event, which illuminates the rest of human experience and helps us to understand ourselves and what has happened to us. Here is Richard Niebuhr's definition of revelation:

> Revelation means for us that part of our inner history which illuminates the rest of it and which is itself intelligible. Sometimes when we read a difficult book, seeking to follow a complicated argument, we come across a luminous sentence from which we can go forward and backward and so attain some understanding of the whole. Revelation is like that. The special occasion to which we appeal in the Christian church is called Jesus Christ. . . . Revelation means this intelligible event which makes all other events intelligible.

The person of Christ is not something we could have deduced from general rational principles; he is a given event in history. But we can know the power of that event to help us understand moral choice, personal relationships, and our corporate experience as a church.

III. Science and Religion: Differences in Method

1. Scientific Selectivity vs. Religious Concern

Turning from similarities to differences, we see first that science and religion ask essentially different questions, even about the same event. Suppose you are asked: "Why is that man climbing the mountain?" You can give a detailed scientific explanation about the contraction of his leg muscles, and the way energy from his lunch activates those muscles. But someone else may say, "The reason he is climbing the mountain is to see the view from the top." Both answers may be correct. The explanation in terms of scientific mechanisms and the explanation in terms of purposes are both important. Again, science asks about *means*, but not about the *ends* for which those means should be used. Scientific results can be used constructively or destructively. The atomic bomb brought home to physicists their involvement in ethical decisions concerning which physics itself is neutral.

In its questions science is necessarily selective. Every community of inquiry has its own symbolic language and replaces complex experiences by models or diagrammatic sketches representing those aspects in which it is interested. In physics problems an elephant on a slippery riverbank becomes a mass with a coefficient of friction, and a Beethoven symphony becomes a set of molecular vibrations. When a field of study can abstract single factors for investigation, it can be more exact; but its schematic representation is further from the total situation of life and from the immediacy and variety of human experience with all its levels of meaning. It is sometimes said that science deals only with the measurable and the quantitative. I do not believe this is the case, though quantitative variables are preferred because they can be treated by the powerful methods of mathematics. But the scientist does limit himself to publicly verifiable sense-data, and he purposely disregards other aspects of experience.

In religion the central question is about man's ultimate allegiance, the objects of his trust and loyalty. It asks about the powers operating in the world for good or evil, the forces of fulfillment and destruction in human life. It is concerned about the goals and values men serve, as we shall see below.

2. Scientific vs. Configurational Understanding

Science aims at a particular type of knowledge, namely reproducible relations expressible in general laws. Scientific understanding is concerned only about repeatable phenomena and considers prediction one test of understanding. Science is not interested in individual events or objects except as instances of general laws. (At the atomic level the physicist is not even able to deal with individual events, and can give precise descriptions only of statistical distributions in a large number of such events.) Consider by way of contrast what a history teacher means when he says he wants to help his students understand an historical event—say the French Revolution. His primary interest is not the formulation of universal laws, but the understanding of a unique pattern among the various social factors and personalities contributing to the French Revolution. History does not repeat itself, and human freedom prevents reduction to rigid laws. We might call this goal *configurational understanding*, the attempt to see how the parts of a unique whole are related to each other. General theories, though they may emerge, are not the main concern here.

There are many fields which aim for such configurational understanding of unique occurrences. Understanding a work of art or of music is primarily a question of insight into the relationships among its parts. A similar approach is called for by a novel or a drama. The clinical psychologist, though concerned about general laws, seeks insight concerning relations between aspects of the unique person whom he is counseling. So also religion asks about the significance of my own unique life—the only one in the universe I experience from the inside—and about my relation to the unique God, who is never one of a general class of objects. This calls for understanding of a configurational rather than a scientific sort.

3. Objective Detachment vs. Personal Involvement

Science tries to minimize the involvement of the observer by enforcing as detached and impersonal an attitude as possible. But this statement needs careful qualification. The popular idea of objectivity as simple "observation" neglects the inevitability of interpretation; we have emphasized the importance of personal factors in constructing hypotheses, in the creative imagination necessary for the invention of new concepts. The personality of the scientist and the particular way in which his mind works is especially important in the creation of original and revolutionary theories. Despite such personal factors in science, the process of verification is impersonal and the results are public. This impersonality is a feature of every scientific article, and we try to impress it on our students as they learn to write laboratory reports. They are not to write "I took the test tube, and even though I was feeling lousy, I put it on the scales"; the report reads instead in the passive voice: "The test tube was found to weigh . . ." Scientific observation, though inherently private *qua* human experience, can achieve a public status because it deals with the public world, standardizes instruments, and specifies operations not subject to individual idiosyncrasies.

But there are many areas of human experience where such detachment is not possible. Art and literature require *personal involvement* and participation. Here man's response is personal, though he is responding to an impersonal object. In other situations both sides of the relationship are personal. Martin Buber, the Jewish philosopher, has described vividly the characteristics which distinguish what he calls an "I-It" from an "I-Thou" situation. The deepest knowledge of another person requires involvement in a personal relationship of trust. Now, in the biblical perspective God is personal and acts primarily in the sphere of the personal, rather than in the sphere of the impersonal with which science deals. Motivational and volitional factors in the private life of the scientist are essential for the pursuit of his work, but they only indirectly influence his conclusions. By contrast, personal attitudes interact strongly with religious beliefs. Egocentricity, for example, has usually been viewed as the major obstacle to love toward either fellow man or God.

Personal involvement is essential to the religious life. To

take the detached attitude of the spectator here is to cut one-self off from the very experiences which are religiously most significant. Here one must be an agent and not just an observer. Religious faith refers to man's ultimate trust, his most basic commitments, what he bets his life on, the final basis by which he justifies all his other values. The religious question is precisely about the object of a person's devotion; it asks to what or to whom a person gives his ultimate allegiance.

It appears that this is a quite different sort of involvement from that of the scientist. Some authors have made much of the fact that in modern physics the observer is involved in the process of observation. It is true that, in relativity, measurements depend on the observer's frame of reference, and that some quantum mechanical phenomena can be interpreted as due to the disturbance of the system by the observer. But here the "observer" really means a measuring process, which might be the automatic recording of results by a camera; the scientist is not involved as a person. Again, Michael Polanyi has shown (e.g., in *Personal Knowledge*) that there is a type of involvement in scientific work which is more nearly parallel to that in religion. He has indicated that there are unavoidable elements of individual judgment in selecting the questions that are considered significant to ask, in weighing the evidence, in assessing a theory and taking responsibility for its truth. Yet in such scientific questions the meaning and purpose of an individual's life are not at stake as they are in religious questions, so only a limited area of the scientist's person is involved in his work.

IV. The Status of Religious Beliefs

In comparing the methods of science and religion, we have suggested that there are both similarities and differences. If the differences are important, religion cannot be completely subsumed under science. If science deals with public sense-data, one cannot be completely scientific about religious beliefs. Moreover, any metaphysical perspective, whether theistic or naturalistic, tries to interpret various types of experience, making totality-assertions and judgments of significance which science itself shuns. Yet basic similarities between science and religion have also been pointed out, especially in regard to the interaction of experience and interpretation in both areas. Such an approach to religion might be called broadly empirical, employing the full activity of reason as interpreter of human experience. The criteria are coherence (or internal consistency), fruitfulness, and adequacy and comprehensiveness in correlating all aspects of experience. To believe in God is also to see man and the world in a certain way which either illuminates or renders more inexplicable ensuing experience. This perspective will either help or hinder one's understanding of oneself, the nature of man and society, the world and history, love and hate, joy and tragedy.

This proposal, in contrast to religious mysticism, suggests that there are no directly apprehended truths. Intuition is a source of insights in both science and religion, but does not take the place of *testing*. We must admit the possibility that any interpretation may be false. The language analysts rightly criticize religious assertions which are so framed that no conceivable evidence could count against them. Should we not say, for example, that suffering and evil, if they were irredeemably pointless, would count against the idea of the infinite goodness and power of God? But interpretive hypotheses are interconnected and seldom stand or fall alone. Just as scientific theories are constituted by webs of constructs, so any world view is indirectly evaluated by the convergence of many lines of inquiry. And religious beliefs, like all hypotheses, are subject to the law of parsimony, the employment of the simplest hypothesis which is adequate. Simplicity is always a secondary criterion, however, and contemporary physics is hardly simple in detail, though it aims at simplicity of form. Occam's razor shaves well if used with care, but wielded with abandon it may slice off important features!

Is the *tentativeness* which such testing requires compatible with the religious life? There are dangers in seeking the security of guaranteed dogmas that close the door to new understanding; tentativeness concerning all our formulations is desirable. Nevertheless, religion does require involvement and commitment, as we have seen. The scientist may have to accept tentatively an hypothesis and act on the basis of its assumed truth if he is to test it. But in religion testing means living in accordance with a choice in which not just a theory but the man himself and the significance of his life is at stake. If one's philosophy of life is one's interpretation of experience, too tentative an attitude may deny one the very sorts of experience which are most crucial in understanding religion. Commitment never in itself turns probabilities into certainties, but it does take one out of a purely theoretic attitude of detachment from life. A partial solution may be a balance and perhaps an alternation between personal involvement and reflection on that involvement. It is not easy to hold beliefs for which you would be willing to die, and yet to remain open to new insights; but it is precisely this combination of commitment and inquiry which constitutes religious maturity.

Now it might be objected that we have reduced God to an hypothesis, and that this is not a true description of actual religious faith. But it has been indicated that we are talking about the philosophy of religion and the philosophy of science, not everyday practice which in both areas is unreflective. It is true that this is not the way most people actually come to religious faith; but the origins of belief are a different question from their analysis and justification. A related charge might be the accusation of subjectivism. In worship itself, the focus is on God, and the Judeo-Christian perspective is radically theocentric. There is a danger that one will end by worshiping one's own experience, a sort of psychological self-idolatry.

Several recent developments in Protestant theology have been in the direction of the approach we have been outlining. Consider the concept of *revelation* presented by Richard Niebuhr, William Temple, and Alan Richardson. To them, revelation never means the disclosure of divine information or the imparting of revealed truths. The human interpretive element is present at all points, from the culturally conditioned factors in the teachings of Jesus and the records of the biblical authors, to the relativity of our own understanding today. Temple sees revelation as occurring in the interaction of minds and events in the world process, that is, in man's interpretation of the significance of historical events. Richardson speaks of revelation as giving us the key categories of interpretation in terms of which our present experience is intelligible, just as every metaphysical perspective makes use of clues or central organizing principles. We have already quoted H. R. Niebuhr's view of revelation which he compares with a sentence in a book or an event in history which illuminates and helps us understand other events. These theologians see revelatory events in dynamic interaction with interpretation of present experience.

There are also currents in contemporary philosophy which are more congenial to the sort of approach outlined here. The logical positivism of the thirties has been subjected to criticism on a number of scores. It asserted: "All statements are either tautologous, empirically verifiable, or meaningless." But this assertion itself proved embarrassing to classify, as it is not a definition and is not verifiable. The antimetaphysical program turned out to have an implicit metaphysics of its own. It is interesting that in recent years a number of the British analysts have taken seriously the use of types of meaning and language other than those of science.

V. The Complementarity of Science and Religion

Since there are both similarities and differences between science and religion, the two fields are neither identical nor contradictory, but *complementary*. The combination of unity and diversity is well expressed by analogy (and it is of course only an analogy) with the Principle of Complementarity in physics. In some experiments, such as diffraction, light behaves as a wave; other experiments, such as photoelectricity, can only be explained if light acts as discrete particles. The word "complementarity" was used by Niels Bohr to refer to the necessity of such sharply contrasting analyses, and he extended it to describe other situations in which alternative categories of explanation for different aspects of a phenomenon appear necessary. The principle must not be used to support uncritical acceptance of apparent dichotomies, undermining any search for unity. At the mathematical level, the wave-particle dualism is largely reconciled in the formalism of wave mechanics. Yet alternative models are still useful to visualize varying aspects of a situation.

Either science or religion alone affords a partial view. We need to use various categories and frames of reference. The man who says "love is not real because I cannot weigh it" is confusing two frames of reference. Love is not a useful concept in the same contexts in which weighing is a useful operation! No single type of language exhausts the description of even one event. Scientist and theologian both depend on experience and interpretation, and both use their minds. Asking differing types of questions, they will not expect the same types of answer. Science and religion thus reflect different aspects of our experience.

If the intelligent citizen can move beyond popular misconceptions of both science and religion, he need feel no conflict between their methods. Today as never before both forces are essential to man's fulfillment and civilization's progress. For science holds in one hand untold promise of health, leisure, prosperity, and knowledge; in the other hand she holds devastating powers of destruction and the exploitation of persons. Whether the power of science contributes to good or evil depends on man's goals, values, and motives, which are central concerns of religion. Understanding the relation of science and religion is no longer an interesting speculation for philosophers only, but a practical necessity, perhaps even for the survival of civilization.

CHAPTER 14

The Role of Religion as Viewed by the Science of Man

by JOHN L. FISCHER

Tulane University

I WOULD LIKE to begin by saying a little about the relation of my discussion to the general theme of religion in an age of science. How can man know what is right for him to do? And what are the various methods of getting valid knowledge generally, with special view to their application to acquiring religious knowledge?

At the same time that we inquire how we may obtain religious knowledge, it is helpful, I believe, to inquire what religious knowledge is, and what is religion generally. How much of religious practice is the acquisition of knowledge? What is religious practice when it is not the acquisition of knowledge? It is these latter questions with which I shall chiefly concern myself. Further, being a cultural anthropologist by training, I shall discuss them mainly from an anthropological point of view.

One of the few statements on religion with which practically all contemporary anthropologists would agree is that all known human societies—though not necessarily all known

216

individuals—have some form of religion, while the lower animals do not. But there are many varied views as to just what practices are religion and what not, and even where there is agreement that some custom or belief is religious, there is disagreement as to why it exists and what its meaning is. There are some anthropologists who would even insist that at this stage of investigation religion is undefinable; all we can do is to continue to study more concrete instances of religion in the hope of eventually arriving at an inductive definition.

However, while anthropologists may be justifiably wary of elaborate discussions of theories of religion or of any other cultural phenomena without reference to concrete field data from a variety of societies, they could hardly select religious data for consideration without at least an implicit definition of religion in the abstract.

A definition of religion as "beliefs in the supernatural and associated practices" would have been acceptable to most nineteenth-century anthropologists as well as many today. The dominant concern of these early anthropologists was to explain religious belief as a cognitive problem. Some, especially in Germany, considered that the important supernatural beings were in origin symbolic representations of the sun and moon and other natural phenomena. The influential English anthropologist Tylor advanced the view that the concept of a separable human soul or spirit (and, from this, ideas of more exalted spirits and gods) arose in an attempt to explain such universal experiences as sleep, dreams, and death.

During the present century these "rationalistic" explanations have been criticized as inadequate for ignoring, on the one hand, the emotional significance of religion for the individual, and on the other hand for ignoring the social significance of religion in helping bind together a society. Questionable speculations based on mere curiosity, it is argued, are insufficient to provide motivation for the elaborate, lengthy, and expensive religious observances of most cultures.

Among those anthropologists emphasizing the individual emotional significance of religion, some have defined religion simply as the complex of practices and beliefs connected with a feeling of awe or submission in the face of any vastly superior power. In this view an atheistic astronomer looking through his telescope at stars many light years away may experience a religious thrill on realizing man's physical insignificance in the universe. A more sharply defined view, of which the typical psychoanalytic view would be one variant, sees religion as a ritual or symbolic means of alleviating insecurity or tension where there is no rational empirical technique easily available to remove the source of insecurity. In this view little distinction is made between religious and neurotic or psychotic behavior, except perhaps that the individual learns religious behavior, at least in its general form, from others who also practice it and approve of it, whereas he presumably largely invents his own neurotic or psychotic behavior, which, moreover, does not meet group approval.

In opposition, or perhaps in complement, to these individualistic views of religion are those views of religion which consider its social aspect as primary. Two exemplars of these views are the French sociologist Durkheim and the English anthropologist Radcliffe-Brown. In the views of these and related authors individual neurotic behavior would be quite dissimilar to religious behavior. Religious behavior would be concerned with insecurity or tension only insofar as some source of insecurity brought together members of a society and caused them to reaffirm their ties to each other in the face of threatened disruption. Moreover, this view can easily account for ceremonies of praise and thanksgiving in the absence of any obvious threat to security or social disruption. These "purely positive" ceremonies are in this view a natural expression of the heightened group consciousness, which occurs at such times as the close of the harvest season when people have just finished working closely together and have some free time to enjoy each other's company. These ceremonies, it is urged, amount to the group formally admiring itself, thus binding its members more closely to it. In brief, God is Society, and the worship of God is the worship of Society, and is the strengthening and inculcation of socially approved values. However, the proponents of this view have been criticized for ignoring, on the one hand, individual "religious" or mystical experience in solitude, and on the other ignoring "nonreligious" occasions of heightened social consciousness and group emotion, such as games, secular dances, or political rallies.

I have distinguished three basic anthropological views of religion which might be called the cognitive-rationalistic, the individual-emotional, and the social. Many variants and combinations of these views could be distinguished, and perhaps other basic views could also be proposed, but my main purpose here is to present a single anthropological view of religion for consideration, and this brief reference to other views is intended to serve as a historical context for the view which I shall present, not as a full summary and analysis of theories of religion.

The definition which I wish to propose here is that religion is the ritual cultivation of socially approved values. Each of the component terms in this definition itself requires explanation before the sense is clear.

By values I mean lasting preferences for some person, thing, quality, state of affairs, or behavior. These preferences exist in individual members of a society or are learned by them from other members, principally their seniors. Not all personal preferences, of course, come under the category of socially approved values. There are many antisocial or asocial preferences—original sin, if you will—which religion recognizes only to combat, not to cultivate.

The phrase "socially approved values" may seem to

exclude the lone religious mystic found in many societies,
but I do not think it does. Such people are found mainly in
societies where a substantial number of members approve
of a hermit's life, at least in the abstract if not as a personal
ideal. Moreover, these individual mystic experiences do not
occur in untutored infants; they occur only after considerable
formal or informal learning of current religious tradition.
Without some sort of social approval and reference, however,
I would not consider hermits as religious.

Many anthropologists regard religion on the whole as
being socially adaptive, that is, conducive to the internal peace
and survival of a society. This is a view with which I would in
general agree, but the definition offered here does not automatically limit religion to socially constructive and adaptive
values, since what is socially approved is not always or necessarily adaptive in the long run. Members of an overpopulated
society may agree, for instance, in wanting to increase their
numbers through childbirth, and may disapprove of attempts
to introduce methods of birth control. Having many children
would then be a socially approved value, which might be
ritually cultivated in fertility ceremonies, but one which in
these circumstances would be maladaptive and could lead to
general poverty, internal disorder, and war.

Likewise even when socially approved values are at the
same time socially adaptive, they are not always adaptive
for the individual from the point of view of his personal survival and fullness of life. Charity to those in need may be a
highly approved and useful value in a society, yet the gen-
erous individual may come to find times when he critically
needs, for his own welfare or survival, things which he has
earlier given to others.

Students of the great world religions have often claimed
that religion in general is concerned with the supreme values
of life, or with the establishment of a hierarchy of values. Anthropologists, on the other hand, have often commented on

the lack of systematic, explicit theories of value or ethics in primitive religions.

For example, most anthropologists would probably include in a description of the native religion on the island of Ponape in the tropical Pacific, where I lived for three years, such things as an annual ceremony dedicating new canoes, the ceremonies offering the first fruits of a number of crops to the gods and the chiefs, rites to cure a wide variety of illnesses thought to be of supernatural origin, the feeding of sacred eels, a ritual involving the manipulation of special egg-shaped stones to ensure an abundant breadfruit harvest, the placing of branches as offerings at certain points on the paths ascending the mountains, etc. But one finds that the question of the relation of these observances to each other was not especially important. Each of these and many other observances had their own time, place, and supernatural spirits and forces; and while some were much more important than others, most of them were disparate and without any clear connection with the others. It would be hard to say that such a heterogeneous assemblage of customs was concerned purely with supreme values or that it clearly reflected a hierarchy of values. The performances listed are certainly not concerned with the meaning of death, although of course other ceremonies were. They are rather concerned with such things as the security of the food supply, health and sickness, the "divine rights" of the chiefs, the sacredness of certain family ties, etc. And the supernatural who protected the chief might have nothing to do with causing or curing one's sickness, or bringing a large breadfruit harvest, or guarding one's family. Such diversity and specificity of values is characteristic of many primitive religions. In view of this I would not want to limit religion to a concern with the "supreme," the "highest good," or the "ultimate," although agreeing that these have been the main concern of the great world religions.

The definition of religion given is not intended to imply that any socially approved value is a religious value. A religious value as defined here is a socially approved value which is moreover ritually cultivated, and many socially approved values are not. The institution of marriage is an example of a highly valued institution which is not the subject of ritual cultivation in many societies, although in our own it is often initiated by a religious ceremony, and religious pressures may be brought to bear to prevent divorce. Presumably in these other societies which treat marriage "rationally" there may be less need for ritual reinforcement of marriage. Perhaps in some of these societies the satisfactions of marriage to the partners are apparent enough so that persons enter into it with little apprehension; or again, where the marriage is arranged by the couple's parents, perhaps family support and pressure alone are usually sufficient to motivate the couple. Mutual economic obligations often help stabilize marriage in many societies, and probably other reasons for religious indifference to marriage might be found.

In further elucidation of the definition we may now consider what is intended by the word "ritual." I am using the term quite broadly—perhaps too broadly—to mean any symbolic act or series of such acts evocative and reductive of emotion but without a clear, empirically achieved external goal. This is not to say that religious rituals may not have external goals which are at times achieved, but from a scientific viewpoint I think we must consider the emotional effect primary and admit that we cannot demonstrate the effectiveness of the ritual on external reality. Thus, if the Ponapeans conduct a ceremony allegedly to ensure an abundant harvest, or if Americans pray for the President's health and these things occur, I assume they do not occur because of the prayers and that the significant effect is on the emotions of those participating in the ritual. To be sure, the President might be told of the prayers, and become encouraged as an important supplementary effect, but presumably prayers never improve the breadfruit harvest. In any case, I assume for scientific purposes that no ritual actually moves any supernatural spirit or force to produce empirical effects.

The sort of act or medium of ritual expression is irrelevant to the definition of ritual as conceived here. Praying, dancing, painting, poetry, reciting or composing a sacred text, music—participating in any of these actively or passively may in a broad sense be regarded as constituting ritual. Admittedly, such a definition of ritual is broad enough to encompass much that is not religion, such as art, social etiquette, play, and much neurotic behavior. These would seem to differ from religion not in any lack of ritual, but in not being primarily concerned with the cultivation of socially approved values. Of course art in many primitive cultures hardly exists apart from religion, and even in Western culture retains connections with religion. Purely secular art is perhaps distinguished from religion in its primary concern with technical mastery of its medium and formal balance; where it is concerned with cultivating socially approved values it would seem to partake of religion, even where it is not connected with an organized multimedium religion.

Play may be distinguished from religion by its primary concern with immediate pleasure and relative indifference to the cultivation of values, that is, lasting preferences. Play relaxes but does not inspire. But the line between play and religion is not absolute in practice, and formal games are a feature of the religion of some societies. To give another example from the Pacific Islands, the people of Truk Lagoon used to have a breadfruit fertility ceremony in which they sailed toy canoes "to bring back the breadfruit from the Southland." The play aspect of this ceremony is shown by the fact that now, many years after adopting Christianity, the people still sail these canoes at odd times, much as we might have a hobby of model railroads.

Etiquette is a form of ritual which is not subject to much confusion with religion, yet one might wonder whether it might not fit the proposed definition of religion. One special characteristic of etiquette to note initially is that it always involves communication or interaction between two or more people. Religious behavior is often performed in solitude, although it always has, I suggest, a concern with socially approved values. The essential difference between etiquette and religion, I believe, is that etiquette is primarily a means of communication to another person, a way of signifying one's conception of one's relative status and one's willingness to perform obligations associated with the status, and perhaps often signifying one's reluctance to do anything more. The primary concern of etiquette thus would appear to be with the immediate specific social situation. While etiquette, like anything in culture, has value attached to it and this value may be reinforced by practice, the universal and constant feature of etiquette is its communication of relative status; the cultivation of social values is a frequent but incidental and not necessary element.

As for neurosis, it has of course been compared to religion by Freud, most notably in his *Future of an Illusion*. According to this view, which is accepted by many social scientists, neurotic behavior proper is to a considerable degree a special individual creation, while religious behavior is distinguished by being shared and openly accepted. This distinction is perhaps true by and large, as far as it goes, but certainly the content of neuroses differs from culture to culture. There is such a thing as shared neurotic behavior which is something other than religion. Moreover, it would also seem useful to be able to distinguish between the idiosyncratic behavior of the religious innovator and the idiosyncratic behavior of the neurotic. I would regard the categories of neurotic and religious behavior as cross-cutting. A person's behavior, idiosyncratic or not, is neurotic as long as it is individually and socially maladaptive, whether religious or not.

The proposed definition of religion also states that religion cultivates values. Most Western intellectuals would probably not be too startled at this idea. However, a good number of anthropologists have objected to it. We have a moral God, they will say, but most primitive peoples have morally imperfect or even outrageous gods. Even the Greek gods were rather naughty at times. Therefore religion has no necessary relation to morality or values. One might counter this argument with the fact that most Christian sects retain the notion of the Devil, who, even though he serves God as His jailer and executioner, has his moral blemishes. The example of the Devil, whom we tend to forget these days, helps illuminate the variety of ways in which religious ritual may reinforce socially approved values. The Devil, unlike Christ, is not regarded as a person to be imitated, but rather as quite the opposite. People in cultures with wicked deities do not condone their misbehavior any more than we condone the Devil's.

Psychologically, myths and rituals representing wicked deities or other evil figures can reinforce values in two ways. On the one hand, they offer a chance for more or less unconscious substitute gratifications of wishes to do evil deeds, such as murder, incest, etc. Presumably in the normal person this substitute gratification offers enough release of tension so that the original wish is less likely to be realized in its true form. On the other hand, these "wicked" myths and rituals —for they are not just verbal myths in some cultures but may be acted out in gruesome detail—call forth and strengthen socially approved sentiments of shock and horror at the evil deeds. One might logically ask why the same ritual should not do just the reverse: strengthen the *anti*social sentiments and provide substitute gratification for the social values. That is, if one has already felt bad for doing something evil *sym-*

bolically or ritually, perhaps one thereby hardens oneself and can do the corresponding *actual* evil with less remorse; alternatively, perhaps if one has already performed *symbolic* charity, one might feel less inclined toward *real* charity. Evidently this sometimes happens, but it seems that religious ritual normally widens the existing gap between conscious social and unconscious antisocial wishes.

Primitive religions with largely evil deities have one further difference from Western religions in that they generally do not assume that the supernatural is the source of morality or the good. While their ritual does reinforce the proper social values, the dogma that without God men would have no morality is not held. Rather, both morality and sin are often held to be in man's nature, regardless of the wishes of the deities. In other words, social values may be cultivated in religious ritual without religious dogma necessarily specifying a supernatural origin for them.

Another argument which is made against the view that primitive religions are concerned with the cultivation of values or morality is that informants in many cultures will tell the anthropologist that the purpose of their religious rituals involves the direct achievement of practical goals, such as an abundant harvest, physical health, or victory in war. No mention may be made of improving personal virtue, and the values which individuals hold appear to be taken for granted. Religion *appears* to these people as a means of achieving empirically values which are assumed to be given and unchangeable, rather than as a means of cultivating or strengthening these values in the minds of the participants, which I have regarded as constituting the essence of religion.

If we take such statements at their face value, we can only conclude that this sort of religion, at least, is a fraud. Some anthropologists, notably Malinowski, have pointed out, however, that these ostensibly "practical" rituals have a very important unintended effect, in that they give a certain amount of increased courage and confidence to the participants. In effect, the rituals strengthen motivation to pursue goals which might otherwise be prematurely judged impossible, and also they prevent people from giving up all hope and lapsing into general apathy in the face of severe threats or disappointment. I would consider this to be an important form of cultivation of values in individual minds, although admittedly a form which is mainly unconscious from the point of view of the religious practitioners.

Let us say, for example, that the participants in a certain agricultural ceremony are largely dependent for food on a certain crop, and naturally value this highly and hope for an abundant yield. Something happens that threatens the prospect of a good yield. One thing the people might do, assuming that they have, for the time being, exhausted their rational agricultural methods, would be to worry awhile and lapse into pessimism; in other words, abandon their value that the crop is good, on the grounds that it is too unreliable and that the yield is not worth their efforts. If a satisfactory substitute crop were readily available, such a pessimistic reaction might be useful, but the world is not always so kind to us. By performing a crop fertility ritual, however, the people reaffirm their valuation of the crop and deny that they should abandon it. From an objective viewpoint this change of attitude may be highly useful to the society and its individual members. They are saved from a certain amount of doubt which might be of no use to them. They do not abandon their values. If the crop does happen to be abundant in spite of the poor prospects, the people have been spared needless worry. If it happens to fail, they have at least been given some extra time relatively free from fear to devote their energies to other pursuits.

Why do these people not tell the anthropologist "Really, the ritual has nothing to do with making the crop abundant; it just reduces our fears and reinforces our valuation of the crop"? The answer does not seem to be too difficult: the ritual paradoxically gains added psychological effect if it is regarded by the participants as having an external effect, rather than a psychological effect. Moreover, the psychological effect is not entirely obvious. The people may not be suddenly swept by a wave of increased esteem for the crop after the ritual; they may in this example simply be prevented from experiencing a loss of esteem for it, or at any rate as severe a loss of esteem as they would have had without the ritual. Of course the anthropologist should take into account the explanation of a religious ritual or any other cultural behavior which the participants offer him but he is not necessarily bound to accept this explanation at its face value nor to assume that acts always have their explicitly stated effect and no other. In the study of religion it would often be misleading to assume this.

But the apparent practical emphasis just suggested as characteristic of primitive religions is too extreme for many. Many primitive societies state quite explicitly that at least some of their rituals help inculcate social values in the participants. This is particularly true of initiation rituals and other rituals marking a change of personal status.

The example of the crop fertility ceremony puts the question as to whether religion is, as claimed by some critics, "simply" a delusion which is comforting to its adherents as long as they believe it literally, but of no use for people with scientific minds, who cannot take it literally. To put it another way, granting that when literal belief in religion is possible the religion may gain a certain strength from this fact, can religion have any significant effect when literal belief is lacking? Moreover, a critic may further ask, even if religion could have some effect without literal belief, is it not a waste of time? Why do we need to cultivate our social values ritually if we can recognize the rational basis for them?

Is not this rational acknowledgment much simpler and sufficient in itself?

To answer these questions we may raise a further question: What kinds of values does religion cultivate or encourage? As noted earlier, anthropologists classify rituals that are concerned with a variety of fairly specific social values as religious, yet not all major social values are involved in religion in all cultures. Why should people feel a need to cultivate some values ritually? I would subscribe to the view that, like the foci of a neurosis, they are all values about which there is some sort of conflict. They may be values which conflict with other values, such as altruistic versus selfish; or they may be values whose prospect of realization is uncertain or attended with much difficulty.

Proceeding rationally, as a computing machine might if appraised of the appropriate facts, one could generally make a rational decision to act in accord with one or another traditional value. But computing machines have an advantage over people: the machines lack emotion. Deciding an important problem has two distinct aspects for people, the rational and the emotional. With a minor problem, a rational solution is enough to take care of the emotional aspect, but with a major problem it is not. Because of the long span of human memory, human emotions cannot be turned on and off so easily. It is here that religion may usefully enter. If a close relative dies, for instance, a rational solution would be simply to dispose of the corpse in sanitary fashion and go about one's other business. But we know that such a rational approach would not help re-establish emotional stability or deal with the shock to the value system of the bereaved. Funeral observances may provide an adequate yet not unlimited expression of grief and remorse, and may reaffirm the value of continuing with life for the survivors. Of course, the bereaved themselves will not necessarily perish or become insane if they fail to participate in funeral ceremonies of some sort. But if they do not do so, they are probably more liable to maladaptive neurotic reactions to the death.

Up to this point I have mainly been emphasizing the positive functions of religion in cultivating socially approved values through the ritual stimulation and release of emotion. But religion, like every other social institution, also entails certain costs. If these costs were only in moderate amounts of time and effort, they might not be begrudged, but, as I am sure the reader is well aware, the cost of some religious systems has been immense in terms of human effort, suffering, and life. To a nonparticipant observer, the cost of some religious systems, for example the bloody pre-Conquest Aztec religion, would seem to far outweigh the social and individual benefits.

Aztec religion was not lacking in moral precepts which excited admiration in Europeans learning of them. Some of the early Spaniards were deeply impressed by resemblances between the Aztec and Christian religions, both in ritual observances and in explicit values. Aztec religion emphasized honesty, individual responsibility, temperance in food and drink, respect for authority, chastity before marriage, etc. The Aztecs did not take their religion lightly. They devoted much time and effort to it. Children received extended formal religious education. There were many temples and a number of sizable orders of monks and nuns.

However this same religion, admirable though it seemed in many ways, carried the practice of human sacrifice to an extreme probably reached in no other culture up to that point in human history. It is said that five thousand prisoners were sacrificed at the coronation of the Emperor Montezuma, and the reports of the number sacrificed at the consecration of the principal temple a few years earlier range from fifteen to sixty thousand. One early Spanish visitor started counting the skulls at one of the five places in Mexico City where the skulls of sacrificial victims were collected. He reported that he gave up after counting 136,000.

Of course it may be argued that these sacrifices were mostly of prisoners of war and criminals—if one is going to have war, does it matter much whether one kills one's enemies on the battlefield or captures them and kills them later? But apart from this, the Aztecs were hard on members of their own society, and many individuals were hard on themselves. The priests, speaking for the gods, sometimes demanded the sacrifice of innocent slaves and children, and in one annual ceremony men were sacrificed who had been honored as incarnations of a deity for the previous year, and accordingly treated up to the time of their death with great indulgence. Discipline of the young was often severe. If a youth in one of the religious schools should be caught drinking wine, he was supposed to have been beaten to death with staves; if the delinquent happened to be of noble birth, however, he had the privilege of being privately strangled instead. The religion was marked by ascetic practices as well as aggressive practices. Fasting was widely practiced, and food was generally rationed for moral reasons. Youths were trained to puncture their tongues with cactus thorns, which they then deposited at remote shrines, running naked through the cold night.

One can explain these cruel rites and restrictions psychologically by a sort of scapegoat mechanism: the Aztecs felt guilty about something, perhaps because of their child training, and so they killed and punished people (even themselves to a certain extent) in order to relieve this guilt. However, one wonders how much of the guilt was fed by the religious ritual itself. Aztec religion was obsessed with problems of penance and sin. The priests explicitly taught the need to feel sinful, along, of course, with the need to do penance. And then the customs of sacrifice and mutilation themselves must have given rise to much guilt independently. Evidently even the Aztecs regarded these practices as frightful and outrageous, although necessary. Thus, human sacrifice and re-lated practices among the Aztecs may be regarded as part of a vicious circle, temporarily reducing old guilt but giving rise to new. In terms of the psychic economy of individual participants, the Aztec religion was, I believe, a failure.

We may diagnose Aztec religion as afflicted by a hypertrophy of ritual. If we regard Aztec religious ritual as dramatizing the punishment of individual selfishness and the need for individual submission in the interest of the general welfare, then the dramatization has become so realistic and costly that it creates new major problems of its own. People are submitting to the ritual more than the general welfare requires. The symbol has been assigned a greater value than the reality it represents.

A tendency toward hypertrophy of ritual seems to be a danger inherent in all ritual. If, as I proposed earlier, ritual —especially religious ritual—involves a special type of symbolism which is highly effective in evoking emotional reactions, then it is not strange that people should be likely to treat the ritual symbol as something very close to reality, and sometimes to ignore or slight the reality which the symbol originally represented. A perception of this danger probably gave rise to the Mosaic prohibition of idol worship and is involved in the whole trend of the evolution of abstract monotheism. Such movements as Unitarianism and Humanism may be regarded as culminations of this age-old trend.

But ritual hypertrophy is not limited to exotic or obsolete customs such as idol worship and ceremonies involving killing or bodily mutilation. We may regard the tendency to think and behave as if many religious scriptures are literally true, as examples of *verbal* ritual hypertrophy. The belief that the resurrection of Christ was a physical event rather than a symbol of the enduring value of his teachings would be a current example from our own society. I would regard the literal belief in personal immortality as another example, and the list of examples could be extended considerably.

It is easy to see that what is called here hypertrophy of verbal ritual, or the tendency to behave as if symbolic religious statements and representations are literally true, is one important source of conflict between science and religion. I do not believe, however, that it is one which needs to be dwelt on at length for this discussion. Most of us would agree that when religious dogma clearly conflicts with scientific findings about the nature of the universe, we should modify our religion.

Perhaps I have given the impression that religion is primarily and necessarily a device which tricks individuals into abandoning rational self-interest; that individuals, from the viewpoint of rational self-interest, would be better off without religion, and that once they recognize its deceptive nature they would naturally abandon it. Men might still be social since the support of a peaceful society is a necessary aim of rational self-interest, but the social values would be subsidiary to selfish values.

I question, however, whether such a view is correct. It seems probable that in man and many other higher social animals, social values exist independently of selfish values, although of course in man they are also reinforced by rational self-interest. In this view, religion could simply help preserve a balance between social and selfish values. Most religions probably reinforce and emphasize social values more than selfish, but this must not necessarily be regarded as purely a treacherous imposition of social values on the ignorant and unsuspecting individual who would otherwise lack them. An alternative interpretation would be that the individual's innate social values are the greater sources of psychological conflict, so it is here that people seek religious support. Moreover, as previously noted, while our definition says that religion cultivates socially approved values, a society may approve apparently selfish values as well as values helpful to the life of the group, e.g., a value on personal salvation through withdrawal from the world.

The question may still be put: once we recognize that religious ritual cultivates values through emotionally evocative symbols, and is neither directly representative nor manipulative of external reality, does not religion thereby lose much or all of its effectiveness? In other words, even if we grant that religion may be reinforcing values which are a "part of human nature," can it continue to have any effect once we stop being "deceived" and in one sense "lose our faith"? I believe that religion can continue to be useful and important without literal belief in any fixed creed of the sort which includes false or questionable descriptions of parts of external reality. To the extent that religion depends for its effect on false or unsupported notions of external reality, it will of course lose this strength when such notions are given up, but this we may regard as fortunate. For it is a principal point of the view of religion which I am presenting that religion does not get its main strength from pseudoscientific theories of nature but rather from its symbolization of values and its evocation of emotion through these symbols.

From an anthropological viewpoint the emphasis on belief in dogma is characteristic only of large societies where problems have arisen of reconciling various religious sects with each other and with an expanding empirical knowledge of the world. Field investigators have observed of many primitive societies that ritual practice rather than dogma is emphasized. The investigator may find that his informants give him conflicting opinions on what may seem to him to be crucial questions of dogma, or that many informants will simply claim ignorance and not even venture an answer. On the other hand, violation of a taboo, or failure to participate in a prescribed ceremony, may bring severe penalties. If we regard religious dogma as the misinterpretation in literal physical terms of what are primarily value symbols, then this lack of concern with dogma would appear to be a healthy feature in primitive religions, and an excessive concern with dogma would involve an obscuring of the "real" meaning and force of religion.

We should not fail to note also that participants of various religious groups usually recognize at least in part the symbolic nature of some of their ritual, hymns, myths, etc. Even the most orthodox Christian would not insist that the parables which Jesus explicitly explained as such have their primary significance as historical events. And I have had a loyal Catholic tell me that the miracle of the loaves and fishes did not mean that Jesus created matter from nothing; rather it referred to his providing symbolic spiritual food, for which the multitude were willing to forget their physical hunger.

If we acknowledge the primary right of science to provide us with knowledge of the external world, as I have done without much discussion, and if we further limit religion to the ritual cultivation of socially approved values, what does this further imply as to the relation between religion and science? Most anthropologists and other social scientists today would agree that social scientists may quite properly study values, in the sense of asking what values people have, how they acquire them, and what makes them alter their values. Since anthropological evidence indicates that religion cultivates values in its participants through ritual, perhaps some will conclude that the scientific study of religion will enable the creation of more effective ritual. I think in fact that there is some possibility of an influence of science on religion in this respect, but the strength of the possible influence should not be exaggerated. To use a close analogy, aestheticians can analyze in part what makes a painting or a piece of sculpture great, and painters and sculptors can gain some profit from the analysis, but the aesthetician himself is as a rule only a mediocre artist, and a good artist at the moment of creation is probably never following an aesthetic handbook of rules. The work of art must apparently spring in large part from unconscious mental processes. Really effective religious ritual, I suspect, originates much in the manner of art. It would seem to be no accident that religious innovations in many cultures originate in dreams, trances, or other more or less nonrational states. The principal practical use of the scientific study of ritual, as I see it, does not lie in the creation of specific new rituals but in evaluating the effect of existing ritual, and in indicating general media suitable for development, and in determining the general principles of effective ritual.

Many social scientists would also agree that they may legitimately ask which values are healthy and which pathological under given social conditions. A social scientist might also ask which healthy values could be cultivated and which pathological values weeded out by religious ritual. Does this then imply that identifying and approving values is primarily a task for science, while the promotion of approved values is a task for religion?

I would say that such a view is too simple and also gives too much weight to the intellect. True, there is some place for science and intellect in that the identification of what is good certainly must involve a prior knowledge of what simply exists, and it is for science to tell us what exists. If we know absolutely nothing about something, we can have no value relative to it. As we learn more and more about it, its value for us may change, depending on what we find out. Moreover, social science may even make statements about what values other people and even we ourselves probably have. However, having values is a matter of being capable of certain emotional reactions toward the objects of value. The ultimate test of the truth of any scientific proposition about our own values is whether we personally and individually care about them. Are we alarmed if our alleged values are obstructed or threatened? Do we rejoice if they are served or achieved? If not—and this test is not quite as easy to apply as it sounds— the alleged value is false, at least for us.

It is quite conceivable, especially now in the infancy of social science and the scientific study of values, that scientists will make important mistakes in the description and explanation of values, and in the ranking of their importance. Perhaps one day our knowledge will be so complete that any scientific mistakes we make about identifying human values will be trivial. But until then it would seem wiser not to try to suppress our conscience and feelings. And when the millennium of nearly perfect social science arrives, the scientific description of values will still be largely superfluous for the healthy individual, since it will simply identify the values he already has. Of course, we may question our mental health if we lack certain values which social science tells us are normal. But even then we would probably require some form of psychotherapy to acquire normal values; the mere scientific-intellectual demonstration of their normality would probably be insufficient to produce any deep and lasting preferences. To expect people to make major value changes, after scientific demonstration of what normal values are, is analogous to expecting the law of gravity to operate more smoothly after Galileo had formulated it.

Nevertheless, while denying the role of science as prescriber of values, I would urge that it has had and will continue to have a profound influence on value changes in two ways: first, by discovering new facts about the universe of relevance to human life, including facts about society and human nature itself, and secondly, by enabling man to manipulate his environment. As a simple example of the first sort of influence, we may take the discovery of the nature of solar eclipses. A solar eclipse is probably an inherently frightening event to human beings and is interpreted as such by many primitive people. In the absence of written records, eclipses are rare enough so that people are uncertain how they will end. They fear an eclipse may mean the life-giving sun has been destroyed or damaged and that the earth will become cold and dark and the plants will die. They therefore conduct religious ceremonies, ostensibly to shorten the eclipse and rescue the sun. But once we learn a little astronomy we can easily see that the eclipse is a short and trivial event, nothing to get at all worried about; and we have long since abandoned ceremonies to save the sun.

A current example of the second sort of influence of science on religion—changing the nature of the world we live in—would be the development of atomic weapons. The vast destructive power and lasting consequences of these weapons has altered the nature of human warfare. Wars have become more dangerous; perhaps so much so that we will have no more open conflicts among the major world powers. It would certainly seem appropriate for those religions which tolerate or favor war under certain circumstances to reconsider their values on this point.

These examples are by no means the only ones which could be given of the value implications of scientific discoveries and inventions. It is obviously important then that religious leaders should be scientifically informed in our modern culture where major scientific innovations are frequent. Certainly it will be helpful to the adjustment of religion to modern conditions if religious leaders are personally acquainted with scientists and if scientists participate in religion. But religious leaders do not need to be scientists, and it seems likely that it is difficult for a single person to be both an effective scientist and a religious leader, since different personality traits are required for the two lines of work.

In conclusion, in the light of my previous remarks, I wish to make a few predictions about the future of religion in our society. It seems clear that barring major catastrophes scientific knowledge of the universe and man's place in it will continue to grow rapidly in the foreseeable future. This growth of science can only have the long-run effect of tend-ing toward the elimination of all magical and pseudoscientific traits from religion; that is, the elimination of all claims of religion to have any direct control of, or to serve as a primary source of information about anything other than the evaluative aspect of the mind of man. This state may be approached through progressive modifications in the beliefs and practices of existing sects or by an increase in the influence of sects which have already largely rid themselves of such traits at the expense of more conservative sects, or in both ways.

However, the elimination of pseudo science from religion does not mean that some sort of "true" science will be left as the reminder of religion, for religion as I see it is not the science of values, but rather an art of cultivating values. Will anything then be left? I would suggest that the remainder will be purified ritual and symbolism.

Unfortunately, an inevitable concomitant of the elimination of pseudo science from religion has been the elimination of much ritual, so that religion has been left impoverished. While the orthodox sects attribute literal significance to myth and ritual, the liberal sects have largely thrown out myth and ritual in the process of questioning their literal significance. In place of ritual we tend to have rationalistic and scientific discussions of religion and values, such as this one. These have their value, but I do not believe they fulfill the same psychological function as religion, nor do I believe that these are sufficient to attract large numbers of people to vital participation in organized churches. Of course, some reduction of religious participation may be desirable. If religion is symbolic of man's reaction to the social and natural universe, we do not want to abandon all direct reaction in favor of symbols. It still seems to me, however, that there is an optimum amount of participation of a society in religion and that contemporary Americans, especially the intellectuals, participate below this optimum.

The liberal sects are not the only ones suffering from

ritual impoverishment. This abandonment of ritual in response to rational considerations has been going on for centuries. Even our most orthodox Western sects are ritually poor in comparison with many primitive sects. It would seem that we have reached an extreme in the impoverishment of religious ritual and that a reaction is inevitable; in fact there are signs of such a reaction in many sects, although on a rather modest scale so far, and often apparently confused with an unnecessary dogmatic reaction.

A really major enrichment of religious ritual cannot be accomplished by simply resurrecting some of the previously abandoned forms. Many of these forms lost much or most of their effect when literal belief in them was abandoned, and to resurrect them now would only embarrass us.

I wish to suggest three possible sources for the enrichment of ritual, namely, (1) the arts, (2) existing ritual in other religions (including primitive and historical religions as well as other contemporary world religions), (3) innovations by contemporary religious leaders. By "the arts" is meant not simply painting and sculpture, but rather all serious arts, including music, poetry, stories, and novels (myth if you will), architecture, dance, and drama. These last two media are very important in many religions and can be especially effective.

Of course it should not be imagined that any and all art or any and all rituals of other religions could be used effectively to enrich our own religious ritual. For one thing, the symbolic value of much exotic art and ritual depends on specific local traditions and would not be significant for contemporary participants in the Western European tradition. Also, many rituals and myths would be excluded on the grounds of incompatibility with the values of our culture, even though their meaning might be clear enough. I would hope and trust, for instance, that Americans would never adopt the Aztec practices of human sacrifice. Nevertheless, symbols and rituals of universal value and significance can be found in many religions throughout the world, and if we judge them by their evocation of emotion rather than their literal cognitive content, there is strong reason for us to adopt them.

In bringing the arts back to religion several developments may be forecast. One would be the salvaging of great art of religious significance in the Western tradition. For instance, the churches might well sponsor productions of the Greek tragedies or the great religious music of Bach, etc., on a fuller scale than at present. Seminaries might pay more attention to the various religious arts and include some training in them in their curricula. And of special importance, the churches and congregations might commission interested artists to produce religious works.

You will gather that I consider the relation of religion to the arts to be fully as critical as the relation of religion to science. But to return briefly to the relation of religion and science, which is a more central concern for this discussion, religious and scientific knowledge appear to me to be quite different and to be acquired differently. Religious knowledge consists of symbols and rituals whose essential function is to stimulate and control emotions in such a way that values are cultivated. To build scientific knowledge our emotional reaction is irrelevant. Science, it is true, may study values, but at second hand. As human beings we inevitably experience values directly before and after studying them. Scientific description *of* human values should probably not be expected to make revolutionary changes *in* human values, which are often founded on more or less permanent features of biological man, on social structure, and on the natural environment.

Yet science and religion do have important interaction. For while it seems futile for science to prescribe what religion should do, religion is a reaction to the world, and science is constantly changing our picture of the world, and even, through application, the world itself.

CHAPTER 15

Faith and the Teaching of Science[*]

by EDWIN C. KEMBLE
Harvard University

AS AN INDIVIDUAL with a strongly religious background who has spent much of his life in the study and teaching of science, let me say at the start that, while I look upon the union of faith and reason as almost a human necessity, I find this union very difficult to maintain. Throughout my life I have been subject to inner tension because science pulls one way, while my basic loyalty to the spirit and aspirations of Christianity pulls another. That tension is still with me.

For a number of years I have had the primary responsibility for teaching a freshman general education course in physical science to Harvard and Radcliffe students. This course attempts to place the subject in its historical and philosophical context. We inevitably discuss the impact of Newtonian science on eighteenth-century philosophical conceptions and are here confronted with the religious issue. My practice has been to face it openly. So it has occurred to me

[*] This is a transcript of an informal veranda talk. Hence its rather personal character. E.C.K.

that you might find some interest in an account of the way in which one teacher has faced the problem of science and religion.

In approaching the subject before a class composed primarily of freshmen, I have a strong feeling of double responsibility. On the one hand, I believe that a university has to function as a place in which teachers and students alike attempt to face up to the truth insofar as they can grasp it, whether agreeable or not. On this basis I conceive it my job to direct the attention of students to the historic, and, for many, upsetting arguments of the eighteenth century between scientific materialists, proponents of natural religion, and defenders of historic Christianity. The members of the class cover much of this part of the course work in collateral reading, and many of them write term papers on some phase of this subject.

The other aspect of my sense of responsibility centers around my conviction that some sort of faith that transcends the search for personal satisfaction is necessary for the mental health of the individual and for the health of society. This does not mean that I conceive it to be part of my job as a teacher to try to persuade students of the existence of God. It does mean, however, that I make clear to them my own belief in the value of religious faith for all who can achieve it. In addition, it means that I make an effort to protect students from too easy acceptance of the conclusion that belief in God is incompatible with the facts of modern science and that a religious interpretation of life is no longer intellectually respectable. In other words, I regard it as my business to acquaint the young people in my class with some of the limitations of science and to preserve among them a sense of freedom to believe, if their total experience of life gives nourishment to belief.

The response of these boys and girls to this part of the course has been most gratifying. They find the discussions of the historical impact of science on philosophy and religion quite stimulating and in their papers they argue about God, the evidences of ultimate purpose in the universe, and the relation of mind to matter without embarrassment and with as much understanding and discrimination as one could realistically hope for. I don't know just what the net long-range effect of the experience on the religious beliefs of these students adds up to. Probably most students leave the course with much the same religious bias that they brought into it. On the other hand, I think the majority carry away a more mature attitude toward religion than they had in the beginning.

Let me now proceed to a brief discussion of some of the points of view that have entered into the annual lectures on science and faith. The presentation varies from year to year, and what I have to say from this point on is not so much a report of the content of these lectures as a fresh attempt to cover some of the more important items.

On the whole, I tend to oppose the common view, which is also the orthodox Catholic view, that because science and religion operate on different planes they are independent of one another. This proposition does not conform to the historic facts regarding the conflict of science and religion.

As a scientist I am instinctively an empiricist, with a healthy skepticism regarding a priori arguments that start with a postulate to be accepted because its converse is inconceivable. Here I use the term "empiricist" in a very broad sense to indicate that in my view all judgments regarding the nature of the world we live in should be based on experience of some kind. Along with scientific experience I would include social experience, emotional experience, religious experience, and the study of history, all of which are in some sense and to some degree legitimate bases for the formation of a personal philosophy, or a religious view.

In speaking of the impact of science on religion, my

tendency has been to focus attention on the issue of materialism, a philosophic view which originated in physical science and symbolizes scientific opposition to traditional religion. This remark raises a question that I have never discussed in my college class, but which seems crucial to a conference like this one, concerned with harmonizing religion and science. Do we seek a reconciliation based on a rejection of materialism, or are we giving serious consideration to a humanistic form of religion that would not necessarily be incompatible with the materialistic, or the naturalistic, view? Perhaps the conference would prefer to leave the question entirely open. It is one that must be faced in any case by each of us as individuals.

For my part, I see a genuine option in the naturalistic view. If religion means an active faith in the future of mankind, reverence for those saints of the past who have devoted their lives to the pursuit of righteousness, truth, and meaning, if it means an organized dedication of men to the idea of universal brotherhood—then surely a humanistic religion is not to be ruled out.

Such a religion would have a great advantage in being totally free from the defensive attitude toward science characteristic of most churches today. Its adherents would not fear any kind of knowledge. Its churches would not be a refuge for those who hide their heads in the sand and refuse to face the difficult and complex facts of the world today. The churches of such a religion could make most effective war on the lies and half-truths that so often becloud the American political atmosphere.

But to those nurtured within the powerful and appealing faith of traditional Christianity, a humanistic religion looks like an effort to lift yourself by your bootstraps. To those who envisage religion as the life of God in the soul of man, to those whose lives have experienced an added dimension through prayer, a purely humanistic religion is no religion

at all. In any case, I, for one, have tended to look for the
reconciliation of science and religion through the rejection of
materialism.

Let us accordingly consider the claims of scientific
materialism and ask ourselves what basis there is for them.
What do they overlook? To begin with a list of claims:

First: The physical universe is a phenomenon that proceeds by invariable, universal, and impersonal law.

Second: The biological universe is but a part of the
physical universe and follows the same invariable and impersonal rule of law.

Third: Mind is a product of the complex organization of
matter in the higher animals. The subjective world of our
own inner experience is a peculiar manifestation of the human
organism created by the accidents of evolution and to be
explained in the long run without the aid of other forces or
other hypotheses than those needed for the scientific interpretation of the nonliving physical universe.

Fourth: The universe unfolds in history by the inherent
necessities of its own purely physical nature. No God is
needed to maintain its evolution. It was not created and
needed no Creator.

Fifth: The universe is guided solely by blind forces. All
evidence of purpose as a determining factor in history is
illusory.

Such is the doctrine of the materialists as I understand it.
The philosophy summarized in these assertions had its origin
in scientific investigations. Many scientists believe, or half
believe, these propositions. To me they stand as an unproved
and dubious extrapolation of the legitimate conclusions of
science.

Let me begin my comment on the materialistic doctrine
with a short discussion of the first two claims, viz., the pre-
sumption that the physical universe, including the biological

universe, is ruled by universal, invariable, mathematical, and impersonal law—the kind of law revealed by physical science. Clearly the prevalence of mathematical law is the primary revelation of scientific inquiry. The universe is orderly and dependable to a degree that our ancestors could not have imagined. Astronomer, chemist, physicist, television expert, physiologist, and geneticist all give testimony to the reign of mathematical law. (The politician is not so sure, but his world has never been conquered by science.) If the universe were not under the rule of laws that defy wishful thinking, it would be no fit home for man.

Moreover, the pluralistic world of the early scientific investigator with its many substances and many independent laws has been subject through the years to a continuous process of consolidation and unification. The laws of mechanics, heat, electricity, optics, and chemistry are not independent. They seem to be merely different manifestations of a single small group of universal laws—laws not yet fully formulated, but apparently almost within our grasp. Chemical analysis has at the same time reduced all forms of matter to different combinations of some one hundred elements that are themselves now known to be different organizations formed from three types of ultimate particles. Finally these three stable species and many others that are unstable appear to be but different forms of physical energy.

The outcome of this process of consolidation is a scientific pattern of the physical universe that fits together like a jigsaw puzzle and possesses as a whole a massive strength beyond that of any of its parts. Although scientists live by the search for new ideas and new facts, they are conscious of a fundamental stability in the general scientific pattern. As a result, the attitude of every working scientist toward new data, new pieces of evidence, new insights into the nature of things is severely conditioned by the questions: "Does this suggestion, this purported information, fit the general pattern? Does it make sense in terms of the other things we have learned so far?" So is created a scientific orthodoxy, a feeling for what is credible, which is by no means completely inflexible, but which is, perhaps, not completely open-minded to new truth.

Scientific orthodoxy is necessary. We need it to protect the scientist from wasting his energy in following up foolish suggestions and to protect the public from hokum. It is needed as a barrier to the activities of the astrologers, to the Velikovskys, to the invasion of flying saucers, to the promoters of schemes for making rubber out of garbage, to all sorts of nonsense.

But orthodox scientific opinion can be wrong and so may block the way to important new truth. We must remember that the exploration of the biophysical universe is not yet complete and that all past experience shows that when a theory which works admirably in one area is applied to a new one, it nearly always requires alteration and must gain a new degree of subtlety. Scientific revolutions of the past should warn us to beware of overconfidence, even with respect to fundamentals. Scientists of the 1890's imagined that physics was nearly finished in their day. That was before the relativity theory, before the Heisenberg uncertainty principle, before cosmic rays, before atom-smashers and atomic energy. Until the time of the First World War orthodox scientific opinion was fully convinced that the ultimate laws of physics were rigidly deterministic, but today we find it expedient to abandon this assumption and to express our results in a language that is fundamentally statistical and therefore not completely causal—a language that assigns a definite and important role in the scheme of things to chance. In the 1920's it was clear to all that electrons and protons were the sole constituents of all species of atoms. There was no room in the picture for any other species of particle. Then neutrons were discovered and the picture changed.

It would be foolish for orthodox scientific opinion to claim immunity from professional prejudice. Einstein's theory of relativity was not welcomed with joy by the physicists of the first decade of this century. Freud had to win his way against the prejudices of the academic psychologists, and even today the development of psychiatric understanding is retarded by the prejudice of orthodox medical science in favor of the therapeutic properties of drugs. Why, for that matter, will the orthodox medical schools have little or nothing to do with osteopathy? Is there nothing in osteopathy that the orthodox medical man should know about?

What about parapsychology, telepathy, automatic writing, and the like? Here is an area of investigation the very mention of which arouses indignant emotions on the part of most scientists. The claims of those who have spent time in studying these so-called supernormal phenomena do not make sense in the light of the general scientific pattern. Fraud and self-deception have many times been exposed in this area of investigation. No wonder the reputable orthodox scientific journals find it necessary to refuse to publish the reports of those who consider the subject one for legitimate research. Shall we then conclude that this area is merely the happy hunting ground for the credulous and close the book?

To be quite frank, I cannot settle the question in this way. Many men of standing, some scientific, some not, have helped in the accumulation of a large literature of evidence that I cannot brush aside. Too many instances of apparently supernormal phenomena have come to my attention from sources that I find it difficult to discount. I have the impression that the debunkers have frequently been a bit too ready to accept the most tenuous evidences as proof of deception. To say before fellow scientists that the obvious difficulty in believing is balanced by a similar difficulty in not believing is like admitting before a Senate committee that one used to be a card-carrying Communist. But there you have it.

The truth is that the doctrine of the universal reign of impersonal physical law is still a vast extrapolation from the results of scientific research to date. Biologists find that within the limits of available experimental information the matter in living organisms is subject to the same laws of behavior as is nonliving matter. The assumption that living organisms are complex physicochemical systems and nothing more, is paying off handsomely in biological research. It is an assumption that must be followed to the limit before any other assumption can take a definite form warranting the serious attention of the research worker. Yet there is a vast deal to be explained about the origin and nature of life and about the nature of mind before this assumption can properly be regarded as established fact.

But let us consider the doctrine of scientific materialism from a more philosophic angle. This conception simultaneously makes a great claim about what the minds of scientists have discovered concerning the universe and plays down the role of mind in the scheme of things. Its proponents are like a man who paints a house and denies the reality of the ladder by which he reached the second story.

Mind and matter seem totally different in spite of the close connection between them. This connection is of a dual nature. There is first of all the high degree of correlation observed between our mental states and the physical states of our body. We know this in part through our ability to trace sensations to physical stimuli, in part through the effect of alcohol and drugs on the mind, in part through physiological changes that occur when we go to sleep or experience strong emotions.

In the second place, there is a connection between mind and matter in that we know matter, or think we do, through mind. Let us briefly examine this second aspect of the relation between mind and matter.

Each of us lives in a private world of conscious experience from which we can never escape, the world of our stream of consciousness. It is alive with vivid sense impressions, memories, emotions, comparisons, and symbols. On the basis of patterns in this stream of experience that repeat themselves, and with the help of verbal symbols thrust upon us by our parents, each of us as a child invents an external world of things and people in space and time. This invented external world gives rationality to our sense impressions and explains our ability to share experiences with other people through language.

The physicist's world of atoms and molecules, of electrons, protons, and neutrons, of electric fields and relativistic space-time, is derived, or constructed, from the primary subjective world of mental states by processes of abstraction that seek a mathematical interpretation of the gross external world of common sense. The physicist selects from his total experience certain aspects that can be correlated with numbers and shared unambiguously with others. These are the abstractions on which he concentrates his attention. From them he has constructed a succession of theories, or symbolic mathematical schemes, related by semantic rules to his observations. These schemes can be used with great effectiveness to control his environment and predict the results of physical experiments.

The value of these mathematical schemes in revealing order in our experience of the external world is truly marvelous. Because of the success of these theories in accounting for the course of events in the physical world, in correlating the different observed properties of material substances, and in accounting for the wide range of stimuli that generate our sensations, the materialist accepts them as essentially complete descriptions of reality. But we must remember that they have been constructed as abstractions from our primary subjective mental worlds. It is apparently impossible to reverse the process and reconstruct a single mental state, or a pattern for one, from, for example, the Newtonian scheme of mass-points moving in space-time, or from any of the more sophisticated modern counterparts of that scheme. No description of events in the brain, however detailed, that is expressed in purely physical terms has any place for the miracle of awareness that bridges the gap between the physical basis of sensation and the subjective perceptions of the stream of consciousness.

For this reason I remain skeptical of the possibility of explaining mind in terms of matter, or energy, or any purely physical conceptions. The faith of the materialistic biologist that he will ultimately succeed in understanding man as a physicochemical system, and nothing but a physicochemical system, is understandable as a professional bias, but to me the case is *not yet proved*.

There are other aspects of the doctrine of scientific materialism that incline me to skepticism, but I will not undertake to discuss them here. My last point has to do not with materialism, but with the legitimacy of faith.

In discussing this subject with students I am accustomed to begin with the observation that only a small fraction of human judgments can possibly be based on a scientific analysis of the situation that makes judgment necessary. Scientific analysis is a long and expensive business appropriate only to a limited class of problems. The method is inapplicable in many cases because analysis implies a separation of the whole into its elementary parts, and this may be destructive. You cannot make a chemical analysis of a living body, nor can you analyze your psychological relations with a close friend without endangering the friendship. For this reason we usually resort in practical matters to intuitive judgments. These are judgments of a complete situation that are not backed up by detailed scientific analysis. They represent the result of a more or less instinctive weighing of the evidence in the light of past experience. We all know how often these judgments are wrong, but we also realize that in human

affairs it is better to risk wrong judgments than to be para-
lyzed because we lack the means for arriving at scientific
certainty. We know, too, how important it is, when a judgment with long-run implications has been made, to stick to
the line of action originally chosen until evidence is encountered that shows pretty clearly and definitely that we
are on the wrong track.

So, faith, in the sense of sustained and active confidence
in conclusions based on intuitive judgment, plays and must
always play a very large role in human affairs. It can be mis-
placed, but that is a risk we have to run.

Religious faith is a particular and centrally important
example. It cannot be based directly on detailed scientific
analysis. It can never be scientific certainty. It should never be
an attempt to accept "what you know isn't so." But faith in
some kind of broad philosophic creed is vital to society and
to the individual. No one can escape some kind of faith. In
a universe of mystery and paradox as marvelously contrived
as ours, religious faith is legitimate and to be coveted. To
those who see in human personality, with all its aspirations
and tragedies, a miracle that transcends its physical environment—to such, a religious faith can be the great gift of God.

CHAPTER 16

Darwin and Religion*

by JOHN C. GREENE
Iowa State University

THE PURPOSE of this communication is to view Darwin and his writings in the broad perspective of the historical conflict between science and religion. The modern history of that conflict may be divided into three overlapping stages. In the first stage, the new physics and cosmology of the seventeenth century, combined with scientific, technological, and economic progress in the eighteenth, gave rise to natural religion, or deism, as a competitor of revealed religion. In the second stage, reaching its climax with Darwin, the further progress of science undermined the traditional conception of nature as a stable framework of rationally contrived structures, a view which had underlain both Christian natural theology and deism. In the third stage, beginning in Darwin's day and extending to the present, the methods of natural science were applied to the study of human nature and society, and these methods came to be regarded by many as the *only* methods which could yield knowledge of man and nature.

* Reprinted with permission from the *Proceedings of the American Philosophical Society*, CIII, No. 5 (1959). This paper is the only one in the volume not associated with the Star Island conferences.

The first of these stages was already well under way by the time Darwin began to think seriously about religion. The Newtonian conception of nature as a law-bound system of matter in motion, when pushed to its logical conclusion, proved irreconcilable with belief in miracles, special providences, prophecies, and the like. These had provided the "external evidences" of the divine origin of the Bible and hence of Christianity. With respect to the "internal evidences," the spread of humanitarian feeling and of optimism concerning the prospects of human life in this world produced a moral revulsion against the God of the Old Testament and the pessimistic view of human nature expressed in traditional Christian doctrines. Finally, the very notion of revealed truth ran counter to the growing demand that all knowledge be based upon clear and distinct ideas derived from experience by reason and observation. In Germany the beginnings of the "higher criticism" made further inroads on belief in the plenary inspiration of the Bible, that is, the belief that everything in the Bible, properly interpreted, is substantially true. Darwin's account of the considerations which led him in the years 1836–1839 to abandon the Christian faith in which he had been reared will serve as a brief summary of these intellectual trends:

> . . . I had gradually come, by this time, to see that the Old Testament from its manifestly false history of the world and from its attributing to God the feelings of a revengeful tyrant, was no more to be trusted than the sacred books of the Hindoos, or the beliefs of any barbarian. The question then continually rose before my mind and would not be banished,—is it credible that if God were now to make a revelation to the Hindoos, would he permit it to be connected with the belief in Vishnu, Siva, etc., as Christianity is connected with the Old Testament. This appeared to me utterly incredible.
>
> By further reflecting that the clearest evidence would be

requisite to make any sane man believe in the miracles by
which Christianity is supported,—that the more we know of
the fixed laws of nature the more incredible do miracles
become,—that the men at that time were ignorant and
credulous to a degree almost incomprehensible by us,—that
the Gospels cannot be proved to have been written simultaneously with the events,—that they differ in many important details, far too important as it seemed to me to be
admitted as the usual inaccuracies of eyewitnesses;—by such
reflections as these, which I give not as having the least
novelty or value, but as they influenced me, I gradually
came to disbelieve in Christianity as a divine revelation. . . .
This disbelief crept over me at a very slow rate, but was at
last complete. The rate was so slow that I felt no distress,
and have never since doubted even for a single second that
my conclusion was correct.[1]

One suspects that the process was painless not only because it was slow but also because Darwin had never felt that
deep anguish of the spirit to which Christianity ministers and
which caused many of his contemporaries to cling to it despite
growing intellectual difficulties. This point will be amplified
in connection with Darwin's anthropology.

What role did Darwin's writings play in the further
transformation of attitudes toward the Bible and the idea of
revealed religion? Most importantly they had the effect of
bringing the Biblical narrative of the early history of man
into doubt. Not that Darwin was the first to suggest that man's
origins had been crude and bestial. Rousseau and Lord Mon-
boddo had sketched the evolution of human nature from
brutelike beginnings, and Lamarck had plainly implied man's
apelike emergence in a long course of organic evolution. But
Darwin converted the scientific community to this view.
He thereby raised it from the status of a subversive specula-

---

[1] Charles Darwin, *The Autobiography of Charles Darwin 1809–1882
with original omissions restored* (New York: Harcourt, Brace and Company, 1959), pp. 85–86.

tion to that of a scientific theory, strenuously defended by scientists in an age when the prestige of science was growing steadily. In this sense, Darwin's writings may be said to have acted as a catalyst, hastening a series of reactions which would have taken place eventually from other causes, such as the progress of Biblical criticism and new discoveries of fossil remains, but which now came rapidly.

Darwin himself avoided attacking the Bible, but for Huxley, his doughty champion against all comers, the battle against the doctrine of inspiration, whether plenary or otherwise, was the crucial engagement in the fight for evolution and for freedom of scientific inquiry.

> I am very glad that you see the importance of doing battle with the clericals [he wrote to Joseph Dalton Hooker]. I am astounded at the narrowness of the view of many of our colleagues on this point. They shut their eyes to the obstacles which clericalism raises in every direction against scientific ways of thinking, which are even more important than scientific discoveries. I desire that the next generation may be less fettered by the gross and stupid superstitions of orthodoxy than mine has been. And I shall be well satisfied if I can succeed to however small an extent in bringing about that result.[2]

Surveying the polemical situation in 1893, Huxley felt that the battle against Biblical authority had largely been won.

> The doctrine of biblical infallibility [he wrote] . . . was widely held by my countrymen within my recollection: I have reason to think that many persons of unimpeachable piety, a few of learning, and even some of intelligence, yet uphold it. But I venture to entertain a doubt whether it can produce any champion whose competency and authority would be recognised beyond the limits of the sect, or theological coterie, to which he belongs. On the con-

---

[2] Thomas Huxley, *Life and Letters of Thomas Huxley* (Vol. III, London: Macmillan, 1913), pp. 123–124.

trary, apologetic effort, at present, appears to devote itself to the end of keeping the name of "Inspiration" to suggest the divine source, and consequently infallibility, of more or less of the biblical literature, while carefully emptying the term of any definite sense. For "plenary inspiration" we are asked to substitute a sort of "inspiration with limited liability," the limit being susceptible of indefinite fluctuation in correspondence with the demands of scientific criticism.

This Parthian policy is carried out with some dexterity; but, like other such manoeuvres in the face of a strong foe, it seems likely to end in disaster.[3]

Actually, the response to evolutionary biology within the Christian camp has been rather more varied than Huxley's words suggest. In some churches, notably the Roman Catholic, a slow but definite accommodation to evolutionary biology has taken place within the context of traditional doctrines concerning the inspiration of Scripture. According to the Reverend E. C. Messenger of Louvain, writing in 1949:

> Most [Catholic] theologians down to very recent times repudiated any form of evolutionary theory, even of plants and animals. Wiser counsels now seem to prevail, and a decided modification of the attitude of theologians is now being witnessed on the possibility of applying some restricted form of evolution to man. Theologians still seem to hold fast to the absolutely literal interpretation of the narrative of the formation of Eve. But the day may come when it will be more generally recognised that, in addition to the core of historical truth, the narrative contains figurative elements. Inevitably this presents the appearance of a losing battle, and of a rearguard action, in which successive positions are defended to the last, only to be abandoned under the pressure of necessity. A different attitude is surely desirable, and it would at least have the merit of a more wholehearted

[3] Thomas Huxley, *Science and Hebrew Tradition: Essays* (New York: Appleton, 1910), p. vii.

recognition that Science as well as Theology reveals to us truth concerning God and the world which He has made.[4]

In Protestant circles the rise of evolutionary biology and of the higher criticism produced the opposing reactions known as modernism (or liberalism) and fundamentalism. Modernism abandoned the doctrine of plenary inspiration in favor of an evolutionary conception of the growth of religious ideas and sentiments; fundamentalism reaffirmed plenary inspiration in its narrowest form and rejected whatever in biology could not be reconciled with the letter of Scripture. This conflict of opinions is too familiar to require description here. Of more recent interest is the development of new conceptions of revelation and inspiration in the Protestant fold.

> In recent Protestant theology [Walter M. Horton writes] the old scholastic distinction between natural and revealed theology is generally questioned, and a new conception of revelation has appeared, based upon a less rationalistic theory of religious knowledge. According to this view, religious revelation does not consist of the communication of propositions about God to be believed; it consists of the confrontation of God and man through actual historical events, such as the Flight from Egypt, the Babylonian Captivity, and the Life of Christ. What is disclosed in such events is "not truth concerning God, but the living God Himself." . . . Since God confronts us through the meaning of events, any report or comment which powerfully conveys that meaning may be divinely inspired, whether or not it is factually in-

---

[4] E. C. Messenger, *Theology and Evolution* (London and Glasgow: Sands & Company, 1949), p. 211. This book is a useful compendium of Catholic opinion, including papal pronouncements on the question of evolution. In connection with Messenger's call for a new attitude toward evolution, it is worth noting the favorable interest recently shown by the Vatican in a lecture in Rome by Professor Johannes Hurzeler, curator of vertebrate paleontology at Basel University. Hurzeler described a skeleton four feet in height recently unearthed in a coal mine in Tuscany. He indicated that this creature must have lived more than ten million years ago and that it represented a high degree of "humanization."

errant. The Bible can thus convey a true revelation of God, and its writers can be God's inspired interpreters, while at the same time they are thoroughly human and fallible.

Again Horton writes:

> For Niebuhr (as indeed for Barth himself . . .) the Word of God is something contemporaneous, or rather something eternal, which impinges upon our age through a human and fallible historic medium. Literal faith in the *ipsissima verba* of Scripture is a form of idolatry which God will punish as he will punish the idolatrous State-worship of our nationalistic contemporaries. But let the words of Scripture be taken as what Niebuhr calls "myths" and Barth calls "tokens" —symbolic expressions of truths too transcendent for human science to grasp, on which nevertheless our human fate depends—and they will lead us back to a fresh appreciation of Christian orthodoxy.

At the same time, say the advocates of this view of revelation, the historic conflict between science and religion will be greatly mitigated, since religion and revelation are conceived to deal with those aspects of reality, especially the value aspect, which are inaccessible to science.

It would appear, then, that although evolutionary biology has done much to stimulate a rethinking of the doctrines of revelation and inspiration, it has by no means relegated them to the limbo of exploded ideas.

In the second stage [5] of the modern conflict between science and religion, further scientific progress undermined the static conception of nature which had informed both Christian natural theology and deism. Here again, traditional views had begun to disintegrate before Darwin published, but his influence was nonetheless decisive. In the static version of the doctrine of creation, set forth in such works as John

[5] [See opening paragraph.—EDITOR.]

Ray's *The Wisdom of God Manifested in the Works of the Creation* (1691) and William Paley's *Natural Theology* (Darwin said he knew it almost by heart), nature was conceived as a framework of rationally contrived structures fitted as a stage for the activities of intelligent beings. The basic structures of nature—stars, seas, mountains, species, etc. —were thought to be permanent and wisely contrived to fulfill certain functions in the general economy of nature. Change, though ever present, was superficial; it could not alter the fundamental aspect of things. Structure was perfectly adapted to function; harmony and balance prevailed in all the operations of nature. The lower forms of existence ministered to the needs of the higher.[6]

In the eighteenth and early nineteenth centuries this view of nature was seriously shaken by the development of the nebular hypothesis in astronomy, by uniformitarian geology, by paleontology with its long catalogue of extinct species, and by the evolutionary speculations of Erasmus, Darwin, and Lamarck. Charles Darwin's contribution to the further disintegration of the traditional view was twofold. On the one hand, by converting the scientific community to belief in organic evolution he multiplied a thousandfold the impact of evolutionary ideas on the traditional faith in the stability and wise design of the fundamental structures of nature. Secondly, in his emphasis on natural selection as the primary mechanism of evolution he knocked the last remaining prop from under the static view. Lamarck had recognized that the perpetual mutability of the inorganic environment implied the perpetual mutability of organic forms, but he believed that living matter was endowed (presumably by the Creator) with a capacity to undergo adaptive transformations in re-

[6] For a fuller analysis of the static view of nature and the factors involved in its decline, see my article, "Objectives and Methods in Intellectual History," *Miss. Valley Hist. Rev.*, XLIV (1957), pp. 58–74; also, my book, *The Death of Adam: Evolution and its Impact on Western Thought* (Ames, Iowa: Iowa State University Press, 1959).

sponse to changing environmental requirements. Hence he was inclined to doubt the real extinction of species. For him, organic change was progressive precisely because it was adaptive. In Darwin's view, however, the variations which determined the survival or extinction of plants and animals were largely unconnected with their efforts to survive. Those organisms which *happened* to vary in such a way as to gain a competitive advantage in the struggle for existence survived; those which happened to vary in less fortunate directions dwindled in numbers and eventually became extinct. Thus, struggle and chance, the antitheses of pre-established harmony and wise design, became the engines of organic change and the architects of such adaptation as could be discerned in nature. This was the last and harshest blow to the traditional view of nature, a blow from which natural theology has not yet fully recovered.

Most of Darwin's contemporaries evaded the full force of the blow by transferring the element of wise design from the structures of nature themselves to the general system of matter in motion which had produced those structures in the course of time. This maneuver gave rise to precisely the kind of evolutionary theism which Immanuel Kant had foreshadowed a hundred years earlier, when, in propounding his theory of cosmic evolution, he declared:

> Matter, which is the primitive constituent of all things, is . . . bound to certain laws, and when it is freely abandoned to these laws it must necessarily bring forth beautiful combinations. It has no freedom to deviate from the perfect plan. Since it is thus subject to a supremely wise purpose, it must necessarily have been put into such harmonious relationships by a First Cause ruling over it; and *there is a God, just because nature even in chaos cannot proceed otherwise than regularly and according to order.*[7]

[7] Immanuel Kant, *Universal Natural History and Theory of the Heavens*, translated by William Hastie in *Kant's Cosmogony* (Glasgow: J. Maclehose & Sons, 1900), p. 26.

Applied to geology, biology, and eventually to history, this view of things harmonized with the nineteenth-century faith in progress and appealed to a wide variety of men and women, ranging from Christian liberals like John Fiske and Asa Gray to out-and-out agnostics like Herbert Spencer.

Darwin himself took a much less cheerful view of the theological consequences of his theory of natural selection. To those who achieved peace of mind by minimizing the role of natural selection and assuming some kind of directive agency or progressive tendency in the process of hereditary variation, Darwin replied that natural selection was the only means which could bring about the adaptation of organisms to their changing environments. To those who, like Asa Gray and Charles Lyell, proposed that God providentially supplied streams of variation in the right direction from which the environment could select, Darwin was equally unresponsive. If God provided the variations which were selected, did He also provide those which were eliminated? Did He also provide the variations which pigeon fanciers selected to please their own or other people's fancy? Did He determine the shape of Darwin's nose? If so, it amounted to saying that all variations were predetermined, those which resulted in beautiful adaptations and those which did not.

As Darwin saw all too clearly, the conception of nature as a law-bound system of matter in motion, when pushed to its ultimate conclusion, eventuated in stoicism. "The old argument of design in nature, as given by Paley, which formerly seemed to me so conclusive, fails, now that the law of natural selection has been discovered," he wrote. "There seems to be no more design in the variability of organic beings and in the action of natural selection, than in the course which the wind blows. Everything in nature is the result of fixed laws." But Darwin could not look on the production of order and adaptation through the operation of natural laws with Immanuel Kant's optimistic enthusiasm. Presumably the laws of nature implied a lawgiver, but what kind of lawgiver would achieve the adaptation of structure to function by proliferating millions of variations at random and leaving it to the environment to eliminate those which did not happen to fit? What kind of lawgiver would permit the enormous amount of suffering evident in nature? "What a book a devil's chaplain might write on the clumsy, wasteful, blundering, low, and horribly cruel works of nature!" Darwin exclaimed in a letter to Hooker. To Asa Gray he confessed like bewilderment:

> There seems to me too much misery in the world. I cannot persuade myself that a beneficent and omnipotent God would have designedly created the Ichneumonidae with the express intention of their feeding within the living bodies of caterpillars, or that a cat should play with mice. Not believing this, I see no necessity in the belief that the eye was expressly designed. On the other hand, I cannot anyhow be contented to view this wonderful universe, and especially the nature of man, and to conclude that everything is the result of brute force. I am inclined to look at everything as resulting from designed laws, with the details, whether good or bad, left to the working out of what we may call chance. Not that this notion *at all* satisfies me. I feel most deeply that the whole subject is too profound for the human intellect. A dog might as well speculate on the mind of Newton. Let each man hope and believe what he can.

And so it went, around and around, in Darwin's head— law and chance, chance and law. The difficulty was that, when nature was conceived as a law-bound system of matter in motion, chance was but the other side of a coin stamped law. In the old view of nature, chance and change had been the antithesis of design and permanence. The forms of the species were regarded as designed by God; varieties were products of time and circumstance, of *chance,* not in the sense of being uncaused or not subject to law, but in the sense of not being a part of the original plan of creation. Now, in the evolutionary view of nature, change was everywhere, and everything was either chance or law depending on how one chose to look at it. Adaptation of structure to function was a *chance* outcome of the operations of nature in the sense of not being specifically arranged in terms of a preconceived plan for the economy of nature, but it was certainly not chance in the sense of being uncaused or spontaneous. Thus, Huxley answered the charge that Darwin had introduced chance into nature by pointing out that "chance variations" must result from the operation of definite laws. Darwin, he declared, had in no way destroyed the teleological view of nature, since the element of design was simply transferred from the present structures of nature to the hidden system of laws, elements, and forces which had produced them. Yet he, like Darwin, asserted repeatedly that he could see no purpose in nature. But what was a teleological view of nature which denied purpose, or *telos,* in nature? The old terms had taken on new meanings. Confusion was rampant.

Oddly enough, it was precisely the element of chance variation (taking *chance* not as the obverse of law but rather as its opposite) which recommended Darwin's theory to the American pragmatists Charles Peirce and William James as a means of deliverance from the mechanical determinism of nineteenth-century physics and chemistry—"the block universe eternal and without a history," as William James described it. Peirce's interpretation of the theory of natural selection was totally at variance with Darwin's conception of nature as a law-bound system of matter in motion.

> In biology [wrote Peirce], that tremendous upheaval caused in 1860 by Darwin's theory of fortuitous variations was but the consequence of a theorem in probabilities, namely, the

theorem that if very many similar things are subject to very many slight fortuitous variations, as much in one direction as in the opposite direction, which when they aggregate a sufficient effect upon any one of those things in one direction must eliminate it from nature, while there is no corresponding effect of an aggregate of variations in other directions, the result must, in the long run, be to produce a change of the average characters of the class of things in the latter direction.

Peirce then went on to substitute a statistical conception of natural law for the traditional idea of natural law as a rigid pattern of behavior imposed on matter by the Creator, and to envisage the world process as a gradual growth of concrete reasonableness in the universe at large. In his opinion, a cosmogonic philosophy capable of representing the state of knowledge at which the West had arrived in his day:

> . . . would suppose that in the beginning—infinitely remote—there was a chaos of unpersonalized feeling, which being without connection or regularity would properly be without existence. This feeling, sporting here and there in pure arbitrariness, would have started the germ of a generalizing tendency. Its other sportings would be evanescent, but this would have a growing virtue. Thus, the tendency to habit would be started; and from this, with the other principles of evolution, all the regularities of the universe would be evolved. At any time, however, an element of pure chance survives and will remain until the world becomes an absolutely perfect, rational, and symmetrical system, in which mind is at last crystallized in the infinitely distant future.

Or, as he put it in another place:

> . . . the coalescence, the becoming continuous, the becoming governed by laws, the becoming instinct with general ideas are but phases of one and the same process of growth of reasonableness. This is first shown to be true with mathe-

matical exactitude in the field of logic, and thence inferred
to hold good metaphysically.

Likewise, William James, Henri Bergson, A. N. Whitehead, and others, each in his own way, found in the idea of
organic evolution the key to a new cosmology in which
spontaneity, novelty, and purpose had a place, a place which
had been denied them in the cosmology inherited from the
seventeenth century. The influence of these new ideas may
be seen in the writings of modern students of evolution, as
when Professor Dobzhansky writes, somewhat mystically: "In
producing life, cosmic evolution overcame its own bounds;
in giving rise to man, biological evolution transcended itself.
Human evolution may yet ascend to a superhuman level."

To summarize concerning Darwin's role with respect
to the second stage of the conflict between science and religion: On the one hand, he gave the death blow to traditional
natural theology by drawing out the ultimate implications for
biology of the conception of nature as a law-bound system
of matter in motion. On the other hand, he helped to precipitate a cosmological revolution (developing independently
within physics itself) which threw into doubt the Newtonian
cosmology that Darwin and Huxley took for granted. Nature
was open once more to the elements of value, purpose, and
novelty which Newton and his contemporaries had extruded
from it except insofar as they thought to find them in the
wise design of the structures of nature.

We come now to the third stage [8] of the conflict between science and religion, the stage in which the methods
and attitudes of natural science were extended to the study
of man, his history and institutions, political, economic, religious, and moral. The hope for a natural science of man and
society had been voiced in the seventeenth and eighteenth
centuries, but it was Herbert Spencer, in the mid-nineteenth

[8] [See opening paragraph.—EDITOR.]

century, who first proposed that the evolution of human history and human institutions be viewed as a simple extension of cosmic and organic evolution, continuous with them and subject to the same general laws. In his essay entitled "Progress: Its Law and Cause," published in 1857, Spencer discerned in the whole universe a progressive development from homogeneity to heterogeneity. Progress seemed written into the structure of things. It was "not an accident, not a thing within human control, but a beneficent necessity." In human history, said Spencer, progress had come about primarily through a competition of individuals and races. Those who were best adapted to the changing requirements of the environment won out over those less well adapted, thus setting the stage for still further progress.[9]

The relation between Darwin and Spencer is an interesting one. On the one hand, Darwin was highly suspicious of Spencer's intellectual methods. "My mind," he wrote Spencer's American disciple John Fiske, "is so fixed by the inductive method, that I cannot appreciate deductive reasoning . . . such parts of H. Spencer as I have read with care impress my mind with the idea of his inexhaustible wealth of suggestion, but never convince me." On the other hand, there can be no question that Darwin shared Spencer's belief in necessary, if somewhat sporadic, improvement in both nature and history and regarded natural selection as the chief engine of progress in both. The modern reader is rather surprised to see how frequently Darwin uses the terms "improve" and "improvement" in discussing natural selection. When Lyell protested that natural selection need not imply natural improvement unless there were some "principle of improvement" at work in nature independently of natural selection, Darwin replied:

[9] For a fuller account of Spencer's ideas as well as those of Auguste Comte, see my article "Biology and Social Theory in the Nineteenth Century: Auguste Comte and Herbert Spencer," *Critical Problems in the History of Science*, Paper No. 14 (Madison: Wisconsin University Press, 1959).

When you contrast natural selection and "improvement," you seem always to overlook . . . that every step in the natural selection of each species implies improvement in that species in relation to its conditions of life. No modification can be selected without it be an improvement or advantage. Improvement implies, I suppose, each form obtaining many parts or organs, all excellently adapted for their functions. As each species is improved, and as the number of forms will have increased, if we look to the whole course of time, the organic condition of life for other forms will become more complex, and there will be a necessity for other forms to become improved, or they will be exterminated; and I can see no limit to this process of improvement, without the intervention of any other and direct principle of improvement. All this seems to me quite compatible with certain forms fitted for simple conditions, remaining unaltered, or being degraded.

But what was the criterion of "improvement"? Not simply survival, for Darwin was quick to concede that natural selection might bring about developments which constituted "retrogression" when viewed against the trend of development as a whole. Improvement in the latter sense seemed to imply some notion of "higher" forms of life capable of surviving in a wider range of environments. But Darwin and his colleagues Hooker and Huxley could never decide just what they meant by "higher" and "lower" forms. "I do not think zoologists agree in any definite ideas on this subject and my ideas are not clearer than those of my brethren," Darwin wrote Hooker. But, if there was no precise criterion of "higher" and "lower," there could be no precise meaning to general improvement as distinct from competitive advantage in a specific situation. Ironically enough, Wallace and Darwin both thought that much of the ambiguity in this respect might have been avoided if instead of using the term "natural selection," loaded with implications of intelligent choice, Darwin had used instead Spencer's term "survival of the fittest."

Nowadays, on the contrary, biologists lament that Spencer's term was ever adopted, even secondarily, because of the difficulty of defining a criterion of fitness and of stripping it of value implications. The moral of the story would seem to be that biologists can neither live with nor live without normative concepts implying standards of excellence. Thus, G. S. Carter, in his recent survey *A Hundred Years of Evolution*,[10] struggles with the "problems raised by the element of progress in evolution. . . . These," he declares, "are the most fundamental of all, for it is the progressive nature of biological evolution, its progress from the simple to the complex, towards a 'better' organism and more 'efficient' life, that is the most outstanding characteristic of evolution in living nature." Professor Carter's liberal use of quotation marks in this passage betrays his uneasiness at introducing what are essentially normative concepts into a science which he regards as "necessarily mechanistic."

Whatever the difficulties involved in the notion of progressive improvement by natural selection in the realm of nature, they were as nothing compared to those which Darwin and Spencer encountered when they attempted to carry the idea over into human history. That mankind *had* progressed and would continue to progress Darwin seldom doubted. "I cannot explain why," he wrote to Lyell in 1860, "but to me it would be an infinite satisfaction to believe that mankind will progress to such a pitch that we should [look] back at [ourselves] as mere Barbarians." Again he wrote: "I am sorry to say that I have no 'consolatory view' on the dignity of man. I am content that man will probably advance, and care not much whether we are looked at as mere savages in a remotely distant future. . . . To believe that man was aboriginally civilised and then suffered utter degradation in so many regions," he declared in *The Descent of Man*, "is to take a pitiably low view of human nature. It is apparently a

[10] (New York: Macmillan, 1957.)

truer and more cheerful view that progress has been much
more general than retrogression; that man has risen, though
by slow and interrupted steps, from a lowly condition to the
highest standard as yet attained by him in knowledge, morals,
and religion." This progress, he added, gave hope for "a still
higher destiny in the distant future."

A very comforting, even inspiring, view of things, this,
but there were ambiguities in it, both as to the criterion of
improvement and as to the method by which it had taken
place and would take place. These difficulties may be illustrated with respect to Darwin's account of the origin and
progress of the *moral sense*, which he regarded as the chief
attribute distinguishing man from the lower animals. In
Darwin's view, the moral sense sprang from the interaction
of the social instincts with man's superior intellectual powers,
the whole process being guided by natural selection.

> It must not be forgotten [he wrote in *The Descent of
> Man*] that although a high standard of morality gives a slight
> or no advantage to each individual man and his children
> over the other men of the same tribe, yet . . . an increase
> in the number of well-endowed men and an advancement in
> the standard of morality will certainly give an immense
> advantage to one tribe over another. A tribe including many
> members who, from possessing in a high degree the spirit
> of patriotism, fidelity, obedience, courage, and sympathy,
> were always ready to aid one another, and to sacrifice them-
> selves for the common good, would be victorious over
> most other tribes; and this would be natural selection.
> At all times throughout the world tribes have supplanted
> other tribes; and as morality is one important element in
> their success, the standard of morality and the number of
> well-endowed men will thus everywhere tend to rise and
> increase. . . . But as man gradually advanced in intellectual
> power, and was enabled to trace the more remote con-
> sequences of his actions; as he acquired sufficient knowledge
> to reject baneful customs and superstitions; as he regarded

more and more, not only the welfare, but the happiness of his fellow-men; as from habit, following on beneficial experience, instruction, and example, his sympathies became more tender and widely diffused, extending to men of all races, to the imbecile, maimed, and other useless members of society, and finally to the lower animals,—so would the standard of his morality rise higher and higher. . . . Looking to future generations, there is no cause to fear that the social instinct will grow weaker, and we may expect that virtuous habits will grow stronger, becoming perhaps fixed by inheritance. In this case the struggle between our higher and lower impulses will be less severe, and virtue will be triumphant.

But, it may be asked, if human sympathies become extended to all mankind, to all races and nations, to the imbecile and the maimed, the so-called useless members of society, what becomes of the competitive struggle and hence of the progress of man? Here, indeed, was a dilemma, and Darwin was caught squarely on the horns of it.

Man, like every other animal [he wrote], has no doubt advanced to his present high condition through a struggle for existence consequent on his rapid multiplication; and if he is to advance still higher it is to be feared that he must remain subject to a severe struggle. Otherwise he would sink into indolence, and the more gifted men would not be more successful in the battle of life than the less gifted. Hence our natural rate of increase, though leading to many and obvious evils, must not be greatly diminished by any means. There should be open competition for all men; and the most able should not be prevented by laws or customs from succeeding best and rearing the largest number of offspring.

This would seem a frank enough avowal of Spencer's "Every man for himself, and the devil take the hindmost," but Darwin immediately adds that the moral qualities, though developed in part by the struggle for existence, are developed even more "through the effects of habit, the reasoning powers, instruction, religion, etc." than through natural selection.

Darwin's reference to the elevating influence of religion on the moral sense is interesting in view of the precarious state of his own religious beliefs. Speaking as an anthropologist, he thought to find the origin of religious ideas in the fears and dreams of primitive peoples. Presumably it was only in the later stages of social advance that religion exercised a beneficial influence on morality. "The idea of a universal and beneficent Creator," he noted, "does not seem to arise in the mind of man, until he has been elevated by long-continued culture." Yet the latest advances in science, to which Darwin himself had contributed mightily, seemed to undermine belief in such a Creator. Science, in discovering the secret of man's lowly origin and the equally humble origin of his highest thoughts and aspirations, seemed to Darwin to have destroyed confidence in man's reason and in his deepest intuitions when confronted with the ultimate questions of human existence. Darwin himself confessed to an "inward conviction" that the universe was not the result of chance. "But then," he added, "with me the horrid doubt always arises whether the convictions of man's mind, which has been developed from the mind of the lower animals, are of any value or at all trustworthy. Would any one trust in the convictions of a monkey's mind, if there are any convictions in such a mind."

Here, indeed, was agnosticism, and agnosticism which trusted in the power of science to trace the origin of stars and planets, mountains and species, morality and religion, but which to all the deepest questions of the human spirit returned an *Ignoro*, followed by an *Ignorabo*. These were gloomy thoughts, and they were but little relieved by Darwin's rather ambiguous belief in the progress of man. For over human progress lay a dark shadow—"the idea," he wrote to Hooker, "or rather I presume the certainty of the sun some day cooling and we all freezing. To think of the progress of millions of years, with every continent swarming with good and enlightened men, all ending in this, and with probably no fresh start until this our planetary system has been again converted into red-hot gas. *Sic transit gloria mundi*, with a vengeance. . . ."

There was, however, an even more dreadful thought which never occurred to Darwin because he assumed that the progress of science and civilization necessarily brought moral improvement in its wake. This was the thought, all too familiar to the present generation, that man might perish not through some natural catastrophe but by his own hand, because the progress of science and technology, of man's intellectual powers, had outrun the progress of human sympathy and understanding.

These difficulties and ambiguities in Darwin's reflections on nature, man, and God would not be worth rehearsing at such great length if they had been *his* difficulties alone. After all, he was primarily a biologist and a very great one. It would perhaps be too much to expect any biologist since Aristotle to be simultaneously a great moral philosopher and social thinker. But Darwin's difficulties and inadequacies were those of his age and of the age which succeeded. They entered deeply into biological and social thought and still do. The genetic fallacy which led Darwin to suppose that the religious beliefs of mankind were adequately accounted for in terms of the dreams and fears of primitive peoples was to permeate sociology and cultural anthropology for many years to come. The sociological positivism which identified Kant's categorical imperative as the voice of society built into the individual by a long course of social training was to reappear in Freud and Durkheim. The antimetaphysical bias which relegated to the realm of the unknowable everything which could not be formulated scientifically was to become even more pronounced. The conception of human progress as an outcome of competitive struggle between individuals, nations, and races was to wreak incalculable havoc in the custody of men less deeply humanitarian than Darwin. Finally, the confident assumption that the progress of intellect, especially of science and the scientific attitude, is necessarily accompanied by moral and cultural progress, still lingers on, despite the shattering events of our own age and the threat of atomic destruction. "Judged by any reasonable criteria," Professor Dobzhansky writes in his recent book, *The Biological Basis of Human Freedom*,[11] "man represents the highest, most progressive, and most successful product of organic evolution. . . . Most remarkable of all, he is now in the process of acquiring knowledge which may permit him, if he so chooses, to control his own evolution. He may yet become 'business manager for the cosmic process of evolution,' a role which Julian Huxley has ascribed to him, perhaps prematurely."

What should a sane man think of this? Should he conclude with Sir Julian that the cosmic process, after billions of years of labor, has finally brought forth a creature, man, who is ready or nearly ready to direct the future course of things? Or should he rather regard the very entertaining of such an idea as a symptom of the madness with which the gods afflict those whom they would destroy?

To summarize: With respect to revealed religion, Darwin's writings helped to precipitate a rethinking of traditional doctrines concerning inspiration and revelation, a rethinking which has proceeded in several directions and is still going on.

With respect to natural religion, Darwin shattered its traditional basis by exhibiting the adaptation of structure to function in the organic world as a necessary outcome of random variation, struggle for existence, and natural selection. For many of his contemporaries the blow was softened by the indomitable faith of the nineteenth century in progress, a faith which enabled them to view the world-machine as a

[11] (New York: Columbia University Press, 1956.)

divinely contrived mechanism for insuring perpetual improvement in nature and history. But Darwin found little comfort in this view. Progress was too slow, too sporadic and haphazard, too precarious to reflect much credit on the Creator, if there was one. But though Darwin remained a prisoner of the law-bound system of matter in motion which he had extended to biology, others found in his theory of organic evolution a way of escape from the gloomy confines of that system. The revolution in biology was soon followed by a revolution in physics and cosmology.

With respect to the third stage of the conflict, in which the methods of natural science were applied to the study of man and society, Darwin played a pioneer role. His writings in this field are valuable not so much for their scientific content as for the light they throw on the difficulties inherent in the concept of social science. Like Spencer, Darwin attempted to apply the concepts of biology to human history; like Spencer, he wound up in hopeless contradictions. Biology afforded no criterion of progress for a creature like man, and Darwin was forced to bring in other criteria, imported surreptitiously from his Christian background. To the very end, he failed to appreciate the morally ambiguous character of human progress. He failed because, like many social scientists today, he had no adequate conception of man. Whatever his origin, man is a very peculiar creature, whose inmost being eludes the abstractions of science. For science, since it adopts the point of view of the detached observer, has no access to those aspects of reality which can be known only from the point of view of the actor. Yet, ultimately, the scientist himself is an actor in the difficult human situation, and science becomes pointless and even destructive unless it takes on significance and direction from a religious affirmation concerning the meaning and value of human existence.

CHAPTER 17

Religion and (or) Science

by PAUL E. SABINE

Palo Alto, California

"CAN SCIENCE BE SEPARATED from ethics and religion?" There cannot be much doubt that the answer of most men of science to this question would be an unqualified affirmative. This separation not only *can* be effected but *has* been effected so far as it relates to scientific knowledge and the intellectual content of Christian faith. This is not to say that a religious attitude and a scientific attitude toward the world of conscious experience are impossible in one and the same individual scientist. Many men of the greatest scientific stature have held deeply rooted religious beliefs. Shortly before his death Newton wrote: "I have kept an eye on such principles as might work with considering men for the belief of a Deity, and nothing can rejoice me more than to find them useful for that purpose." Michael Faraday throughout his lifetime was a devout follower of a simple religious faith that in modern terms would be classed as "fundamentalist."

On the other hand Laplace, the great French mathematician, questioned as to the omission of all reference to the Deity in his *Méchanique Céleste* characterized the existence of God as an unnecessary hypothesis in his account of the stellar universe. The whole trend of modern physical science is in line with Laplace's secular neutralism rather than with Newton's pious wish. Newtonian physics leads to a world view of atomistic mechanism presenting the material universe as a machine calling for no *deus ex machina* to maintain it as a going concern. With this background, the God of the Hebraic-Christian tradition, having created a perfect machine and completely fulfilled his creative function, has retired to the remoteness of interstellar space to contemplate his handiwork and serve as an object of veneration for sinful mortals. Later, biological science robbed the God of traditional Christianity of his creator role. The biblical account of the creation of the physical world out of the void has been replaced by the scientific concept of cosmic evolution. The best that scientific thought can do with the scriptural account of the origin of life on this planet is to consider it an allegorical picture of an evolutionary process that originated in the darkness of geological time and to assign to the human species a modest place as the contemporary phase of the development of the order of primates. Man is described by science not as being "a little lower than the angels" but rather as being a bit higher than the apes.

A century ago, psychology deserted the ranks of philosophy and joined the procession of the physical sciences in its concepts and methodology. Measurement is the road to knowledge of the physical world, and modern psychology started on this road early in the last century with a most impressive collection of devices for measuring stimulus and response in the human organism. This earlier phase, which began in Germany, gave way in this country to a behaviorism that eliminated the effect of conscious mental processes on overt behavior, thus reducing personality to a collection of conditioned reflexes that automatically determine the activities of the individual human organism. At the other extreme of present-day psychology is the psychoanalytic school of thought that grew out of the researches of Freud and his disciples and today commands a wide following among psychologists. In this, the idea of the existence of a human soul with its religious connotations has been supplanted by the somewhat nebulous concept of the human psyche which is compounded of both conscious and unconscious elements and is the source of the psychic drives that motivate conduct and control the development of personality. Having abandoned the notion of the reality of the soul of man, psychologists of this school find the correlative postulate of the existence of God no more necessary than Laplace found it in astronomical theory.

This neutral attitude of the teachings of science and psychology toward ethical and religious problems is doubtless responsible for the widely accepted notion that the scientific and the religious world views are mutually opposed to each other. This state of mind was expressed by a professor of philosophy in a widely discussed paper that appeared in a popular magazine a few years ago. The writer of the article, a professed atheist, agreed with a statement of the Catholic Bishops of America to the effect that the chaotic state of the world today is due to the abandonment of God and religion. He found support from another quarter in the writings of Bertrand Russell and Jean Paul Sartre. He ascribed this state of affairs to the general spirit and basic assumptions of modern science and psychology. In support of his position, he cited the fact that the skepticism of the Age of Enlightenment in the eighteenth century followed hard upon the rise of modern science in the century preceding. His logic was one that any schoolboy can follow. Said he: "Before Galileo, European man, whether ancient pagan or modern Christian, thought of the world as controlled by plan and purpose. After Galileo, European man thinks of it as utterly purposeless.

This is the great revolution of which I spoke." Further he announces with a voice of final authority: "It is this that has killed religion."

To this masterpiece of sophomoric logic, the religious-minded scientist may well reply: "If science has killed religion, then this type of philosophy has gone all out to bury it beyond all hope of resurrection." This negative type of existentialism finds its historic counterpart in the escape philosophy of Stoicism, which served as a substitute for a positive faith in the centuries of decline and decay of Greco-Roman culture at the beginnings of the Christian era.

Now this revolution which, according to our atheistic philosopher, has caused the demise of religion, has taken place in every field of thought including science itself. During the last sixty years there has been a change in the thinking of physicists as radical as that which came when Copernicus shifted the center of man's universe from the earth to the sun.

In that excellent piece of reporting, *Dialogues of Alfred North Whitehead*,[1] Lucien Price quotes this great modern philosopher as saying in effect that since the beginning of the present century absolutely nothing of the seemingly solid structure of mathematical physics, built by the great men of science such as Newton and Descartes, has been left unshaken and unchallenged—"not a single major concept." Further in reply to the question as to whether this is equally true of religion and ethics, he said, "Yes, but with the difference that philosophy and science welcomed these new hypotheses which upset their old ones and thus profited by them, whereas religion resisted the new ideas and suffered in consequence."

In retrospect, ten years after the expression of this opinion, one finds it substantially true of the present situation, but with one slight change in wording. Taking the

[1] (Boston: Little Brown, 1954.)

program of a conference of the World Council of Churches as a criterion, today it would seem nearer the truth to say that Protestant religious leadership has not resisted the "new ideas" of science but has simply ignored them as being of no importance to religion. One does not find a discussion of "Religion in an Age of Science" assigned any very prominent place in the deliberations of the program of the conference.

Science has demonstrated its ability to arrive at its proper goals without the aid of religion. It would seem to be vastly more important to inquire as to whether a Protestant faith can survive in the intellectual climate of our day. The devout Catholic has the authority of an historic Church to promote his acceptance of a religious philosophy compounded of the metaphysics of Aristotle and an authoritative interpretation of scriptural teachings by his Church. This for him is a rational basis for his religious belief. The Protestant Christian has no such unified body of orthodox teaching. Until fairly recently, the major branches of the non-Catholic church have accepted the formulations of denominational theologians as statements of their official creeds. During the course of the last half century these doctrinal lines have gradually become less important in the minds of the laity and in the preaching of the clergy.

At the risk of oversimplifying a situation that is far from simple, one ventures the assertion that the most important division in Protestant thought today is between a liberal and a fundamentalist attitude toward religious teachings. For the most part this cleavage does not follow denominational lines. Both attitudes are to be found among the clergy and the laity of all the larger Protestant churches.

The integration of the religious and the scientific interpretations is a problem that concerns liberals more than fundamentalists. The latter seem to feel that faith alone is sufficient and needs no scientific prop to sustain it. Liberals, on the other hand, facing the "either-or" dilemma as between scientific knowledge and religious belief, are of divided mind. The choice of either to the exclusion of the other is difficult, and the state of mind following a choice is uncomfortable.

If the liberal happens to be a scientist—which is quite frequently the case—he should feel quite at home in dealing with this particular quandary. Being in quandaries is a normal state of the scientific mind, and modern science has arrived at an effective way out. Nature has a perplexing habit of giving seemingly contradictory answers to questions put to her in the language of experiment. Scientific procedure in such cases is to replace the "either-or" of the dilemma for a "both-and" synthesis of the contradictory interpretations of the experimental facts. In short, science abandons Aristotelian logic in favor of Hegelian dialectic.

The revolutionary change in scientific thought of which Whitehead was speaking, is in large measure due to this shift from analysis to synthesis in theoretical physics. Einstein's abandonment of the Newtonian ideas of absolute space and absolute time in favor of the space-time continuum of the relativity theory, not only resolved the apparent contradiction of the fact of the aberration of starlight and the results of the Michelson-Morley experiment, but led to an entirely new concept of the nature of the stellar universe. A similar synthesis was made in quantum physics when the antithetical properties of waves and particles were combined in the mathematical concept of the "wave-particle."

Admittedly this revolution in scientific thought as to the ultimate nature of the physical world carries no necessary religious implications. Belief in the reality that is symbolized by the word "God" calls for an act of faith, no less when we describe physical reality in the symbolic relationships of the new physics than if we employ the older concepts of inert atoms and mechanical forces. But mathematical relations are the products of mental processes, and the existence of *mind* is a necessary corollary of the operation of a mental process.

That mind may be limited to the individual mind of the mathematical physicist. It may, on the other hand, be conceived as a cosmic mind that bears the same relation to the material universe as the human mind bears to the material body with which it is associated. Acceptance of the second alternative does not necessitate belief in the existence of God in any religious sense, but it does make the belief tenable if one is disposed toward a religious view of scientific concepts. Neither a radical skepticism nor a positive religious faith is based on wholly rational grounds. Both involve a "will to believe." The difference lies in what one chooses to believe.

Although the new physics allows the existence of a cosmic mind as a tenable belief, we still have to face the fact that, God or no God, all that can occur in the natural world is ultimately subject to the limitation of the inescapable second law of thermodynamics. Put in its simplest terms, this is a statement of the observed fact that all physical processes involve a dissipation of the available energy of the universe, thus diminishing the supply that remains available to maintain future processes. Under the continuing operation of this law, the ultimate fate of the physical universe is a state of complete thermodynamic equilibrium, the "heat death" that marks the complete running down of the cosmos considered as a machine. This aspect of the scientific picture of the world has led to a deal of pessimistic and fatalistic philosophizing that induces a negative attitude toward the meaning of human life. If man and his world are only a passing phase of a process that is finally to end in a state of universal stagnation, what possible reason is there to search for meaning, either religious or scientific, in a process that in the long run has no meaning? Such a prospect makes human life a "tale told by an idiot, full of sound and fury, signifying nothing."

Taking a more comprehensive view, the running-down process can be seen as only part of the totality of Nature. An equally significant part is the presence and proliferation of life. This latter is beyond the scope of physical science, as are also religious and ethical values. Physical science gives no account of vital processes. But in biophysics and biochemistry, the biologist crosses the line between physical and natural science. In so doing he discovers that all life processes dissipate available energy just as do those that are considered to be wholly physical or chemical. Although all life has its origin in antecedent life, yet the energy that sustains it comes ultimately from the dissipative process of solar radiation. In a very real sense, life as we know it on our globe is made possible by some sort of running-down process in the sun. "Life on this earth is sustained by the material disintegration of a dying star." This gives a cosmic significance to the mundane drama of organic life and should be a ground for devout gratitude rather than for fatalistic pessimism.

The great generalization of biological science is the doctrine of evolution. In very broad terms, this doctrine describes the organic world as a continuous creative process. Looked at in this way, it may be said to complement the thermodynamic concept of physical reality. The latter, viewing nature only in its purely physical aspects, describes it as an essentially disorganizing process. Here as elsewhere in our quest of reality, a synthesis of two opposing concepts gives a closer approximation to the truth than is reached by either alone. The world, as we can know it from our interior point of view, is a cyclic process of creation and destruction, growth and decay, life and death. The rise and fall of historic societies present a similar pattern. The life of an individual organism is a rhythmic synthesis of these same elements.

Biological science does not see evolution as a triumphal march toward a predestined goal, with man as the crowning achievement of a creative principle. The scientific picture is rather that of a vital urge inherent in matter that finds expression in living forms not by an act of creation of something out of nothing, but by the intellectual process of bringing order out of chaos. Now, order in a biological sense implies functional correlation of processes which in turn involves the idea of purpose. We can describe the action of lungs in mechanical terms as similar to that of a bellows. We understand the action of the lungs only in terms of the contribution that action makes to the life of the whole organism, that is to say, the *purpose* they serve. Vital processes differ from the purely physical in that they operate to future ends. In conscious processes we humans are subject to both, and there is the crux of the age-old philosophical problem of human freedom. Here again we can have recourse to the scientific way out and see human conduct as both free and conditioned. That sense of incompleteness with a feeling of guilt that theologians ascribe to "original sin," stems from the tensions between these two elements of conscious personality.

The religious urge has its origin in this area of man's nature as a self-conscious being. It is here that modern psychology and religious teaching need to find some common ground if they are to satisfy the spiritual hunger of men and women in a sensate culture so completely lacking in spiritual vitamins as is that of today. On the whole, psychology has not gone very far toward supplying this lack. For the behaviorists, physical stimulus and overt response comprise the whole area of psychological interest. Someone has called the behaviorist approach "psychology with the psyche left out." According to behaviorist theory, conscious thought, feeling, and will are negligible factors in determining conduct or in developing personality. Naturally, religion as a conscious experience of the individual lies outside the field of interest of behaviorist psychology. However, the behavioristic technic has proved a powerful means of creating and developing a mass psychology, as evidenced by the success of a small minority in gaining control of the group mind of Nazi Germany and in Communistic Russia.

On the credit side, it should be noted that liturgical religious worship finds its psychological significance as a response in behavior to religious stimuli. Conversely, religious experience may well be engendered and enhanced by religious rites no less than by religious thoughts. Perhaps it is the lack of a ritual that is meaningful to the modern mind that confines the appeal of liberalism to a relatively small minority of religious people.

Analytical psychology stands at the other extreme from behaviorism in present-day psychology. Probably its concepts and theories of the structure of the mind and the source and development of personality have had more profound and far-reaching influence on the religious attitude of liberals than any other single element in contemporary life. Quite probably its net effect has been to undermine rather than to support a positive attitude toward Christian teaching. This is not surprising, in view of the fact that the psychoanalytical view of personality grew out of the study of the nature and causes of mental illness. Psychoanalysis as a therapeutic technic has justified its existence, but its value as a philosophy for healthy minds may well be questioned. Those that are whole have no need of a physician, and it is entirely possible that an overlong occupancy of the psychiatrist's couch may bear a causal as well as a curative relation to a disturbed state of a healthy mind.

Here, as in the case of objective science, a religious interpretation of secular truth may be the most creative approach to a problem that lies in both fields. Dr. C. G. Jung in the title of his volume of essays, *Modern Man in Search of a Soul*, points the way toward such a synthesis. Psychoanalytical theory is based upon the premise of the real existence of the psyche, the dynamic, vital aspect of the personality. It is the center and source of conscious experience, but is at the same time dominated by instinctive emotional and volitional drives that exist in the "unconscious" level of mental processes.

The best that psychology has to offer to modern man

in search of his soul is a psyche that is the organizing principle of an integrated personality. The mentally ill can turn to a doctor of the mind, the psychiatrist. But the great majority of religious-minded people today are not spiritually sick, only spiritually undernourished.

The whole history of mankind bears out the statement that all historic societies of the past have grown out of and with a religion of some sort. Moreover, as Arnold Toynbee has cogently indicated in his *Study of History*, the disintegration of a civilization begins with a schism in the soul of the individual. Evidence of the rift in the soul of modern man is all too easy to find, and it is a reasonable assumption that there is no small measure of correlation between that fact and the disintegrating process of Western civilization.

"Doctors are told they fail in treating 'Basic Unhappiness.'" This is a newspaper headline of a report on a paper read before the recent meeting of the American Medical Association in San Francisco. In the body of the paper the author describes that syndrome of physical and mental disorders for which the doctor can find no organic cause and about which he conceals his ignorance and frustration by calling them "functional" in their origin. These cases he gladly turns over to a colleague whom he doesn't like or even to a Christian Science practitioner.

It would be fatuous to assign a single cause for this widespread lack of durable satisfaction in the life of our times. A part of it is probably because thoughtful people today are searching and failing to find the soul that is lost in a welter of sensations and things that science and technology have heaped on modern man. He lives in a bewildering world of material "blessings" so-called, of things, gadgets running all the way from television to atom bombs, and like a spoiled child with a surfeit of toys, he suffers from basic unhappiness. As a substitute for his lost soul, psychology offers him a psyche, almost buried in an underworld of the unconscious.

But it is only a favored few who find the stone of psychological analysis transmuted into the bread of life.

Here again quest of truth leads to a synthesis of two antithetical ideas. The psyche of analytical psychology is rooted in the unconscious in which the nonrational elements of the total personality find themselves. For the most part these stem from the animal side of man's nature and are oriented toward the satisfaction of purely biological drives that motivate his behavior. The complete co-ordination of these elements would make the human individual a splendid animal. At that point his evolution as a spiritual being would stop, and his quest of a soul would be abandoned. The human species would become a dead branch on the tree of life.

A religion whose intellectual content and motivation are congruent with those of science sees the soul of man as the reverse side of the psyche of psychology. It is this psychological side that is oriented toward man's destiny rather than toward his origin. It is on this side that human evolution is a continuing process. Here, in a portion of man's being that has not yet come to the surface of his conscious life, lie the creative factors that find expression in poetry, music, and art, as well as the expanding intellectual horizons of science, philosophy, and religion.

Christian teaching can include the religious implications of modern science and psychology by a simple change of tense in the biblical account of cosmic and human origins. Thus the liberal Christian can read "from the beginning God *is* creating the heavens and the earth" and thus get a stereoscopic view of the scientific and scriptural accounts of the process of creation. In like fashion, he can read "God *is* creating man in his own image" and arrive at a satisfying synthesis of the two supreme mysteries of existence, God and the human soul.

CHAPTER 18

Science, Faith, and Human Nature*

by C. JUDSON HERRICK

University of Chicago

The Natural and the Supernatural

Did God make man or did man make his gods? This is the sort of question that theologians and naturalists have wrangled about for hundreds of years. The fires of controversy have usually produced more heat than light, and still do, in part because the appeal from both sides is often to traditional dogma and emotional prejudice and in larger part because of failure to define precisely the things we are talking about. It is, for example, silly to debate about the "supernatural" without first explaining just what we mean by the "natural."

It should be emphasized at the start that this essay is not a brief in defense of either the natural or the supernatural. It may be claimed that the natural needs no defense, for

* Reprinted with the permission of the University of Chicago from *PERSPECTIVES in Biology and Medicine*, Autumn, 1958. Copyright 1958 by the University of Chicago.

most of our common affairs and all of natural science deal only with unequivocal natural things and events. There is no such agreement about what the supernatural is and its influence (if any) on human conduct. It is certain that *belief* in the supernatural does influence behavior. The visions of the mystics are real events. However they may be explained, they often have consequences as obvious as the one which converted Saul of Tarsus into a Christian evangelist, and the supernaturalism indoctrinated by the metaphysicians and theologians motivates the behavior of multitudes of people. Let us look at these facts from the standpoint of the student of behavior.

It is not my purpose here to try to give a definite answer to the question set at the beginning or to any other question about what we should believe or what faiths we should entertain. What I want to do is to clear the air of some smog arising from fuzzy definitions and to suggest some considerations that may help to heal the schism between the naturalists and the supernaturalists.[1]

It will be shown that faith plays an indispensable role as a common denominator in both science and religion. It is, then, pertinent to ask: What is the appropriate role of knowledge and of faith in all human affairs, as well as in science and religion? Critical examination of our definitions and of the behavioral significance of both knowledge and faith, from the naturalist's standpoint, will show, I am convinced, that rigorously mechanistic science may keep the peace with a rational supernaturalism stripped of the crude mythologies and traditional dogmas with which it is usually garnished. Let us, then, first try to agree upon some definitions, not as final or absolute truths, but as necessary instruments for profitable approach to these problems.

[1] C. J. Herrick, *Texas Quarterly*, I:1 (1958). With the kind permission of the publisher of the *Texas Quarterly*, this article is here revised and expanded so as to clarify some passages and bring out more sharply the contrasts between the faiths of science and the religious faiths.

Definitions

In common usage the term "unnatural" is applied in so many different ways that the word is practically meaningless, and this implies, of course, that the word "natural" is no better off. What, then, is nature? A classical definition was written by T. H. Huxley in 1872: [2]

> For myself, I am bound to say that the term "Nature" covers the totality of that which is. The world of psychical phenomena appears to me to be as much a part of "Nature" as the world of physical phenomena; and I am unable to perceive any justification for cutting the Universe into two halves, one natural and one supernatural.

Most scientists and naturalistic philosophers accept Huxley's last statement without qualification; but does it follow that nature, as science views it, comprises "the totality of that which is"? A revised version of Huxley's definition is given by Van Rensselaer Wilson,[3] who writes: "The whole domain of the *possible* must be included, along with the domain of the actual, when we speak of the natural in this inclusive sense." I grant that science can and does deal theoretically with the possible, including the "superactual," but the question remains whether there may not be domains of the actual that are forever inaccessible to human science.

Natural science is a human construction derived from human experience, and it can go no further than the range of possible or conceivable experience. The totality of that which is and of that which is possible may extend to infinity, that is, beyond the reach of experience, which is limited to a finite

[2] T. H. Huxley, *Science and Christian Tradition*, reprinted in *Collected Essays by T. H. Huxley* (Vol. V, New York: Appleton, 1902), p. 39.
[3] H. Van R. Wilson, *Humanist*, XIV (1954), p. 265.

world. The normative sciences, like logic and mathematics, can use symbols for that which is unknown, unknowable, or actually impossible; but these symbols, which are useful tools of thought, may stand for fictions that the empirical scientist never can encounter in his exploration of the actual world. Because natural science is limited to the domain accessible to finite minds, a logical and an actual operational limit is set to nature as envisaged scientifically and practically.

If we accept either Huxley's or Wilson's definition of nature, our argument is closed. Everything is natural. The supernatural cannot exist, and there is nothing more to be said about it. But the limitation of the scope of natural science to which reference has just been made leaves the question open, for it demands consideration of the possibility that nature as envisaged by science may be only a small fraction of the totality of that which is. Even if this possibility is recognized, I grant that it remains true that the unknowable is none of the naturalist's business. He must be careful, of course, not to set arbitrary limits to the knowable. No one can tell what these limits are. Some accepted facts prove to be fictions, and some fictions assumed to be miraculous have been factually realized. Newton's knowledge of optics would not have justified either a prediction of television as we see it today or a denial of the possibility of such a miraculous achievement. Facts, like axioms and definitions, are sometimes tricky things, for human experience is not infallible, and it is often misinterpreted.

The limitation of the scope of scientific inquiry here recognized does not involve any splitting of the total universe of the actual into two independent and interacting halves, as postulated by the dualists, as will be explained further.

We may, then, regard the natural as the knowable part of total reality. For our present purpose, we accept the concise definition written by Santayana in 1905.[4] "Nature," he said, "is the sum total of things potentially observable, some observed actually, others interpolated hypothetically." In another context he insisted upon "regarding nature as the condition of mind and not mind as the condition of nature."

The preceding appeal to experience perhaps calls for further explanation. The philosophers have not reached any agreement about the definition of experience, and in Chapter XIII of a recent book [5] I have outlined a natural history of experience. We need not bother with these details now, for we have all had experiences, and the word in this context has the ordinary vernacular meaning as used in dealing with human adjustments, with the qualification that our primary concern here is with consciously recognized experiences.

These experiences are of two radically different sorts. First, there are our experiences about obviously physical things and events. This gives us our knowledge of the objective world—our natural bodies, everything that acts upon these bodies, and all observable events. From this knowledge, our science of mechanics in the broad meaning of that term has been constructed. Here we are looking at nature as spectators, and hence this has been called "perceptual" or "extraspective experience." Experiences of the second class are not projected outward in this way. They are concerned with subjective mental processes of various kinds, including emotion, reasoning, illusion, hallucination, and imaginative fantasies in endless variety. This "introspective experience" is of the self as an experiencing subject.

The distinction between these two kinds of experience is basic, and it has given rise to the popular conception of human nature as split into "physical" and "spiritual" seg-

[4] G. Santayana, *Reason and Common Sense* (New York: Charles Scribner's Sons, 1905).

[5] C. J. Herrick, *The Evolution of Human Nature* (Austin: University of Texas Press, 1956). Short extracts from this book are included here by permission of the publisher.

ments. But the integrity of the normal personality cannot be sundered in this way. The two types of experience are organically related, and the nature of this relationship is critically examined in the book just cited [5] and in many other works.

Knowledge, as we have just seen, has been fabricated from experience, and the two kinds of experience give us two kinds of knowledge, which are called, for short, "perceptual knowledge" and "conceptual knowledge." This knowledge provides the raw data for the motivation of all rational behavior.

Much of our conduct, however, is not motivated rationally but by subconscious impulses derived from our animal heritage and from unrecognized or forgotten influences of family and community surroundings, or by passions and sentiments that have little intelligent control. We also look forward and plan for today in view of probable future contingencies; expectation and fear or hope shape the course of action. Here faith goes beyond knowledge. A faith is more than a belief based on factual evidence. There is always an extension into the unknown and usually a more or less vivid factor of expectancy and desire or aversion, a factor which gives the faith its great motivating efficiency. This faith "means the assurance of what we hope for; it is our conviction about things that we cannot see" (Paul's Letter to the Hebrews, 11:1, Goodspeed's translation). Because faith has always played so large a part in indoctrination about the supernatural, we next examine its status in other domains of human interest. This examination is needed because the word "faith" has always had many different meanings, from the original Latin *fides* to its derivatives in current usage. In all these meanings there is implicit a union of belief and trust.

A scientific code is a body of knowledge acquired by experience and the appropriate ways to get it. A religious creed is a confession of faith. In advanced cultures, science and religion have a common objective—the betterment of men —but the methods used are radically different. The conflict between science and religion has resulted largely from failure by both parties to recognize the significance of this difference and to adjust their beliefs and practices so as to be able to co-operate harmoniously, each in his own way, without antagonism or rivalry. This mutual understanding cannot be gained without forbearing tolerance of diverse ideologies and the resulting conduct and without some important concessions on both sides.

Science knows no absolutes of truth, of perfection, of right, or of anything else. These are the ideals toward which we work, but in actual practice these values are all relative, and success in our endeavors depends on the breadth of experience and the validity of the knowledge acquired.

Knowledge and Faith

Faith influences our behavior more than most people realize. I believe that the sun will rise tomorrow morning. I hope that it will, and I would be greatly disturbed if it did not. This belief is a fact, but the thing believed is not a fact. It is a faith. This particular faith is more firmly based on past experience than are many others, such as faith in the weather prediction for tomorrow.

In all ordinary transactions, there is a factor of faith —faith in the orderly recurrence of some natural events like the change of seasons and the flow of tides, faith in ourselves and our ability to adjust conduct to these events and to unforeseen exigencies, and faith in our fellow men and their institutions. Every time I write a check on my bank, I express a faith in the reliability of that institution. All business and government transactions necessarily involve this factor of trust based on more or less reliable knowledge.

Every belief we entertain has these two factors: a more or less substantial body of knowledge reinforced by a faith in its accuracy. Because our factual knowledge is never complete or final, it must be supplemented by this factor of faith, and the less complete the knowledge, the larger the uncertainty and the faith required for its acceptance. Some primitive mythologies which were invoked in early times to fill these gaps in knowledge survive to our day as fantasies that many people trust more implicitly than they do their own actual experiences.

In the history of the practice of medicine, we see instructive illustrations of the interplay of knowledge and faith. In primitive cultures, the medicine man habitually invokes supernatural powers. In our own communities today, we have many illustrations of similar practices, as in the various bizarre cults of faith-cure. That these treatments are sometimes effective, there can be no question. The motivating power of faith is real, whether it is faith in some supernatural intervention, faith in the doctor and his treatment, or reinforcement of the patient's faith in his own ability to overcome his weaknesses. The eminently successful work of Alcoholics Anonymous and of all regular medical practice gives many demonstrations of this fact. Sir William Osler said: "Faith has always been an essential factor in all medical treatment," and "As a profession, consciously or unconsciously, more often the latter, *faith* has been one of our most valuable assets." [6]

These faiths are real vectors in life; they are directional toward recognizable goals more or less clearly discerned. We cannot dispense with them in any field of human interest, and assuredly we should not want to. Bertrand Russell shot wide of the mark when he defined faith as "a firm belief in something for which there is no evidence." Those scien-

[6] H. Cushing, *The Life of Sir William Osler* (Vol. II, Oxford: Clarendon Press, 1925), pp. 181 and 222.

tists who accept Earl Russell's definition (as some do) ignore both the primary meaning of the word and its actual significance in past and present usage. It has long been recognized that there are faiths supported by more or less reliable knowledge and other faiths which may be justified or rejected, depending on their practical effects. The real issues are: What is the evidence for any particular faith, and what consequences follow from its exercise?

In our various codes of belief and practice, the relative parts played by knowledge and faith vary between the widest possible limits. In natural science, the end sought is verifiable knowledge, and in this pursuit faith plays an ancillary, but nevertheless essential, role. As Donald H. Barron has expressed it to me, "A law of science is a prediction based on faith in a probability of the highest known order." In religion, faith plays a quite different role. The end sought is the satisfaction of hopes and aspirations or escape from fear and distress, with strong emotional pressure. Faith is the cement that gives unity to experience of all sorts—practical, aesthetic, scientific, and religious.

These faiths are of two kinds, which are related to the two kinds of experience and knowledge to which reference has been made. There are faiths that are supported by abundant evidence, that is, by what we have called perceptual knowledge. These are the faiths that play so large a part in all scientific exploration by extrapolation from the known to the unknown. Other faiths which are nurtured by fears, hopes, or aspirations may be justified or rejected on behavioristic grounds, even if there is little or no evidence for or against them. We may ask: How do they work? Do they contribute to personal health of body and mind and to social betterment, or do they foster personal and social disorder?

A faith that has not been shown to be erroneous factually must nevertheless be rejected if, in practice, it results in personal conduct or social movements that are injurious. Faith

in demoniacal possession retarded the progress of psychiatry
for many centuries, and faith in divine authority for the ex-
termination of heresy led to fanatical intolerance and such
atrocities as the Holy Inquisition and burning of witches.
We have it on eminent authority that "faith without works
is dead," and to this we may add that a faith whose works are
evil is a source of corruption. It is not only dead, it stinks.

The converse is equally true. A faith for which there is
little factual evidence may justifiably be entertained if it
promotes moral culture and social welfare. It was said of the
prophets of old, "by their fruits ye shall know them," and by
the same token any faith can be judged today. On these
grounds the justification of a faith is a factual matter to be
decided on available evidence.

In his youth, Santayana wrote in his *Reason in Science*
(1906): "Religion and art have had their day." Science, he
then thought, had come at last to displace religion. Fifty
years later he said: "Of course we were wrong. . . . Always
bear in mind that my naturalism does not exclude religion;
on the contrary it allows for it. I mean that religion is the
natural reaction of the imagination when confronted by the
difficulties of a truculent world." [7]

Human imagination is the source of the greatest triumphs
of science, technology, art, and philosophy. We must be careful not to cripple its exercise by arbitrary restrictions. It gives
us our pre-eminence over the brutes. The creative imagination of poets and dramatists have always had a powerful influence upon people's conduct, often for good and sometimes
for evil. In religion the imagination has tended to run riot-
ously, with disastrous consequences. Common sense and scientific knowledge should check these excesses. A few illustrations of present scientific movements are now mentioned,
in order to show what readjustments of current thinking are
needed.

[7] D. Cory, *Atlantic Monthly*, CXCI:4 (1953), p. 66.

Science and Faith

Our present age of science is characterized by a general attitude of skepticism. We want to know what to believe and why. What we believe as scientists is (or should be) based on factual evidence, and yet every acceptable fact and every generalization rests upon a large and complicated system of faiths—faith in the lawful ordering of natural processes, faith in the reliability of the observations and the trustworthiness of the record, faith in the predictive value of every sound scientific principle, and many more. Without these and similar faiths, some of which are products of informed creative imagination, science would die of senile sclerosis.

Exploration has been the passion of some men since the beginning of history. The scientist, like every other explorer, works for the joy of it, that is, for the satisfaction won by entering a terrain never before seen by man. But the vast expenditures now made by government and other organizations in support of science would not be appropriate if the shrewd administrators of these funds did not have faith that these investments would yield profits of human welfare sufficient to justify the cost.

Our knowledge of the essential qualities of the physical world has been revolutionized during the last fifty years, and a brief reference to these changes may help us to understand the nature of the relationship between the "physical" and the "spiritual" components of human nature. Today's natural science is radically mechanistic. Man's so-called spiritual nature, which includes all conscious processes, seems to be non-mechanistic, and so there is strong prejudice against scientific meddling with spiritual values.

From the earliest recorded stages of the development of human cultures until now, men have split the world as they experience it into natural and supernatural domains. Where knowledge fails, magic is invoked to fill the gap. Throughout the world today most people cherish the belief in some sort of supernatural intervention in mundane affairs. In its more sophisticated patterns, this faith usually takes the form of belief in a spiritual nature set over against a physical nature. These independent domains of "spiritual reality" and "physical reality" are supposed to be somehow so linked as to constitute the human person; but no one has been able to explain how a nonphysical agency which is released from the limitations of the physical world can act upon a physical body so as to influence human conduct. Any dualistic hypothesis closes the door to the scientific investigation of man's spiritual nature, for mechanistic science cannot deal with the nonmechanistic.

We must not let the matter rest here. Dualism is a confession of defeat, and defeatism is not a healthy attitude in science. The hoary mind-body problem will not be solved until we find psychophysical principles that are consistent with what we know about both psychology and physics. This goal has not yet been reached, but investigations now in process point to new avenues of approach which give promise of a satisfactory solution. The details are very technical and cannot be summarized here. The hopeful feature of the present situation lies in the recent development of radically new ideas about the nature of mechanism and its physical operations.[8]

The principles of mechanism (or physicalism, if you prefer) have been fundamentally changed within the memory of men now living. Matter and energy have been shown to be interconvertible, and recently discovered physical processes have opened vistas that fifty years ago could not even have

---

[8] I have discussed this topic at length in Chap. V and elsewhere in the book cited in reference 5 and also in two articles in *The Humanist*, XVI (1956), p. 210, and *Psychological Review*, LXI (1955), p. 333.

been imagined. In the present state of knowledge, we can set no limits to the kinds of products natural mechanisms can make, call them physical or spiritual or what you will. The impenetrable wall which traditionally separates the "physical" from the "spiritual" man is breaking down.

It must not be overlooked, however, that there is a real difference between those processes that we call "physiological" and the mental functions that we call "subjective." The laws of physiology and the principles of introspective psychology do not seem to be directly commensurable. We do not yet know enough about those operations of the brain which have as one of their properties some awareness of what is going on to be able to formulate a satisfactory theory of psychophysics. This is just one of many other vital functions that have not yet been fully explained.[9]

We do know that every mental experience is an act performed by a living body; it is not the adroitness of a mystic *anima* that can flout the laws of the physical world, a ghost that lives in the body as a tenant but is not a part of it. No natural mechanism needs a jinni to tell it what to do. This is as true of the human machine as of the solar system. Helios has been banished from the domain of optics, and Psyche can no longer be charged with responsibility for human conduct. We know where the organs are that do our thinking, and we know a great deal about how they operate. This knowledge is increasing very fast, and we are confident that an acceptable description of the mechanics of thinking as a vital process will sooner or later be possible.

New and hitherto unsuspected ways of clarifying some of these mysteries may be possible. To cite one illustration, we now know that our ideas of three-dimensional space and of time as a linear sequence, measurable in arbitrary units like inches and seconds, are not innate intuitions. The newborn babe has no such ideas. His body operates in integrated space-

[9] S. S. Stevens, *Science*, CXXVII (1958), p. 383.

time, just as does every other structure in our known universe when its movements are analyzed in terms of current physics. The infant's knowledge of the measurable relations of things in space and time is acquired by experience, and out of this experience our artificial standards of measurement of things perceived have been constructed. These artifacts are useful as adequate instruments for practical adjustments in the "man-sized" world, but they cannot satisfy the requirements of subatomic physics and metagalactic astronomy. They must be supplemented by a different system of mathematical artifacts, that is, by quantum mechanics, a system which dispenses with arbitrary units of measurement based on fixed points of reference and replaces them with the relativistic conception of integrated space-time.

Quantum mechanics, in turn, is by no means a finished discipline. It employs postulates or assumptions, in all of which there is an element of faith, a faith supported by more or less reliable experimental evidence. Some of the most fundamental of these assumptions are still in controversy, and there are many unsolved problems. It is safe to say that, just as quantum mechanics has supplemented Newtonian mechanics, so there may remain to be discovered still unknown physicalistic principles that will justify our faith in the lawful order of everything there is. This faith was cherished by Einstein as long as he lived, and he refused to accept chance or random disorder as a basic principle of physical science.[10] There is, then, no justification for cutting the universe into two halves, one "physical" and one "spiritual."

We cannot foresee what changes in our present conceptions of the operations of cosmic energies may occur. Most scientists now believe that there is no acceptable evidence that natural processes are influenced in any way by unnatural

[10] Compare in this connection two articles in the *Scientific American* for January, 1958, where the opinions of George Gamow (p. 51) and David Bohm (p. 111) are contrasted.

agencies. Nature is regarded as self-contained and self-regulating. The naturalists, accordingly, have no interest, as naturalists, in the supernatural. But if a naturalist, or anybody else, wishes to speculate about what may lie beyond the range of possible human experience, that is his privilege. No scientist can object to it, provided that these excursions into transcendentalism do not invade his own domain. It is legitimate to extrapolate from the known facts into the unknown but not to reverse the procedure. Our metaphysics must not be divorced from our physics and from all veridical knowledge. The naturalist may properly insist that any hypothesis about the supernatural must not be inconsistent or incompatible with what we know about nature, and that is as far as he can justifiably go. He cannot prove the existence of anything supernatural, nor can he deny such a possibility.

If, then, one entertains any faith or hypothesis about the supernatural, it must be on other than scientific grounds. But human experience embraces more than science, and, because these faiths so profoundly influence human conduct, this aspect of the subject is worth looking into.

The astronomers tell us that there may now be on other planets of our stellar systems people with some kind of mentality similar to ours. Some of these may be far more efficient than ours. Some philosophers go further and admit the possibility of a cosmic mind of higher order than those embodied anywhere locally. The only basis for such a faith is the appeal to analogy with the only kind of mind of which we have accurate knowledge—our own. But it is not unreasonable to extrapolate from the observed properties of the human mind to the larger domain of total reality, for the properties of our minds are the highest manifestations of cosmic energy known to us.

We do not know what energy is. We know only some patterns of its operations, and from these observed events we postulate an active agency common to all of them. This as-

sumption is frankly an act of faith, a faith that is supported
by a vast amount of information that would otherwise be
inexplicable.

A faith in a supreme intelligence can claim no such
scientific support; yet I think it must be granted that there
are no scientific or philosophical grounds for denying the
possibility of an "All Knower" (to borrow Josiah Royce's
term), that is, of an intelligent regulating agency of the total
cosmos, of which the limited universe known to man is an
integral part, however improbable this may seem to many
scientists. Any such belief is, I repeat, a faith supported only
by analogy with our own minds.

From time immemorial men have ascribed to their gods
thoughts and passions like their own. The material or ideal
images of these gods have taken an amazing variety of forms
in the various religions of the world. They may have qualities
selected from all sorts of experience, including fantastic
recombinations of animate and inanimate things—beasts with
human heads, angels with wings, thunderbolts in the hands of
Thor.

The scientific study of comparative religion seems to
indicate that all the gods of all religions are inventions of the
human imagination, made in the image of man or endowed
with human qualities. Among these mystic conceptions there
is one that stands pre-eminent—the conception of a personal
God who is the apotheosis of the most noble qualities of
human nature and the benevolent Father of his children. This
ideal of the perfection which we crave inspires multitudes of
people to resist evil impulses and to cherish the finest aspirations of which men are capable.

This faith sustained one of the most productive and saga-
cious scientists I have ever known, a deeply religious man
who was an active member of the Society of Friends as long
as he lived. The late Warder Clyde Allee wrote: "Religion

is ill-served by past and present emphasis on mystical and supernatural improbabilities. To me 'God' is a possible permissible personification of all the best that the human race has been able to think and do and of all the beauty we have created, together with all the natural beauty we can appreciate." [11]

This faith, I claim, is "permissible" because it is impossible to prove that it is unjustified, and like the imaginative creations of poets and dramatists, when cultivated wisely and practiced judiciously, it influences behavior in ways that make for righteousness. It is for many people their strongest motivation for moral conduct and sustenance of spiritual values. It may bring more comfort in affliction and stronger courage in the face of disaster than is available to these people from any other source, and it may be literally a saving faith in times of distress and despair. As such, it has biological value which the naturalist should frankly recognize, however much he may deplore the irrational dogmatism and fanaticism of some of its defenders. There are times when knowledge and courage fail and when it is better to walk by faith than to perish in the slough of despond. Faith in a good God promotes acceptable behavior and relief of tensions more effectually than faith in demons or fear of hell-fire.

In the thousands of years since Job was asked, "Canst thou by searching find out God?" it has become increasingly clear that the existence of the God of Job or of the God whose name is stamped on the currency of our United States cannot be proved by factual evidence. This trust can be supported only by faith, a faith justified by works that enhance human welfare.

If this faith is clothed in the garb of religion, we should not fail to heed Professor Haydon's warning that by too much faith in gods and other worlds and too little faith in

[11] W. C. Allee, *Science,* XCVII (1943), p. 517.

man, a practical program of vital religion has been all too long delayed.[12] Here the sciences of man provide us with our most powerful implements of cultural development.

We may, then, render to God the things that are God's and to science only the things that are nature's.

Conclusion

Most of the people of the world today are firm believers in some form of supernaturalism, which usually is cherished as religious faith. Religion is so deeply intrenched in almost every society that there is no probability that it will be given up in the foreseeable future. The Communists' attempt to suppress it has failed, and they have nothing better to offer.

Those who reject all religious faiths that appeal to the supernatural find support for their opposition in the tragic history of the atrocities that have been perpetrated by religious organizations in both ancient and modern times. Faith in evil gods, who demand human sacrifices and other crimes, and fanatical intolerance of all religions other than one's own have fostered bigotry leading to persecutions, holy wars, sectarian control of government, and worship of ritual rather than the spiritual values which they symbolize. These abuses, some of which are still prevalent, have discredited all religion to many observers.

These critics fail to appreciate that the great motivating power of refined religious faith may have value in some situations where no other incentives for righteousness have any force. Since we have to live with religion, whether we like it or not, it must be recognized that its abolition is neither practicable nor desirable. What we should do is to try in every possible way to redirect all religious thought and prac-

[12] A. E. Haydon, in F. H. Burkhardt (ed.), *The Cleavage in Our Culture* (Boston: Beacon Press, 1952), p. 133.

tice away from its evil perversions and toward those true values that come to expression in refined standards of personal morality and social responsibility.

The current movements that can be grouped under the name "naturalistic humanism" put the emphasis on human nature as a going concern in today's surroundings, and they work for a more efficient integration of all human endeavors and aspirations so as to get a more rich, productive, and satisfying life for all people. To this end, the appeal is to natural science as the source of the necessary knowledge of ourselves and our surroundings rather than to the doctrines of traditional metaphysics and theology. The ideas of supernatural intervention in the operations of nature and of revelation from supernatural sources are generally dismissed as unproved and objectionable.

Those of us who prefer to keep our speculations about the unknown within the domain of the natural as here defined should recognize that within our own field of experience there are many things for which we have as yet no natural explanation. This is a call for further search.

If, in this search, we recognize that, at best, our findings will be incomplete because only a part of total reality is knowable by finite minds, then the naturalist must assume that the knowable part, which we call the "domain of nature," is inseparable from the whole of which it is part and is harmoniously integrated with it. The natural and the supernatural cannot be regarded as independent and disparate realms of existence. Our "laws of nature," which are human constructions based on limited and fallible observation, cannot be incompatible with those of the total cosmic order. Any arbitrary "supernatural" interference with natural processes must be ruled out, and any apparent evidence of such miraculous events must be due to imperfections in our knowledge of natural law.

We already know enough about our natural cosmos to

be humbled by the stupendous magnitude and splendor of it and to be inspired by the fact that the human population of it plays a part in cosmic evolution that is by no means insignificant. The personal worth and dignity of a man are his natural birthright. It is essential that this be everywhere recognized, for it is the cardinal factor of all previous human achievements and our only hope of further progress. The glory of man lies not only in his ability to understand but also in his aspirations. We live by faith, faith in the order of nature, faith in ourselves, and faith in our fellow men. This faith is our most prevalent motivation, and it is a reliable guide just so far as it is founded on knowledge. Where knowledge is lacking, we may extrapolate with due regard for the uncertainties arising from the incompleteness of our knowledge. We must avoid dogmatism, and dogmatism about the unknown is especially reprehensible. The mystics often neglect this caution. The naturalists must not, and they find within the bounties of nature ample scope for their best endeavors and for the satisfaction of their highest aspirations.

We are citizens of the universe. Our cosmos is dynamic and intrinsically creative at all levels of organization. This native creativity is amplified in the domain of organic evolution and glorified when aware of itself in human purposive planning. The sublimity of this conception of man's place in nature commands our reverence and our utmost effort to meet the demands imposed upon us by that nature which is our alma mater.

If one wishes to go further than this and add to his faith in nature, and especially in human nature, an additional faith in the supernatural as here defined, the naturalist has no legitimate ground for objection, provided that this faith is not in conflict with veridical knowledge and that it promotes acceptable conduct. It is unseemly for any man of science or any philosopher to condemn that faith, even though he himself may not entertain it.